Fundamental Identities

$$\csc t = \frac{1}{\sin t}$$

$$\tan t = \frac{\sin t}{\cos t}$$

$$\sin^2 t + \cos^2 t = 1$$

$$\sec t = \frac{1}{\cos t}$$

$$\cot t = \frac{\cos t}{\sin t}$$

$$\tan^2 t + 1 = \sec^2 t$$

$$\cot t = \frac{1}{\tan t}$$

$$\cot^2 t + 1 = \csc^2 t$$

Formulas for Negatives

$$\sin(-t) = -\sin t \qquad \cos(-t) = \cos t \qquad \tan(-t) = -\tan t$$

Addition Formulas

$$\sin(u + v) = \sin u \cos v + \cos u \sin v$$

$$\cos(u + v) = \cos u \cos v - \sin u \sin v$$

$$\tan(u + v) = \frac{\tan u + \tan v}{1 - \tan u \tan v}$$

Subtraction Formulas

$$\sin(u - v) = \sin u \cos v - \cos u \sin v$$

$$\cos(u - v) = \cos u \cos v + \sin u \sin v$$

$$\tan(u - v) = \frac{\tan u - \tan v}{1 + \tan u \tan v}$$

Double-Angle Formulas

$$\sin 2u = 2 \sin u \cos u$$

$$\cos 2u = \cos^2 u - \sin^2 u = 1 - 2\sin^2 u = 2\cos^2 u - 1$$

$$\tan 2u = \frac{2 \tan u}{1 - \tan^2 u}$$

Half-Angle Formulas

$$\left| \sin \frac{u}{2} \right| = \sqrt{\frac{1 - \cos u}{2}}$$

$$\left| \cos \frac{u}{2} \right| = \sqrt{\frac{1 + \cos u}{2}}$$

$$\tan \frac{u}{2} = \frac{1 - \cos u}{\sin u} = \frac{\sin u}{1 + \cos u}$$

$$\sin^2 u = \frac{1 - \cos 2u}{2}$$

$$\cos^2 u = \frac{1 + \cos 2u}{2}$$

$$\tan^2 u = \frac{1 - \cos 2u}{1 + \cos 2u}$$

Product Formulas

$$2 \sin u \cos v = \sin(u + v) + \sin(u - v)$$

$$2 \cos u \sin v = \sin(u + v) - \sin(u - v)$$

$$2 \cos u \cos v = \cos(u + v) + \cos(u - v)$$

$$2 \sin u \sin v = \cos(u - v) - \cos(u + v)$$

Factoring Formulas

$$\sin u + \sin v = 2 \cos \frac{u - v}{2} \sin \frac{u + v}{2}$$

$$\sin u - \sin v = 2 \cos \frac{u + v}{2} \sin \frac{u - v}{2}$$

$$\cos u + \cos v = 2 \cos \frac{u + v}{2} \cos \frac{u - v}{2}$$

$$\cos u - \cos v = 2 \sin \frac{v + u}{2} \sin \frac{v - u}{2}$$

EARL W. SWOKOWSKI

MARQUETTE UNIVERSITY

FUNDAMENTALS OF TRIGONOMETRY

FIFTH EDITION

PRINDLE, WEBER & SCHMIDT

BOSTON, MASSACHUSETTS

PWS PUBLISHERS

Prindle, Weber & Schmidt •  • Willard Grant Press • **wg** • Duxbury Press • ♠
Statler Office Building • 20 Park Plaza • Boston, Massachusetts 02116

PWS Publishers is a division of Wadsworth Inc.

Printed in the United States of America.
10 9 8 7 6 5 4 3 — 87 86 85 84 83

Library of Congress Cataloging in Publication Data

Swokowski, Earl William
    Fundamentals of trigonometry.

    Includes index.
    1. Trigonometry, Plane. I. Title.
QA533.S95 1981   516.2'4   80-27922
ISBN 0-87150-311-5

ISBN 0-87150-311-5

Cover design by Novum, Inc. Text design by Nancy Blodget. Text composition in Monophoto Times Roman and Univers by Technical Filmsetters Europe Ltd. Cover printed by New England Book Components, Inc. Text printed and bound by R.R. Donnelley & Sons Company.

PREFACE

The fifth edition of *Fundamentals of Trigonometry* reflects the continuing change in the needs and abilities of students who enroll in precalculus mathematics courses. The goal of this new edition is to maintain the mathematical soundness of earlier editions, but to make some of the discussions less formal by rewriting, placing more emphasis on graphing and applications, and adding new examples, figures, and exercises.

Chapter 1 consists of topics that are fundamental for the study of trigonometry. These include properties of real numbers, functions, and graphs. A noteworthy change from earlier editions is the additional emphasis on symmetry, horizontal or vertical shifts, and stretching of graphs.

In Chapter 2, an accessible introduction to trigonometric functions using a unit circle is managed by emphasizing examples and keeping the discussion relatively brief. Angles are introduced early in the chapter, and the unit circle approach is then supplemented by an angular description of the trigonometric functions. Later, examples are again emphasized to help students learn to sketch graphs rapidly. A new section on harmonic motion was added at the end of the chapter to provide some non-triangular applications of trigonometry.

Most of Chapter 3 consists of work with trigonometric identities and equations. Inverse trigonometric functions are discussed in Section 3.7.

The standard methods of solving oblique triangles appear in Chapter 4. Section 4.5 provides an introduction to geometric and algebraic properties of vectors in two dimensions. Section 4.6 is new to this edition, and contains a discussion of properties and applications of the dot product.

Complex numbers are covered in Chapter 5. Exponential and logarithmic functions are discussed in Chapter 6. Computational aspects of logarithms are considered in the last two sections, and may be omitted without interrupting the continuity of the book. Chapter 7 contains the standard topics in analytic geometry.

There is a review section at the end of each chapter consisting of a list of important topics and pertinent exercises. The review exercises are similar in scope to those which appear throughout the chapter and may be used to prepare for examinations. Answers to odd-numbered exercises are given at the end of the text. An answer booklet for the even-numbered exercises may be obtained from the publisher.

This revision has benefited from comments and suggestions of users of previous editions. I wish to thank the following individuals, who reviewed all or parts of the manuscript and offered many helpful suggestions: Ben P. Bockstege, Jr. (Broward Community College), Gary L. Ebert (University of Delaware), Leonard E. Fuller (Kansas State University), F. Cecilia Hakeem (Southern Illinois University), Douglas

W. Hall (Michigan State University), Arthur M. Hobbs (Texas A&M University), Adam J. Hulin (University of New Orleans), William B. Jones (University of Colorado), Jimmie Lawson (Louisiana State University), Burnett Meyer (University of Colorado), Eldon L. Miller (University of Mississippi), Robert W. Owens (Lewis and Clark College), Anthony L. Peressini (University of Illinois), Jack W. Pope (University of San Diego), Larry H. Potter (Memphis State University), Sandra M. Powers (The College of Charleston), Billie Ann Rice (Dekalb Community College), John Riner (Ohio State University), Mary W. Scott (University of Florida), William F. Stearns (University of Maine), Janet T. Vasak (University of Wisconsin-Milwaukee), Richard G. Vinson (University of South Alabama), T. Perrin Wright, Jr. (Florida State University), and Paul M. Young (Kansas State University).

I am also grateful to the staff of Prindle, Weber & Schmidt, for their painstaking work in the production of this book. In particular, Mary Lu Walsh, John Martindale, and Nancy Blodget gave valuable assistance with the revision.

Special thanks are due to my wife Shirley and the members of our family: Mary, Mark, John, Steve, Paul, Tom, Bob, Nancy, Judy, and Jay. All have had an influence on the book—either directly, through working exercises, proofreading, or typing, or indirectly, through continued interest and moral support.

To all of the people named here, and to the many unnamed students and teachers who have helped shape my views about precalculus mathematics, I express my sincere appreciation.

Earl W. Swokowski

TABLE OF CONTENTS

COMMENTS ABOUT HANDHELD CALCULATORS

There is disagreement among mathematics educators as to the extent that electronic handheld calculators should be employed in courses involving algebra and trigonometry. Those who favor their use point out that, in addition to reducing the time spent on numerical computations, calculators are useful for illustrating and reinforcing mathematical concepts. It is unlikely that any teacher would recommend that a calculator be used as a tool for solving the quadratic equation $x^2 + 2x - 3 = 0$; however, the process of approximating the solutions of $241x^2 + 527x - 73 = 0$ *without* a calculator is pure drudgery, adding little to a student's mathematical knowledge. On the theoretical side, some claim that calculating $10^{\log x}$ for various values of x will help beginning students accept, and remember, the identity $10^{\log x} = x$. The extent to which this is true is, of course, difficult to measure.

Teachers who oppose the use of calculators in courses involving algebra and trigonometry argue that they distract from the mainstream of study, and that classroom time is better spent on theoretical and manipulative aspects which are needed in advanced courses such as calculus. Clearly, it is essential to understand basic results about equations before using a calculator to approximate solutions. As another illustration, working with logarithmic and trigonometric tables has some worthwhile side-effects concerning the variation of functions and intermediate values.

In this text an attempt is made to satisfy both those instructors who wish to use calculators as a teaching aid, and those who prefer not to use them. Specifically, optional problems labeled *Calculator Exercises* have been included in appropriate sections of the text, following the regular exercises. They may either be omitted or assigned, depending on course objectives. In order to make proper use of these exercises, it is necessary to have access to a scientific calculator which has the capability to deal with exponential, logarithmic, trigonometric, and inverse trigonometric expressions.

If calculators are used, students should be aware of the fact that inaccuracies may occur due to round off, truncation, or algorithms which the calculator employs to compute certain numerical values. For example, to use a calculator to demonstrate that $(\frac{1}{3}) \cdot 3 = 1$, we may enter 3, press the reciprocal key $\boxed{1/x}$, and then multiply by 3. However, if the decimal approximation 0.33333333 is entered, then multiplying by 3 results in 0.99999999. Similarly, to demonstrate that $\sqrt{2}\sqrt{3} = \sqrt{6}$ we may, on the one hand, calculate $\sqrt{2}\sqrt{3}$ and $\sqrt{6}$ separately, and verify that the same decimal approximation is obtained in each case. On the other hand, calculating $\sqrt{6} - \sqrt{2}\sqrt{3}$ with a typical calculator, we may obtain 0.000000000013 (this number may vary, depending on the type of calculator). If we agree to round off answers to eight decimal places, then this result may be considered as a calculator demonstration that $\sqrt{6} - \sqrt{2}\sqrt{3} = 0$, and hence that $\sqrt{6} = \sqrt{2}\sqrt{3}$.

Other discrepencies may occur. For example, given a calculator which displays a maximum of eight digits, if we enter 10,000,000 and then add 0.1, we obtain 10,000,000, a result not in keeping with laws of algebra! Similarly, laws such as $a(b + c) = ab + ac$ may not hold if certain values are entered for a, b, and c.

It should also be noted that if calculators are used to solve the *regular* exercises involving logarithmic or trigonometric functions, some answers may differ from those given in the text, since the latter were obtained using the four-place tables in the Appendix, whereas calculators produce a higher degree of accuracy.

Finally, instructions on how to operate a calculator are not provided in this text. The large variety of calculators on the market make it impractical to do so. Owner manuals should be consulted for information and illustrations.

1

PREREQUISITES FOR TRIGONOMETRY

This chapter contains topics necessary for the study of trigonometry. After a review of real numbers, coordinate systems, and graphs in two dimensions, we turn our attention to one of the most important concepts in mathematics—the notion of function.

1.1 REAL NUMBERS

Real numbers are used in all phases of mathematics, and you are undoubtedly well acquainted with symbols used to represent them, such as

$$1, \quad 73, \quad -5, \quad 49/12, \quad \sqrt{2}, \quad 0, \quad \sqrt[3]{-85}, \quad -8.674, \quad 0.33333\ldots, \quad 596.25$$

We shall assume familiarity with the fundamental properties of addition, subtraction, multiplication, division, exponents, and radicals. Throughout this chapter, unless otherwise specified, lower-case letters a, b, c, ... will denote real numbers.

The **positive integers** 1, 2, 3, 4, ... may be obtained by adding the real number 1 successively to itself. The **integers** consist of all positive and negative integers together with the real number 0. A **rational number** is a real number that can be expressed as a quotient a/b, where a and b are integers and $b \neq 0$. Real numbers that are not rational are called **irrational**. The ratio of the circumference of a circle to its diameter is irrational. This real number is denoted by π and the notation $\pi \approx 3.1416$ is used to indicate that π is *approximately equal* to 3.1416. Another familiar example of an irrational number is $\sqrt{2}$.

Real numbers may be represented by nonterminating decimals. For example, the decimal representation for the rational number 7434/2310 is found by long division to be 3.2181818..., where the digits 1 and 8 repeat indefinitely. Rational numbers may always be represented by repeating decimals. Decimal representations for irrational

1

numbers may also be obtained; however, they are nonterminating and nonrepeating. For numerical applications, nonterminating decimals are approximated by terminating decimals, where the number of decimal places is determined by the degree of accuracy which is desired.

It is possible to associate real numbers with points on a straight line *l* in such a way that for each real number *a* there corresponds one and only one point, and conversely, to each point *P* on *l* there corresponds precisely one real number. Such an association is referred to as a **one-to-one correspondence**. We first choose an arbitrary point *O*, called the **origin**, and associate with it the real number 0. Points associated with the integers are then determined by laying off successive line segments of equal length on either side of *O* as illustrated in Figure 1.1. The points corresponding to rational numbers such as 23/5 and −1/2 are obtained by subdividing the equal line segments. Points associated with certain irrational numbers, such as $\sqrt{2}$, can be found by geometric construction. For other irrational numbers such as π, no construction is possible. However, the point corresponding to π can be approximated to within any degree of accuracy by locating successively the points corresponding to 3, 3.1, 3.14, 3.141, 3.1415, 3.14159, etc.

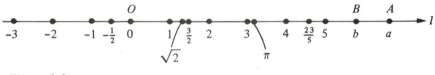

Figure 1.1

The number *x* that is associated with a point *X* on *l* is called the **coordinate** of *X*. An assignment of coordinates to points on *l* is called a **coordinate system** for *l*, and *l* is called a **coordinate line**, or a **real line**. A direction can be assigned to *l* by taking the **positive direction** along *l* to the right and the **negative direction** to the left. The positive direction is noted by placing an arrowhead on *l* as shown in Figure 1.1.

The numbers that correspond to points to the right of *O* in Figure 1.1 are called **positive real numbers**, whereas those that correspond to points to the left of *O* are **negative real numbers**. The real number 0 is neither positive nor negative. The positive real numbers are **closed** relative to addition and multiplication; that is, if *a* and *b* are positive, then so is the sum $a + b$ and the product *ab*.

If *a* and *b* are real numbers, and $a - b$ is positive, we say that *a* **is greater than** *b* and write $a > b$. An equivalent statement is *b* **is less than** *a*, written $b < a$. The symbols $>$ and $<$ are called **inequality signs**, and expressions such as $a > b$ or $b < a$ are called **inequalities**. From the manner in which we constructed the coordinate line *l* in Figure 1.1, we see that if *A* and *B* are points with coordinates *a* and *b*, respectively, then $a > b$ (or $b < a$) *if and only if A lies to the right of B.* The following definition is stated for reference, where *a* and *b* denote real numbers.

Definition of > and <

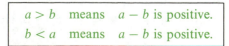

$a > b$ means $a - b$ is positive.
$b < a$ means $a - b$ is positive.

Note that $a > b$ and $b < a$ have exactly the same meaning. As illustrations,

$$5 > 3 \quad \text{since} \quad 5 - 3 = 2 \text{ is positive}$$
$$-6 < -2 \quad \text{since} \quad -2 - (-6) = -2 + 6 = 4 \text{ is positive}$$
$$-\sqrt{2} < 1 \quad \text{since} \quad 1 - (-\sqrt{2}) = 1 + \sqrt{2} \text{ is positive}$$
$$2 > 0 \quad \text{since} \quad 2 - 0 = 2 \text{ is positive}$$
$$-5 < 0 \quad \text{since} \quad 0 - (-5) = 5 \text{ is positive.}$$

The last two illustrations are special cases of the following general properties.

> $a > 0$ if and only if a is positive.
> $a < 0$ if and only if a is negative.

These properties are consequences of the definitions of $>$ and $<$. We sometimes refer to the **sign** of a real number as being positive or negative according to whether the number is positive or negative.

There are several other useful symbols that involve inequality signs. In particular, $a \geq b$, which is read *a* **is greater than or equal to** *b*, means that either $a > b$ or $a = b$ (but not both). The symbol $a \leq b$ is read *a* **is less than or equal to** *b* and means that either $a < b$ or $a = b$. The expression $a < b < c$ means that both $a < b$ and $b < c$, in which case we say that *b* **is between** *a* **and** *c*. We may also write $c > b > a$. For instance,

$$1 < 5 < \frac{11}{2}, \quad -4 < \frac{2}{3} < \sqrt{2}, \quad 3 > -6 > -10.$$

Other variations of the inequality notation are used. For example, $a < b \leq c$ means both $a < b$ and $b \leq c$. Similarly, $a \leq b < c$ means both $a \leq b$ and $b < c$. Finally, $a \leq b \leq c$ means both $a \leq b$ and $b \leq c$.

If a is a real number, then it is the coordinate of some point A on a coordinate line l, and the symbol $|a|$ is used to denote the number of units (or the distance) between A and the origin, without regard to direction. The number $|a|$ is called the *absolute value* of a. Referring to Figure 1.2, we see that for the point with coordinate -4 we have $|-4| = 4$. Similarly, $|4| = 4$. In general, if a is negative, we change its sign to find $|a|$, whereas if a is nonnegative, then $|a| = a$. The next definition summarizes this discussion.

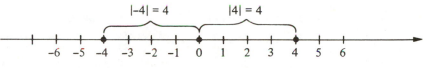

Figure 1.2

Definition

> If a is a real number, then the **absolute value** $|a|$ of a defined by
> $$|a| = \begin{cases} a & \text{if } a \geq 0 \\ -a & \text{if } a < 0. \end{cases}$$

Example 1   Find $|3|$, $|-3|$, $|0|$, $|\sqrt{2}-2|$, and $|2-\sqrt{2}|$.

Solution   Since $3, 2-\sqrt{2}$, and 0 are nonnegative, we have

$$|3| = 3, \quad |2-\sqrt{2}| = 2-\sqrt{2}, \quad \text{and} \quad |0| = 0.$$

Since -3 and $\sqrt{2}-2$ are negative, we use the formula $|a| = -a$ to obtain

$$|-3| = -(-3) = 3 \quad \text{and} \quad |\sqrt{2}-2| = -(\sqrt{2}-2) = 2-\sqrt{2}. \qquad \blacksquare$$

Note that in Example 1, $|-3| = |3|$ and $|2-\sqrt{2}| = |\sqrt{2}-2|$. It can be shown that

$$\boxed{|a| = |-a| \text{ for every real number } a.}$$

We shall use the concept of absolute value to define the distance between any two points on a coordinate line. Let us begin by noting that the distance between the points with coordinates 2 and 7 shown in Figure 1.3 equals 5 units on l. This distance is the difference, $7-2$, obtained by subtracting the smaller coordinate from the larger. If we employ absolute values, then since $|7-2| = |2-7|$, it is unnecessary to be concerned about the order of subtraction. We shall use this as our motivation for the next definition.

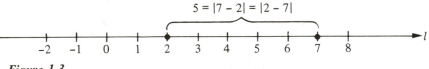

Figure 1.3

Definition   Let a and b be the coordinates of two points A and B, respectively, on a coordinate line l. The **distance between A and B**, denoted by $d(A,B)$, is defined by
$$d(A,B) = |b-a|.$$

The number $d(A,B)$ is also called the **length of the line segment AB**.

Observe that since $d(B,A) = |a-b|$ and $|b-a| = |a-b|$, we may write

$$d(A,B) = d(B,A).$$

Also note that the distance between the origin O and the point A is

$$d(O,A) = |a-0| = |a|$$

which agrees with the geometric interpretation of absolute value illustrated in Figure 1.2. The formula $d(A,B) = |b-a|$ is true regardless of the signs of a and b, as illustrated in the next example.

Example 2 Let A, B, C, and D have coordinates -5, -3, 1, and 6, respectively, on a coordinate line l (see Figure 1.4). Find $d(A, B)$, $d(C, B)$, $d(O, A)$, and $d(C, D)$.

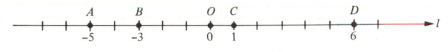

Figure 1.4

Solution By definition,

$$d(A, B) = |-3 - (-5)| = |-3 + 5| = |2| = 2$$
$$d(C, B) = |-3 - 1| = |-4| = 4$$
$$d(O, A) = |-5 - 0| = |-5| = 5$$
$$d(C, D) = |6 - 1| = |5| = 5.$$

These answers can be checked geometrically by referring to Figure 1.4. ∎

The concept of absolute value has uses other than that of finding distances between points. Generally, it is employed whenever one is interested in the magnitude or numerical value of a real number without regard to its sign.

Sometimes it is convenient to use the notation and terminology of sets. A **set** may be thought of as a collection of objects of some type. The objects are called **elements** of the set. Capital letters A, B, C, R, S, ... will often be used to denote sets. Lower-case letters a, b, x, y, ... will represent elements of sets. The notation $x \in S$ is used to specify that x is an element of the set S. Throughout our work $\mathbb{R}$ will denote the set of real numbers and $\mathbb{Z}$ the set of integers. If every element of a set S is also an element of a set T, then S is called a **subset** of T. For example, $\mathbb{Z}$ is a subset of $\mathbb{R}$. Two sets S and T are said to be equal, written $S = T$, if S and T contain precisely the same elements. The notation $S \neq T$ means that S and T are not equal.

If the elements of a set S have a certain property, then we write $S = \{x : \ldots\}$ where the property describing the arbitrary element x is stated in the space after the colon. For example, $\{x : x > 3\}$ may be used to represent the set of all real numbers greater than 3.

Finite sets are sometimes denoted by listing all the elements within braces. For example, if S consists of the first five letters of the alphabet, we write $S = \{a, b, c, d, e\}$. When sets are given in this way, the order used in listing the elements is considered immaterial; that is, $S = \{a, c, b, e, d\}$, or $S = \{d, c, b, e, a\}$, etc.

We frequently make use of symbols to denote arbitrary elements of a set. For example, we may use x to denote a real number, although no *particular* real number is specified. A letter that is used to represent any element of a given set is sometimes called a **variable**. Throughout this text, unless otherwise specified, variables will represent real numbers. In some cases it is necessary to restrict the numbers that are represented by a variable. We shall use the following terminology.

Definition | The **domain of a variable** is the set of real numbers represented by the variable.

The domain of a variable x is often referred to as the set of "permissible" or "allowable" values for x. To illustrate, given the expression $\sqrt{x}$, we note that in order to obtain a real number we must have $x \geq 0$, and hence, in this case the domain of x is assumed to be the set of nonnegative real numbers. Similarly, when working with the expression $1/(x - 2)$, we must exclude $x = 2$ (Why?), and consequently, we take the domain of x to be the set of all numbers different from 2.

If x is a variable, then expressions such as

$$x + 3 = 0, \quad x^2 - 5 = 4x, \quad (x^2 - 9)\sqrt[3]{x + 1} = 0$$

are called **equations** in x. If certain numbers are substituted for x in these equations, true statements are obtained, whereas other numbers produce false statements. For example, the equation $x + 3 = 0$ leads to a false statement for every value of x except -3. If 2 is substituted for x in the equation $x^2 - 5 = 4x$, we obtain $4 - 5 = 8$, or $-1 = 8$, a false statement. However, if we let $x = 5$, then we obtain $(5)^2 - 5 = 4 \cdot 5$, or $20 = 20$, which is true. If a true statement is obtained when x is replaced by some real number a from the domain of x, then a is called a **solution** or a **root** of an equation. We also say that a **satisfies** the equation. To **solve** an equation means to find all the solutions.

Sometimes every number in the domain of the variable is a solution of the equation. In this case the equation is called an **identity**. To illustrate,

$$\frac{1}{x^2 - 4} = \frac{1}{(x + 2)(x - 2)}$$

is an identity, since it is true for every number in the domain of x. If there are numbers in the domain of x that are not solutions, then the equation is called a **conditional equation**.

The solutions of an equation depend on the system of numbers under consideration. For example, if we demand that solutions be rational numbers, then the equation $x^2 = 2$ has no solutions, since there is no rational number whose square is 2. However, if we allow *real* numbers, then the solutions are $-\sqrt{2}$ and $\sqrt{2}$. Similarly, the equation $x^2 = -1$ has no real solutions; however, we shall see later that this equation has solutions if *complex* numbers are allowed.

Two equations are said to be **equivalent** if they have exactly the same solutions. For example, the equations

$$x - 1 = 2, \quad x = 3, \quad 5x = 15, \quad \text{and} \quad 2x + 1 = 7$$

are all equivalent.

One method of solving an equation is to replace it by a chain of equivalent equations, each in some sense simpler than the preceding one and terminating in an equation for which the solutions are obvious. This is often accomplished by using various properties of real numbers. For example, since x represents a real number, we may add the same expression in x to both sides of an equation without changing the solutions. Similarly, we may subtract x from both sides of an equation. We may also multiply or divide both sides of an equation by an expression that represents a nonzero real number.

We shall assume that the reader has had experience in finding solutions of equations in one variable. In particular, recall that the solutions of a *quadratic equation* $ax^2 + bx + c = 0$, where $a \neq 0$, may be obtained as follows.

Quadratic Formula

If $a \neq 0$, then the solutions of the equation $ax^2 + bx + c = 0$ are given by
$$x = \frac{-b \pm \sqrt{b^2 - 4ac}}{2a}.$$

The solutions are real if $b^2 - 4ac$ is nonnegative. The case $b^2 - 4ac < 0$ is discussed in Chapter Five.

Example 3   Find the solutions of $2x^2 + 7x - 15 = 0$.

Solution   Using the Quadratic Formula with $a = 2$, $b = 7$, and $c = -15$ gives us

$$x = \frac{-7 \pm \sqrt{49 + 120}}{4} = \frac{-7 \pm \sqrt{169}}{4} = \frac{-7 \pm 13}{4}.$$

Hence,

$$x = \frac{-7 + 13}{4} = \frac{3}{2} \quad \text{or} \quad x = \frac{-7 - 13}{4} = -5.$$

Consequently, the solutions are $3/2$ and -5.

The given equation can also be solved by factoring. We begin by writing

$$2x^2 + 7x - 15 = (2x - 3)(x + 5) = 0.$$

Since a product can equal zero only if one of the factors is zero, we obtain

$$2x - 3 = 0 \quad \text{or} \quad x + 5 = 0.$$

This leads to the same solutions, $3/2$ and -5.   ∎

EXERCISES 1.1

In Exercises 1–4, replace the symbol □ between each member of the given pairs of real numbers with the appropriate symbol $<$, $>$, or $=$.

1   (a) $-7 \,\square\, -4$ (b) $3 \,\square\, -1$
   (c) $1 + 3 \,\square\, 6 - 2$

2   (a) $-3 \,\square\, -5$ (b) $-6 \,\square\, 2$
   (c) $1/4 \,\square\, 0.25$

3   (a) $1/3 \,\square\, 0.33$ (b) $125/57 \,\square\, 2.193$
   (c) $22/7 \,\square\, \pi$

4   (a) $1/7 \,\square\, 0.143$ (b) $(3/4) + (2/3) \,\square\, 19/12$
   (c) $\sqrt{2} \,\square\, 1.4$

In each of Exercises 5–16, express the given statement in terms of inequalities.

5   -8 is less than -5 6   2 is greater than 1.9

7 0 is greater than -1 **8** $\sqrt{2}$ is less than π

9 x is negative   **10** y is positive

11 a is between 5 and 3

12 b is between 1/10 and 1/3

13 b is greater than or equal to 2

14 x is less than or equal to -5

15 c is not greater than 1

16 d is nonnegative

Rewrite the numbers in Exercises 17–20 without using symbols for absolute value.

17 (a) $|4 - 9|$ (b) $|-4| - |-9|$
(c) $|4| + |-9|$

18 (a) $|3 - 6|$ (b) $|0.2 - (1/5)|$
(c) $|-3| - |-4|$

19 (a) $3 - |-3|$ (b) $|\pi - 4|$
(c) $(-3)/|-3|$

20 (a) $|8 - 5|$ (b) $-5 + |-7|$
(c) $(-2)|-2|$

In each of Exercises 21–24, the given numbers are coordinates of three points A, B, and C (in that order) on a coordinate line l. Find (a) $d(A, B)$; (b) $d(B, C)$; (c) $d(C, B)$; (d) $d(A, C)$

21 $-6, -2, 4$ **22** $3, 7, -5$

23 $8, -4, -1$ **24** $-9, 1, 10$

Use the Quadratic Formula to solve the equations in Exercises 25–36.

25 $2x^2 - x - 3 = 0$ **26** $u^2 + 2u - 6 = 0$

27 $3x^2 - 2x - 8 = 0$ **28** $v^2 + 3v - 5 = 0$

29 $2x^2 - 4x - 5 = 0$ **30** $3x^2 - 6x + 2 = 0$

31 $4y^2 - 20y + 25 = 0$ **32** $9t^2 + 6t + 1 = 0$

33 $4x^4 - 37x^2 + 9 = 0$ **34** $2x^4 - 9x^2 + 4 = 0$

35 $3z^4 - 5z^2 + 1 = 0$ **36** $2y^4 + y^2 - 5 = 0$

1.2 COORDINATE SYSTEMS IN TWO DIMENSIONS

In Section 1.1 we discussed how coordinates may be assigned to points on a straight line. Coordinate systems can also be introduced in planes by means of ordered pairs. The term **ordered pair** refers to two real numbers, where one is designated as the "first" number and the other as the "second." The symbol (a, b) is used to denote the ordered pair consisting of the real numbers a and b where a is first and b is second. We consider two ordered pairs (a, b) and (c, d) equal, and write

$$(a, b) = (c, d) \quad \text{if and only if} \quad a = c \text{ and } b = d.$$

This implies, in particular, that $(a, b) \neq (b, a)$ if $a \neq b$.

A **rectangular**, or **Cartesian,*** **coordinate system** may be introduced in a plane by considering two perpendicular coordinate lines in the plane which intersect in the origin O on each line. Unless specified otherwise, the same unit of length is chosen on each line. Usually one of the lines is horizontal with positive direction to the right, and the other line is vertical with positive direction upward, as indicated by the arrowheads

* The term "Cartesian" is used in honor of the French mathematician and philosopher René Descartes (1596–1650), who was one of the first to employ such coordinate systems.

in Figure 1.5. The two lines are called **coordinate axes** and the point O is called the **origin**. The horizontal line is often referred to as the **x-axis** and the vertical line as the **y-axis**, and they are labeled x and y, respectively. The plane is then called a **coordinate plane** or, with the preceding notation for coordinate axes, an **xy-plane**. Although the symbols x and y are used to denote lines as well as numbers, there should be no misunderstanding as to what these letters represent when they appear alongside of coordinate lines, as in Figure 1.5. In certain applications different labels such as d, t, etc., are used for the coordinate lines. The coordinate axes divide the plane into four parts called the **first, second, third,** and **fourth quadrants** and labeled I, II, III, and IV, respectively, as shown in Figure 1.5.

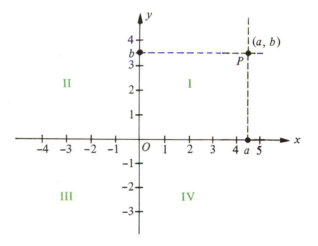

Figure 1.5

Each point P in an xy-plane may be assigned a unique ordered pair. If vertical and horizontal lines through P intersect the x- and y-axes at points with coordinates a and b, respectively (see Figure 1.5), then P is assigned the ordered pair (a, b). The number a is called the **x-coordinate** (or **abscissa**) of P, and b is called the **y-coordinate** (or **ordinate**) of P. We sometimes say that P *has coordinates* (a, b), or that P *is the point* (a, b).

Conversely, every ordered pair (a, b) determines a point P in the xy-plane with coordinates a and b. Specifically, P is the point of intersection of lines perpendicular to the x-axis and y-axis at the points having coordinates a and b, respectively. This establishes a one-to-one correspondence between the set of all points in the xy-plane and the set of all ordered pairs.

The symbol $P(a, b)$ will denote the point P with coordinates (a, b). To **plot a point** $P(a, b)$ means to represent P by a dot in the appropriate position, as illustrated in Figure 1.5. Note that abscissas are positive for points in quadrants I or IV and negative for points in quadrants II or III. Ordinates are positive for points in quadrants I or II and negative for points in quadrants III or IV. Some typical points in a coordinate plane are plotted in Figure 1.6.

We shall next derive a formula for finding the distance between any two points in a coordinate plane. The distance between two points P and Q will be denoted by $d(P, Q)$.

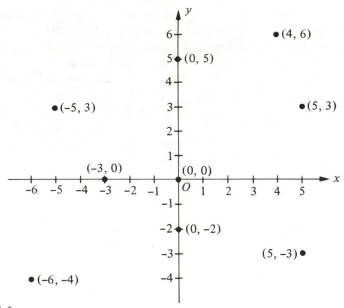

Figure 1.6

If $P = Q$, then we agree that $d(P, Q) = 0$, whereas if $P \neq Q$, the distance is positive. Let us consider any two points $P_1(x_1, y_1)$ and $P_2(x_2, y_2)$ in the plane. If the points lie on the same horizontal line, then $y_1 = y_2$, and we may denote the points by $P_1(x_1, y_1)$ and $P_2(x_2, y_1)$. If lines through P_1 and P_2 parallel to the y-axis intersect the x-axis at $A_1(x_1, 0)$ and $A_2(x_2, 0)$, as shown in (i) of Figure 1.7, then $d(P_1, P_2) = d(A_1, A_2)$. However, from Section 1.1, $d(A_1, A_2) = |x_2 - x_1|$, and hence,

$$d(P_1, P_2) = |x_2 - x_1|.$$

Since $|x_2 - x_1| = |x_1 - x_2|$, the last formula is valid whether P_1 lies to the left of P_2 or to the right of P_2. Moreover, the formula is independent of the quadrants in which the points lie.

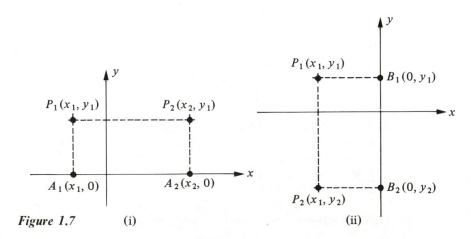

Figure 1.7   (i)   (ii)

In similar fashion, if P_1 and P_2 are on the same vertical line, then $x_1 = x_2$, and we may denote the points by $P_1(x_1, y_1)$ and $P_2(x_1, y_2)$. If we consider the points $B_1(0, y_1)$ and $B_2(0, y_2)$ on the y-axis, as shown in (ii) of Figure 1.7, then

$$d(P_1, P_2) = d(B_1, B_2) = |y_2 - y_1|.$$

Finally, let us consider the general case, in which the points $P_1(x_1, y_1)$ and $P_2(x_2, y_2)$ do not lie on the same horizontal or vertical line. The line through $P_1(x_1, y_1)$ parallel to the x-axis and the line through $P_2(x_2, y_2)$ parallel to the y-axis intersect at some point P_3. Since P_3 has the same y-coordinate as P_1 and the same x-coordinate as P_2, we can denote it by $P_3(x_2, y_1)$ (see Figure 1.8). From the previous discussion

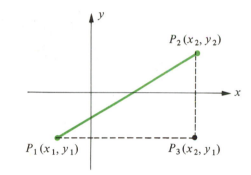

Figure 1.8

$d(P_1, P_3) = |x_2 - x_1|$ and $d(P_3, P_2) = |y_2 - y_1|$. Since P_1, P_2, and P_3 form a right triangle with hypotenuse from P_1 to P_2, we have, by the Pythagorean Theorem,

$$[d(P_1, P_2)]^2 = [d(P_1, P_3)]^2 + [d(P_3, P_2)]^2$$

and hence,

$$[d(P_1, P_2)]^2 = |x_2 - x_1|^2 + |y_2 - y_1|^2.$$

Using the fact that $d(P_1, P_2)$ is nonnegative and that $|a|^2 = a^2$ for every real number a, we obtain the following important formula.

Distance Formula

> If $P_1(x_1, y_1)$ and $P_2(x_2, y_2)$ are points in a coordinate plane, then the **distance between P_1 and P_2** is given by
>
> $$d(P_1, P_2) = \sqrt{(x_2 - x_1)^2 + (y_2 - y_1)^2}.$$

Although we referred to the special case indicated in Figure 1.8, the argument used in the proof of the Distance Formula is independent of the positions of P_1 and P_2.

Example 1 Plot the points $A(-1, -3)$, $B(6, 1)$, and $C(2, -5)$, and prove that the triangle with vertices A, B, and C is a right triangle.

Solution   The points and the triangle are shown in Figure 1.9. From plane geometry, a triangle is a right triangle if and only if the sum of the squares of two of its sides is equal to the square of the remaining side. Using the Distance Formula, we obtain

$$d(A, B) = \sqrt{(-1 - 6)^2 + (-3 - 1)^2}$$

$$= \sqrt{49 + 16} = \sqrt{65}$$

$$d(B, C) = \sqrt{(6 - 2)^2 + (1 + 5)^2}$$

$$= \sqrt{16 + 36} = \sqrt{52}$$

$$d(A, C) = \sqrt{(-1 - 2)^2 + (-3 + 5)^2}$$

$$= \sqrt{9 + 4} = \sqrt{13}$$

Since $[d(A, B)]^2 = [d(B, C)]^2 + [d(A, C)]^2$, the triangle is a right triangle with hypotenuse joining A to B.

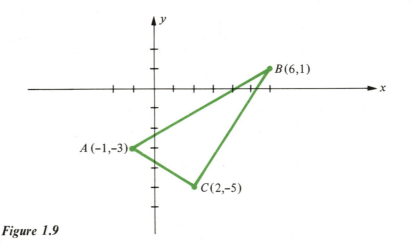

Figure 1.9

It is easy to obtain a formula for the midpoint of a line segment. Let $P_1(x_1, y_1)$ and $P_2(x_2, y_2)$ be two points in a coordinate plane, and let M be the midpoint of the segment $P_1 P_2$. The lines through P_1 and P_2 parallel to the y-axis intersect the x-axis at $A_1(x_1, 0)$ and $A_2(x_2, 0)$, and, from plane geometry, the line through M parallel to the y-axis bisects the segment $A_1 A_2$ (see Figure 1.10). If $x_1 < x_2$, then $x_2 - x_1 > 0$, and hence,

$$d(A_1, A_2) = x_2 - x_1.$$

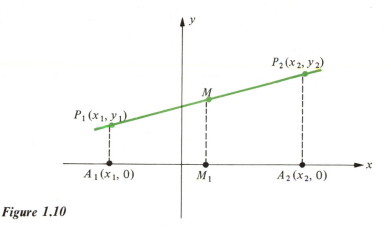

Figure 1.10

Since M_1 is halfway from A_1 to A_2, the abscissa of M_1 is

$$x_1 + \tfrac{1}{2}(x_2 - x_1) = x_1 + \tfrac{1}{2}x_2 - \tfrac{1}{2}x_1$$
$$= \tfrac{1}{2}x_1 + \tfrac{1}{2}x_2$$
$$= \frac{x_1 + x_2}{2}.$$

It follows that the abscissa of M is also $(x_1 + x_2)/2$. It can be shown in similar fashion that the ordinate of M is $(y_1 + y_2)/2$. Moreover, these formulas hold for all positions of P_1 and P_2. This gives us the following result.

Midpoint Formula

> The midpoint of the line segment from $P_1(x_1, y_1)$ to $P_2(x_2, y_2)$ is
>
> $$\left(\frac{x_1 + x_2}{2}, \frac{y_1 + y_2}{2} \right).$$

Example 2   Find the midpoint M of the line segment from $P_1(-2, 3)$ to $P_2(4, -2)$. Plot the points P_1, P_2, and M, and verify that $d(P_1, M) = d(P_2, M)$.

Solution   Applying the Midpoint Formula, the coordinates of M are

$$\left(\frac{-2 + 4}{2}, \frac{3 + (-2)}{2} \right) \quad \text{or} \quad \left(1, \frac{1}{2} \right)$$

The three points P_1, P_2, and M are plotted in Figure 1.11. Using the Distance Formula, we obtain

$$d(P_1, M) = \sqrt{(-2 - 1)^2 + (3 - \tfrac{1}{2})^2} = \sqrt{9 + (\tfrac{25}{4})}$$
$$d(P_2, M) = \sqrt{(4 - 1)^2 + (-2 - \tfrac{1}{2})^2} = \sqrt{9 + (\tfrac{25}{4})}.$$

Hence, $d(P_1, M) = d(P_2, M)$.

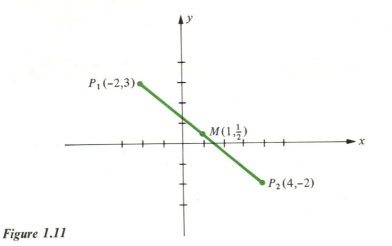

Figure 1.11

■

EXERCISES 1.2

1 Plot the following points on a rectangular coordinate system: $A(5, -2)$, $B(-5, -2)$, $C(5, 2)$, $D(-5, 2)$, $E(3, 0)$, $F(0, 3)$.

2 Plot the points $A(-3, 1)$, $B(3, 1)$, $C(-2, -3)$, $D(0, 3)$, and $E(2, -3)$ on a rectangular coordinate system, and then draw the line segments AB, BC, CD, DE, and EA.

3 Plot $A(0, 0)$, $B(1, 1)$, $C(3, 3)$, $D(-1, -1)$, and $E(-2, -2)$. Describe the set of all points of the form (x, x) where x is a real number.

4 Plot $A(0, 0)$, $B(1, -1)$, $C(2, -2)$, $D(-1, 1)$, and $E(-3, 3)$. Describe the set of all points of the form $(a, -a)$ where a is a real number.

5 Describe the set of all points $P(x, y)$ in a coordinate plane such that
(a) $x = 3$ (b) $y = -1$ (c) $x \geq 0$ (d) $xy > 0$
(e) $y < 0$.

6 Describe the set of all points $P(x, y)$ in a coordinate plane such that
(a) $y = 0$ (b) $x = -5$ (c) $x/y < 0$ (d) $xy = 0$
(e) $y > 1$.

In Exercises 7–12, find (a) the distance $d(A, B)$ between the given points A and B; (b) the midpoint of the segment AB.

7 $A(4, -3)$, $B(6, 2)$ **8** $A(-2, -5)$, $B(4, 6)$

9 $A(-5, 0)$, $B(-2, -2)$

10 $A(6, 2)$, $B(6, -2)$ **11** $A(7, -3)$, $B(3, -3)$

12 $A(-4, 7)$, $B(0, -8)$

In Exercises 13 and 14, prove that the triangle with the indicated vertices is a right triangle and find its area.

13 $A(8, 5)$, $B(1, -2)$, $C(-3, 2)$

14 $A(-6, 3)$, $B(3, -5)$, $C(-1, 5)$

15 Prove that the following points are vertices of a square: $A(-4, 2)$, $B(1, 4)$, $C(3, -1)$, $D(-2, -3)$.

16 Prove that the following points are vertices of a parallelogram: $A(-4, -1)$, $B(0, -2)$, $C(6, 1)$, $D(2, 2)$.

17 Given $A(-3, 8)$, find the coordinates of the point B such that $M(5, -10)$ is the midpoint of AB.

18 Given $A(5, -8)$ and $B(-6, 2)$, find the point on AB that is three-fourths of the way from A to B.

19 Given $A(-4, -3)$ and $B(6, 1)$, prove that $P(5, -11)$ is on the perpendicular bisector of AB.

20 Given $A(-4, -3)$ and $B(6, 1)$, find a formula that expresses the fact that $P(x, y)$ is on the perpendicular bisector of AB.

21 Find a formula that expresses the fact that $P(x, y)$ is a distance 5 from the origin. Describe the totality of all such points.

22 If r is a positive real number, find a formula that states that $P(x, y)$ is a distance r from a fixed point $C(h, k)$. Describe the totality of all such points.

1.3 GRAPHS

If W is a set of ordered pairs, we may consider the point $P(x, y)$ in a coordinate plane which corresponds to the ordered pair (x, y) in W. The **graph** of W is the set of all such points. The phrase "sketch the graph of W" means to illustrate the significant features of the graph geometrically on a coordinate plane, as illustrated in the next example.

Example 1 Sketch the graph of $W = \{(x, y) : y = 2x - 1\}$.

Solution We begin by finding points with coordinates of the form (x, y), where the ordered pair (x, y) is in W. It is convenient to list these coordinates in tabular form, as shown below, where for each real number x the corresponding value for y is $2x - 1$.

x	-2	-1	0	1	2	3
y	-5	-3	-1	1	3	5

Plotting indicates that the points with these coordinates all lie on a line, and we sketch the graph accordingly (see Figure 1.12). Ordinarily the few points we have plotted would not be enough to illustrate the graph; however, in this elementary case we can be reasonably sure that the graph is a line. It will be proved in Chapter Seven that our conjecture is correct.

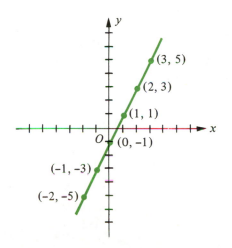

Figure 1.12

It is impossible to sketch the entire graph in Example 1 since x may be assigned values that are numerically as large as desired. Nevertheless, we often call a drawing of the type given in Figure 1.12 *the graph of* W *or a sketch of the graph*, where it is understood that the drawing is only a device for visualizing the actual graph and the line does not terminate as shown in the figure. In general, when sketching a graph you should illustrate enough of the graph so that the remaining parts are evident.

Given an equation in x and y, we say that an ordered pair (a, b) is a **solution** of the equation if equality is obtained when a is substituted for x and b for y. For example, $(2, 3)$ is a solution of $y = 2x - 1$, since substitution of 2 for x and 3 for y leads to $3 = 4 - 1$, or $3 = 3$. Two equations in x and y are **equivalent** if they have exactly the same solutions. The solutions of an equation in x and y determine a set S of ordered pairs, and we define the **graph of the equation** as the graph of S. Note that the graph of the equation $y = 2x - 1$ is the same as the graph of the set W in Example 1 (see Figure 1.12).

For some equations encountered in this chapter, the technique used for sketching the graph will consist of plotting a sufficient number of points until some pattern emerges, and then sketching the graph accordingly. This is obviously a crude (and often inaccurate) way to arrive at the graph; however, it is a method often employed at the beginning of elementary courses. In order to give accurate descriptions of graphs when complicated expressions are involved, it is usually necessary to employ more advanced mathematical tools of the types introduced in the study of calculus.

Example 2   Sketch the graph of the equation $y = x^2$.

Solution   The following table exhibits the coordinates of some points on the graph.

x	-3	$-\frac{5}{2}$	-2	$-\frac{3}{2}$	-1	$-\frac{1}{2}$	0	$\frac{1}{2}$	1	$\frac{3}{2}$	2	$\frac{5}{2}$	3
y	9	$\frac{25}{4}$	4	$\frac{9}{4}$	1	$\frac{1}{4}$	0	$\frac{1}{4}$	1	$\frac{9}{4}$	4	$\frac{25}{4}$	9

Larger numerical values of x produce even larger values of y. For example, the points $(4, 16)$, $(5, 25)$, and $(6, 36)$ are on the graph, as are $(-4, 16)$, $(-5, 25)$, and $(-6, 36)$. Plotting the points given in the table and drawing a smooth curve through these points, we obtain the sketch in Figure 1.13, where we have labeled several points.

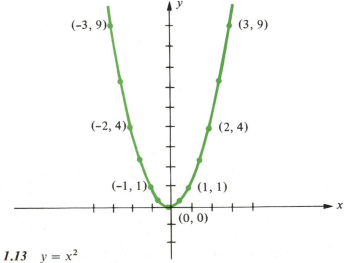

Figure 1.13 $y = x^2$

The graph in Example 2 is called a **parabola.** The lowest point $(0,0)$ is called the **vertex** of the parabola, and we say that the parabola **opens upward.** If the graph were inverted, as would be the case for $y = -x^2$, then the parabola would **open downward.** The y-axis is called the **axis of the parabola**.

If the coordinate plane in Figure 1.13 is folded along the y-axis, then the graph that lies in the left half of the plane coincides with that in the right half. We say that **the graph is symmetric with respect to the y-axis**. As in (i) of Figure 1.14, a graph is symmetric with respect to the y-axis provided that the point $(-x, y)$ is on the graph whenever (x, y) is on the graph. Similarly, as in (ii) of Figure 1.14, **a graph is symmetric with respect to the x-axis** if whenever a point (x, y) is on the graph, then $(x, -y)$ is also on the graph. In this case, if we fold the coordinate plane along the x-axis, that part of the graph which lies above the x-axis will coincide with the part which lies below. Another type of symmetry which certain graphs possess is called **symmetry with respect to the origin**. In this situation, whenever a point (x, y) is on the graph, then $(-x, -y)$ is also on the graph, as illustrated in (iii) of Figure 1.14.

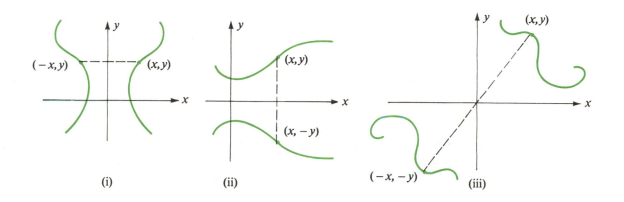

Figure 1.14

The following tests are useful for investigating these three types of symmetry.

Tests for Symmetry

(i)   The graph of an equation is symmetric with respect to the y-axis if substitution of $-x$ for x leads to an equivalent equation.

(ii) The graph of an equation is symmetric with respect to the x-axis if substitution of $-y$ for y leads to an equivalent equation.

(iii) The graph of an equation is symmetric with respect to the origin if the simultaneous substitution of $-x$ for x and $-y$ for y leads to an equivalent equation.

If, in the equation of Example 2, we substitute $-x$ for x, we obtain $y = (-x)^2$, which is equivalent to $y = x^2$. Hence, by Symmetry Test (i) the graph is symmetric with respect to the y-axis.

If symmetry with respect to an axis exists, then it is sufficient to determine the graph in half of the coordinate plane, since the remainder of the graph is a mirror image, or reflection, of that half.

Example 3   Sketch the graph of $y^2 = x$.

Solution   Since substitution of $-y$ for y does not change the equation, the graph is symmetric with respect to the x-axis. (See Symmetry Test (ii).) It is sufficient, therefore, to plot points with nonnegative ordinates and then reflect through the x-axis. Since $y^2 = x$, the ordinates of points above the x-axis are given by $y = \sqrt{x}$. Coordinates of some points on the graph are tabulated below. A portion of the graph is sketched in Figure 1.15. The graph is a parabola with vertex at the origin and which opens to the right. In this case the x-axis is the axis of the parabola.

x	0	1	2	3	4	9
y	0	1	$\sqrt{2}$	$\sqrt{3}$	2	3

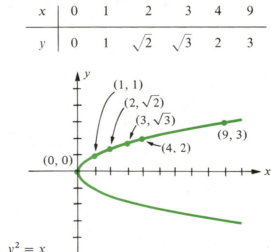

Figure 1.15 $y^2 = x$

Example 4   Sketch the graph of the equation $y = x^3$.

Solution   If we substitute $-x$ for x and $-y$ for y, then

$$-y = (-x)^3 = -x^3.$$

Multiplying both sides by -1, we see that the last equation has the same solutions as the given equation $y = x^3$. Hence, from Symmetry Test (iii), the graph is symmetric with respect to the origin. The following table lists some points on the graph.

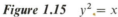

x	0	$\frac{1}{4}$	$\frac{1}{2}$	$\frac{3}{4}$	1	$\frac{3}{2}$	2
y	0	$\frac{1}{64}$	$\frac{1}{8}$	$\frac{27}{64}$	1	$\frac{27}{8}$	8

By symmetry (or substitution) we see that the points $(-\frac{1}{4}, -\frac{1}{64})$, $(-\frac{1}{2}, -\frac{1}{8})$, etc., are on the graph. Plotting points leads to the graph in Figure 1.16.

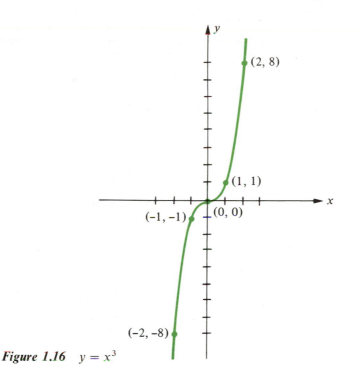

Figure 1.16 $y = x^3$

If $C(h, k)$ is a point in a coordinate plane, then a circle with center C and radius r may be defined as the collection of all points in the plane that are r units from C. As shown in (i) of Figure 1.17 a point $P(x, y)$ is on the circle if and only if $d(C, P) = r$, or, by the Distance Formula, if and only if

$$\sqrt{(x - h)^2 + (y - k)^2} = r.$$

The equivalent equation

$$\boxed{(x - h)^2 + (y - k)^2 = r^2, \text{ where } r > 0}$$

is called the **standard equation of a circle of radius r and center (h, k)**. If $h = 0$ and $k = 0$, this reduces to

$$\boxed{x^2 + y^2 = r^2}$$

which is an equation of a circle of radius r with center at the origin (see (ii) of Figure 1.17). If $r = 1$, we obtain a **unit circle** with center at the origin. Note that a point $P(x, y)$ is on this unit circle if and only if $x^2 + y^2 = 1$.

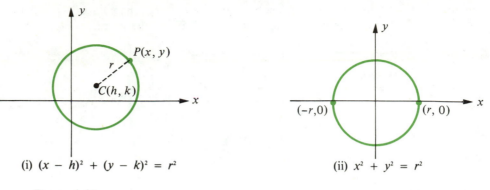

(i) $(x - h)^2 + (y - k)^2 = r^2$ (ii) $x^2 + y^2 = r^2$

Figure 1.17

Example 5   Find an equation of the circle having center $C(-2, 3)$ and containing the point $D(4, 5)$.

Solution   The circle is illustrated in Figure 1.18. Since D is on the circle, the radius r is the distance from the center to D. By the Distance Formula,

$$r = d(C, D) = \sqrt{(-2 - 4)^2 + (3 - 5)^2}$$
$$= \sqrt{36 + 4} = \sqrt{40}.$$

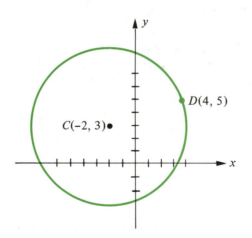

Figure 1.18

Using the standard equation of a circle with $h = -2$ and $k = 3$, we obtain

$$(x + 2)^2 + (y - 3)^2 = 40.$$

Squaring the indicated terms and simplifying gives us the equivalent equation

$$x^2 + y^2 + 4x - 6y - 27 = 0.$$ ∎

EXERCISES 1.3

In each of Exercises 1–20 sketch the graph of the equation after plotting a sufficient number of points.

1 $y = 3x + 1$

2 $y = 4x - 3$

3 $y = -2x + 3$

4 $y = 2 - 3x$

5 $2y + 3x + 6 = 0$

6 $3y - 2x = 6$

7 $y = 2x^2$

8 $y = -x^2$

9 $y = 2x^2 - 1$

10 $y = -x^2 + 2$

11 $4y = x^2$

12 $3y + x^2 = 0$

13 $y = -\frac{1}{2}x^3$

14 $y = \frac{1}{2}x^3$

15 $y = x^3 - 2$

16 $y = 2 - x^3$

17 $y = \sqrt{x}$

18 $y = \sqrt{x} - 1$

19 $y = \sqrt{-x}$

20 $y = \sqrt{x - 1}$

Describe the graphs in Exercises 21–28.

21 $x^2 + y^2 = 16$

22 $x^2 + y^2 = 25$

23 $9x^2 + 9y^2 = 1$

24 $2x^2 + 2y^2 = 1$

25 $(x - 2)^2 + (y + 1)^2 = 4$

26 $(x + 3)^2 + (y - 4)^2 = 1$

27 $x^2 + (y - 3)^2 = 9$ **28** $(x + 5)^2 + y^2 = 16$

In each of Exercises 29–38, find an equation of a circle satisfying the stated conditions.

29 Center $C(3, -2)$, radius 4

30 Center $C(-5, 2)$, radius 5

31 Center $C(\frac{1}{2}, -\frac{3}{2})$, radius 2

32 Center $C(\frac{1}{3}, 0)$, radius $\sqrt{3}$

33 Center at the origin, passing through $P(-3, 5)$

34 Center $C(-4, 6)$, passing through $P(1, 2)$

35 Center $C(-4, 2)$, tangent to the x-axis

36 Center $C(3, -5)$, tangent to the y-axis

37 Endpoints of a diameter $A(4, -3)$ and $B(-2, 7)$

38 Tangent to both axes, center in the first quadrant, radius 2

1.4 DEFINITION OF FUNCTION

The notion of **correspondence** is encountered frequently in everyday life. For example, to each book in a library there corresponds the number of pages in the book. As another example, to each human being there corresponds a birth date. To cite a third example, if the temperature of the air is recorded throughout a day, then at each instant of time there is a corresponding temperature.

The examples of correspondences we have given involve two sets X and Y. In our first example, X denotes the set of books in a library and Y the set of positive integers. For each book x in X there corresponds a positive integer y, namely the number of pages in the book.

We sometimes represent correspondences by diagrams of the type shown in Figure 1.19, where the sets X and Y are represented by points within regions in a plane. The curved arrow indicates that the element y of Y corresponds to the element x of X. We have pictured X and Y as different sets. However, X and Y may have elements in common. As a matter of fact, we often have $X = Y$.

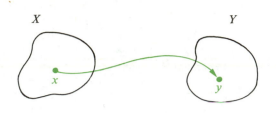

Figure 1.19

Our examples indicate that to each x in X there corresponds *one and only one y* in Y; that is, *y is unique* for a given x. However, the same element of Y may correspond to different elements of X. For example, two different books may have the same number of pages, two different people may have the same birthday; and so on.

In most of our work X and Y will be sets of numbers. To illustrate, let X and Y both denote the set $\mathbb{R}$ of real numbers, and to each real number x let us assign its square x^2. Thus to 3 we assign 9, to -5 we assign 25 and to $\sqrt{2}$ the number 2. This gives us a correspondence from $\mathbb{R}$ to $\mathbb{R}$.

All the examples of correspondences we have given are *functions*, as defined below.

Definition

> A **function** f from a set X to a set Y is a correspondence that assigns to each element x of X a unique element y of Y. The element y is called the **image** of x under f and is denoted by $f(x)$. The set X is called the **domain** of the function. The **range** of the function consists of all images of elements of X.

The notation $f(x)$ for the element of Y that corresponds to x is read "f of x." We also call $f(x)$ the **value** of f at x. In terms of the pictorial representation given earlier, we may now sketch a diagram as in Figure 1.20. The curved arrows indicate that the elements $f(x), f(w), f(z)$, and $f(a)$ of Y correspond to the elements x, w, z, and a of X. Let us repeat the important fact that to each x in X there is assigned precisely one image $f(x)$ in Y; however, different elements of X, such as w and z in Figure 1.20, may have the same image in Y.

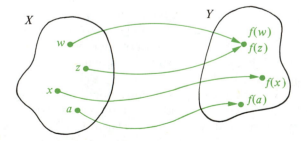

Figure 1.20

Beginning students are sometimes confused by the symbols f and $f(x)$. Remember that f is used to represent the function. It is neither in X nor in Y. However, $f(x)$ is an element of Y, namely the element that f assigns to x.

Two functions f and g from X to Y are said to be **equal**, and we write

$$f = g \quad \text{if and only if} \quad f(x) = g(x)$$

for every x in X.

Example 1 Let f be the function with domain $\mathbb{R}$ such that $f(x) = x^2$ for every x in $\mathbb{R}$. Find $f(-6)$, $f(\sqrt{3})$, and $f(a)$, where a is any real number. What is the range of f?

Solution Values of f (or images under f) may be found by substituting for x in the equation $f(x) = x^2$. Thus,

$$f(-6) = (-6)^2 = 36, \quad f(\sqrt{3}) = (\sqrt{3})^2 = 3, \quad \text{and} \quad f(a) = a^2.$$

If T denotes the range of f, then by definition T consists of all numbers of the form $f(a)$ where a is in $\mathbb{R}$. Hence T is the set of all squares a^2, where a is a real number. Since the square of any real number is nonnegative, T is contained in the set of all nonnegative real numbers. Moreover, every nonnegative real number c is an image under f, since $f(\sqrt{c}) = (\sqrt{c})^2 = c$. Hence the range of f is the set of all nonnegative real numbers. ∎

If a function is defined as in the preceding example, the symbol used for the variable is immaterial; that is, expressions such as $f(x) = x^2$, $f(s) = s^2$, $f(t) = t^2$, and so on, all define the same function f. This is true because if a is any number in the domain of f, then the same image a^2 is obtained no matter which expression is employed.

Example 2 Let X denote the set of nonnegative real numbers, and let f be the function from X to $\mathbb{R}$ defined by $f(x) = \sqrt{x} + 1$ for every x in X. Find $f(4)$ and $f(\pi)$. If b and c are in X, find $f(b + c)$ and $f(b) + f(c)$.

Solution As in Example 1, finding images under f is simply a matter of substituting the appropriate number for x in the expression for $f(x)$. Thus,

$$f(4) = \sqrt{4} + 1 = 2 + 1 = 3$$
$$f(\pi) = \sqrt{\pi} + 1$$
$$f(b + c) = \sqrt{b + c} + 1$$
$$f(b) + f(c) = (\sqrt{b} + 1) + (\sqrt{c} + 1) = \sqrt{b} + \sqrt{c} + 2.$$
∎

Many formulas that occur in mathematics and the sciences determine functions. As an illustration, the formula $A = \pi r^2$ for the area A of a circle of radius r assigns to each positive real number r a unique value of A. This determines a function f, where $f(r) = \pi r^2$, and we may write $A = f(r)$. The letter r, which represents an arbitrary number from the domain of f, is often called an **independent variable.** The letter A, which represents a number from the range of f, is called a **dependent variable,** since its value depends on the number assigned to r. If two variables r and A are related in this manner, it is customary to use the phrase A *is a function of* r. To cite another example, if an automobile travels at a uniform rate of 50 miles per hour, then the distance d (miles) traveled in time t (hours) is given by $d = 50t$, and hence, the distance d is a function of time t.

We have seen that different elements in the domain of a function may have the same image. If images are always different, then, as in the next definition, the function is called *one-to-one.*

Definition

A function f from X to Y is a **one-to-one function** if, whenever $a \neq b$ in X, then $f(a) \neq f(b)$ in Y.

If f is one-to-one, then each $f(x)$ in the range is the image of *precisely one* x in X. The function illustrated in Figure 1.20 is not one-to-one, since two different elements w and z of X have the same image in Y. A one-to-one function is often called a **one-to-one correspondence**. The association between real numbers and points on a coordinate line is an example of a one-to-one correspondence.

Example 3
(a) If $f(x) = 3x + 2$, where x is real, prove that f is one-to-one.
(b) If $g(x) = x^2 + 5$, where x is real, prove that g is not one-to-one.

Solution

(a) If $a \neq b$, then $3a \neq 3b$, and thus, $3a + 2 \neq 3b + 2$, or $f(a) \neq f(b)$. Hence, f is one-to-one.

(b) The function g is not one-to-one, since different numbers in the domain may have the same image. For example, although $-1 \neq 1$, both $g(-1)$ and $g(1)$ are equal to 6. ∎

In the remainder of our work, unless specified otherwise, the phrase f *is a function* will mean that the domain and range are sets of real numbers. If a function is defined by means of some expression, as in Examples 1–3, and the domain X is not stated explicitly, then X is considered to be the totality of real numbers for which the given expression is meaningful. To illustrate, if $f(x) = \sqrt{x}/(x-1)$, then the domain is assumed to be the set of nonnegative real numbers different from 1. If x is in the domain, we sometimes say that f **is defined at** x, or that $f(x)$ **exists**. If a subset S is contained in the domain, we often say that f **is defined on** S. The terminology f **is undefined at** x means that x is not in the domain of f.

The types of functions described in the next definition occur frequently.

Definition

> A function f with domain X is
>
> (i) **even** if $f(-x) = f(x)$ for every x in X.
> (ii) **odd** if $f(-x) = -f(x)$ for every x in X.

Example 4
(a) If $f(x) = 3x^4 - 2x^2 + 5$, show that f is an even function.
(b) If $g(x) = 2x^5 - 7x^3 + 4x$, show that f is an odd function.

Solution   If x is any real number, then

(a) $\quad f(-x) = 3(-x)^4 - 2(-x)^2 + 5$
$\qquad\qquad = 3x^4 - 2x^2 + 5 = f(x).$

Hence, f is even.

(b) $\quad g(-x) = 2(-x)^5 - 7(-x)^3 + 4(-x)$
$\qquad\qquad = -2x^5 + 7x^3 - 4x = -g(x).$

That is, g is odd.   ∎

The concept of ordered pair can be used to obtain an alternative approach to functions. We first observe that a function f from X to Y determines the following set W of ordered pairs:

$$W = \{(x, f(x)) : x \text{ is in } X\}.$$

Thus W is the totality of ordered pairs for which the first number is in X and the second number is the image of the first. In Example 2, where $f(x) = \sqrt{x} + 1$, W consists of all pairs of the form $(x, \sqrt{x} + 1)$, where x is a nonnegative real number. It is important to note that for each x there is exactly one ordered pair (x, y) in W having x in the first position.

Conversely, if we begin with a set W of ordered pairs such that each x in X appears exactly once in the first position of an ordered pair, and numbers from Y appear in the second position, then W determines a function from X to Y. Specifically, for any x in X there is a unique pair (x, y) in W, and by letting y correspond to x, we obtain a function from X to Y.

It follows from the preceding discussion that the statement given below could also be used as a definition of function. We prefer, however, to think of it as an alternative approach to this concept.

Alternative Definition of a Function

> A function with domain X is a set W of ordered pairs such that for each x in X there is exactly one ordered pair (x, y) in W having x in the first position.

In terms of the preceding definition, the function f of Example 1, where $f(x) = x^2$, is the set of all ordered pairs of the form (x, x^2). Similarly, the ordered pairs $(x, \sqrt{x} + 1)$ determine the function of Example 2, where we had $f(x) = \sqrt{x} + 1$.

EXERCISES 1.4

1 If $f(x) = 2x^2 - 3x + 4$, find $f(1)$, $f(-1)$, $f(0)$, and $f(2)$.

2 If $f(x) = x^3 + 5x^2 - 1$, find $f(2)$, $f(-2)$, $f(0)$, and $f(-1)$.

3 If $f(x) = \sqrt{x - 1} + 2x$, find $f(1)$, $f(3)$, $f(5)$, and $f(10)$.

4 If $f(x) = \dfrac{x}{x - 2}$, find $f(1)$, $f(3)$, $f(-2)$, and $f(0)$.

In Exercises 5–8, find each of the following, where a, b, and h are real numbers:

(a) $f(a)$ (b) $f(-a)$
(c) $-f(a)$ (d) $f(a + h)$
(e) $f(a) + f(h)$
(f) $\dfrac{f(a + h) - f(a)}{h}$ provided $h \neq 0$

5 $f(x) = 5x - 2$ **6** $f(x) = 3 - 4x$

7 $f(x) = 2x^2 - x + 3$ **8** $f(x) = x^3 - 2x$

In Exercises 9–12, find the following:

(a) $g(1/a)$ (b) $1/g(a)$
(c) $g(a^2)$ (d) $(g(a))^2$
(e) $g(\sqrt{a})$ (f) $\sqrt{g(a)}$

9 $g(x) = 3x^2$ **10** $g(x) = 3x - 8$

11 $g(x) = \dfrac{2x}{x^2 + 1}$ **12** $g(x) = \dfrac{x^2}{x + 1}$

In each of Exercises 13–20, find the largest subset of $\mathbb{R}$ that can serve as the domain of the function f.

13 $f(x) = \sqrt{3x - 5}$ **14** $f(x) = \sqrt{7 - 2x}$

15 $f(x) = \sqrt{4 - x^2}$ **16** $f(x) = \sqrt{x^2 - 9}$

17 $f(x) = \dfrac{x + 1}{x^3 - 9x}$

18 $f(x) = \dfrac{4x + 7}{6x^2 + 13x - 5}$

19 $f(x) = \dfrac{\sqrt{x}}{2x^2 - 11x + 12}$

20 $f(x) = \dfrac{x^3 - 1}{x^2 - 1}$.

In each of Exercises 21–26, find the number that has the image 4. If $a > 0$, what number has the image a? Find the range of f.

21 $f(x) = 7x - 5$ **22** $f(x) = 3x$

23 $f(x) = \sqrt{x - 3}$ **24** $f(x) = 1/x$

25 $f(x) = x^3$ **26** $f(x) = \sqrt[3]{x - 4}$

In each of Exercises 27–34, determine if the function f is one-to-one.

27 $f(x) = 2x + 9$ **28** $f(x) = 1/(7x + 9)$

29 $f(x) = 5 - 3x^2$ **30** $f(x) = 2x^2 - x - 3$

31 $f(x) = \sqrt{x}$ **32** $f(x) = x^3$

33 $f(x) = |x|$ **34** $f(x) = 4$

In each of Exercises 35–44, determine whether f is even, odd, or neither even nor odd.

35 $f(x) = 3x^3 - 4x$ **36** $f(x) = 7x^6 - x^4 + 7$

37 $f(x) = 9 - 5x^2$ **38** $f(x) = 2x^5 - 4x^3$

39 $f(x) = 2$ **40** $f(x) = 2x^3 + x^2$

41 $f(x) = 2x^2 - 3x + 4$

42 $f(x) = \sqrt{x^2 + 1}$

43 $f(x) = \sqrt[3]{x^3 - 4}$

44 $f(x) = |x| + 5$

45 Find a formula that expresses the radius r of a circle as a function of its circumference C. If the circumference of *any* circle is increased by 12 inches, determine how much the radius increases.

46 Find a formula that expresses the volume of a cube as a function of its surface area. Find the volume if the surface area is 36 square inches.

47 An open box is to be made from a rectangular piece of cardboard having dimensions 20 inches by 30 inches by cutting out identical squares of area x^2 from each corner and turning up the sides. Express the volume V of the box as a function of x.

48 Find a formula that expresses the area A of an equilateral triangle as a function of the length s of a side.

49 Express the perimeter P of a square as a function of its area A.

50 Express the surface area S of a sphere as a function of its volume V.

51 A weather balloon is released at 1:00 P.M. and rises vertically at a rate of 2 meters per second.

An observer is situated 100 meters from a point on the ground directly below the balloon. If t denotes the time (in seconds) after 1:00 P.M., express the distance d between the balloon and the observer as a function of t.

52 Two ships leave port at 9:00 A.M., one sailing south at a rate of 16 mph and the other west at a rate of 20 mph. If t denotes the time (in hours) after 9:00 A.M., express the distance d between the ships as a function of t.

In each of Exercises 53–60, determine whether the set W of ordered pairs is a function in the sense of the alternative definition of function.

53 $W = \{(x, y) : 2y = x^2 + 5\}$

54 $W = \{(x, y) : x = 3y + 2\}$

55 $W = \{(x, y) : x^2 + y^2 = 4\}$

56 $W = \{(x, y) : y^2 - x^2 = 1\}$

57 $W = \{(x, y) : y = 3\}$

58 $W = \{(x, y) : x = y\}$

59 $W = \{(x, y) : xy = 0\}$

60 $W = \{(x, y) : x + y = 0\}$

1.5 GRAPHS OF FUNCTIONS

Graphs—or, more precisely, *sketches* of graphs—are often used to describe the variation of physical quantities. For example, a scientist may use Figure 1.21 to indicate

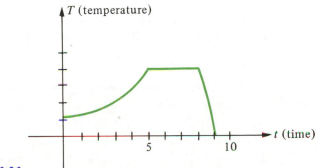

Figure 1.21

the temperature T of a certain solution at various times t during an experiment. The sketch shows that the temperature increased gradually from time $t = 0$ to time $t = 5$, did not change between $t = 5$ and $t = 8$, and then decreased rapidly from $t = 8$ to $t = 9$. A visual aid of this type reveals the behavior of T more clearly than a long table of numerical values.

If f is a function, we may use a graph to exhibit the behavior of $f(x)$ as x varies through the domain of f. By definition, the **graph of a function** f is the set of all points $(x, f(x))$ in a coordinate plane, where x is in the domain of f. Thus the graph of f is the same as the graph of the equation $y = f(x)$, and if $P(a, b)$ is on the graph, then the ordinate b is the functional value $f(a)$, as illustrated in Figure 1.22. It is important to note that since there is a unique $f(a)$ for each a in the domain, there is only *one* point on the graph with abscissa a, and hence, every vertical line intersects the graph of a function in at most one point. Consequently, for graphs of functions it is impossible to obtain a sketch such as that shown in Figure 1.15, where some vertical lines intersect the graph in more than one point.

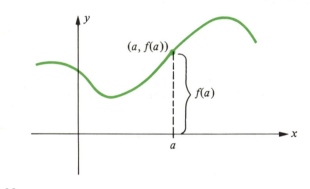

Figure 1.22

Example 1   Sketch the graph of f if $f(x) = 2x + 3$.

Solution   The graph consists of all points $(x, f(x))$, where $f(x) = 2x + 3$. The following table lists coordinates of several points on the graph, where $y = f(x)$.

x	-3	-2	-1	0	1	2
y	-3	-1	1	3	5	7

Plotting, it appears that the points lie on a straight line, and we sketch the graph as in Figure 1.23. (In Chapter Seven we shall *prove* that the graph is a straight line.) The graph of f is the same as the graph of the equation $y = 2x + 3$.

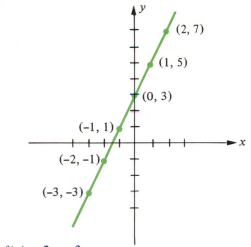

Figure 1.23 $f(x) = 2x + 3$

It is useful to determine the points at which the graph of a function f intersects the x-axis. The abscissas of these points are called the **x-intercepts** of the graph and are found by locating all points $(x, f(x))$ such that $f(x) = 0$. In Example 1 the x-intercept is $-3/2$, since that number is the solution of $2x + 3 = 0$. A number a such that $f(a) = 0$ is also called a **zero of the function** f.

If the number 0 is in the domain of f, then $f(0)$ is called the **y-intercept** of the graph of f. It is the ordinate of the point at which the graph intersects the y-axis.

The graph of a function can have at most one y-intercept. The y-intercept in Example 1 is 3.

If f is the function in Example 1 and if $x_1 < x_2$, then $2x_1 + 3 < 2x_2 + 3$; that is, $f(x_1) < f(x_2)$. This means that as abscissas of points increase, ordinates also increase. The function f is then said to be *increasing*. If f is increasing, then the graph rises as x increases. For certain functions, we have $f(x_1) > f(x_2)$ whenever $x_1 < x_2$. In this case the graph of f falls as x increases, and the function is called a *decreasing* function. In general we shall speak of functions that increase or decrease on certain subsets of their domains, as in the following definition. Functions that neither increase nor decrease are called *constant*.

Definition

> If S is a subset of the domain of a function f, then
> (i) f is **increasing** on S if $f(x_1) < f(x_2)$ whenever $x_1 < x_2$ in S
> (ii) f is **decreasing** on S if $f(x_1) > f(x_2)$ whenever $x_1 < x_2$ in S
> (iii) f is **constant** on S if $f(x_1) = f(x_2)$ for every x_1, x_2 in S.

If we regard Figure 1.21 as the graph of a function f, then f is increasing on $\{x : 0 \le x \le 5\}$, is constant on $\{x : 5 \le x \le 8\}$, and is decreasing on $\{x : 8 \le x \le 9\}$.

Example 2   Sketch the graph of f if $f(x) = x^2 - 3$.

Solution   We list coordinates $(x, f(x))$ of some points on the graph of f in tabular form, as follows:

x	-3	-2	-1	0	1	2	3
$f(x)$	6	1	-2	-3	-2	1	6

The x-intercepts are the solutions of the equation $f(x) = 0$, that is, of $x^2 - 3 = 0$. These are $\pm\sqrt{3}$. The y-intercept is $f(0) = -3$. Plotting points leads to the sketch in Figure 1.24. Evidently f decreases on the set of nonpositive real numbers and f increases on the set of nonnegative real numbers. It follows that $f(x)$ takes on its least value when $x = 0$. This smallest value, -3, is called the **minimum value** of f. The corresponding point is the lowest point on the graph. Clearly $f(x)$ does not take on a **maximum value**, that is, a *largest* value.

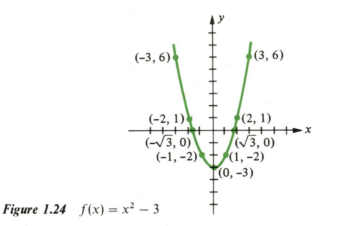

Figure 1.24 $f(x) = x^2 - 3$ ■

The solution to Example 2 could have been shortened by observing that, since $(-x)^2 - 3 = x^2 - 3$, the graph of $y = x^2 - 3$ is symmetric with respect to the y-axis. This fact also follows from (i) of the next theorem.

Theorem on Symmetry

(i) The graph of an even function is symmetric with respect to the y-axis.

(ii) The graph of an odd function is symmetric with respect to the origin.

Proof   If f is even, then $f(-x) = f(x)$, and hence, the equation $y = f(x)$ is not changed if $-x$ is substituted for x. Statement (i) now follows from Symmetry Test (i) of Section 1.3. The proof of (ii) is left to the reader. ■

Example 3   Sketch the graph of f if $f(x) = |x|$.

Solution   If $x \geq 0$, then $f(x) = x$, and hence, the points (x, x) in the first quadrant are on the graph of f. Some special cases are $(0, 0)$, $(1, 1)$, $(2, 2)$, $(3, 3)$, and $(4, 4)$. Since

$|-x| = |x|$, we see that f is an even function, and hence, by the preceding theorem, the graph is symmetric with respect to the y-axis. Plotting points and using symmetry leads to the sketch in Figure 1.25. As in Example 2, this function decreases for nonpositive real numbers and increases for nonnegative real numbers, with a minimum value 0 at $x = 0$.

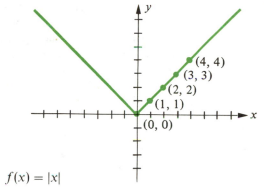

Figure 1.25 $f(x) = |x|$

Example 4   Sketch the graph of f if $f(x) = \sqrt{x-1}$.

Solution   The domain of f does not include values of x such that $x - 1 < 0$, since $f(x)$ is not a real number in this case. Consequently there are no points (x, y) on the graph with $x < 1$. Moreover, no part of the graph lies below the x-axis. (Why?)

The following table lists some points $(x, f(x))$ on the graph.

x	1	2	3	4	5	6
$f(x)$	0	1	$\sqrt{2}$	$\sqrt{3}$	2	$\sqrt{5}$

Plotting points leads to the sketch shown in Figure 1.26. The function is increasing throughout its domain. The x-intercept is 1, and there is no y-intercept.

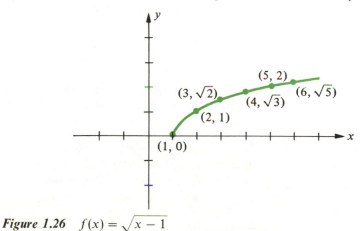

Figure 1.26 $f(x) = \sqrt{x-1}$

Example 5   Given $f(x) = x^2 + c$, sketch the graph of f if (a) $c = 4$; (b) $c = -2$.

Solution   We shall sketch both graphs on the same coordinate axes. The graph of $y = x^2$ was sketched in Figure 1.13, and for reference it is represented by dashes in Figure 1.27. To find the graph of $f(x) = x^2 + 4$, we may simply increase the ordinate of each point on the graph of $y = x^2$ by 4, as shown in the figure. (Why?) This amounts to *shifting* the graph of $y = x^2$ *upward* 4 units. For $c = -2$, we decrease ordinates by 2, and hence, this graph may be obtained by shifting the graph of $y = x^2$ downward 2 units. Each graph is a parabola symmetric with respect to the y-axis. In order to get the correct position it is advisable to plot several points on each graph.

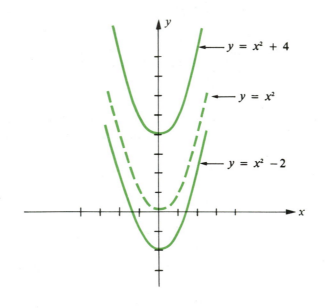

Figure 1.27 $f(x) = x^2 + c$

The graphs in the preceding example illustrate **vertical shifts** of the graph of $y = x^2$, and are special cases of the following general rules.

Vertical Shifts of Graphs ($c > 0$)

To obtain the graph of:	shift the graph of $y = f(x)$:
$y = f(x) - c$	c units downward
$y = f(x) + c$	c units upward

Similar rules can be stated for **horizontal shifts**. Specifically, if $c > 0$, consider the graphs of $y = f(x)$ and $y = f(x - c)$ sketched on the same coordinate axes, as illustrated in Figure 1.28.

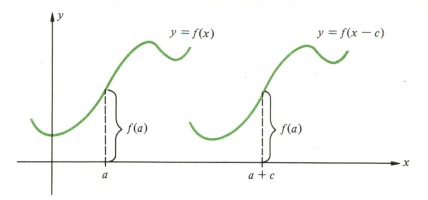

Figure 1.28

Since $f(a) = f(a + c - c)$, we see that the point with abscissa a on the graph of $y = f(x)$ has the same y-coordinate as the point with abscissa $a + c$ on the graph of $y = f(x - c)$. This implies that the latter graph can be obtained by shifting the graph of $y = f(x)$ to the right c units. Similarly, the graph of $y = f(x + c)$ can be obtained by shifting the graph of f to the left c units. These rules are listed for reference in the next box.

Horizontal Shifts of Graphs ($c > 0$)

To obtain the graph of:	shift the graph of $y = f(x)$:
$y = f(x - c)$	c units to the right
$y = f(x + c)$	c units to the left

Example 6 Sketch the graph of f if

(a) $f(x) = (x - 4)^2$ (b) $f(x) = (x + 2)^2$.

Solution   The graph of $y = x^2$ is sketched, with dashes, in Figure 1.29. According to the last two rules, shifting this graph to the right 4 units gives us the graph of $y = (x - 4)^2$, whereas shifting to the left 2 units leads to the graph of $y = (x + 2)^2$. Students who are not convinced of this technique are urged to plot several points on each graph.

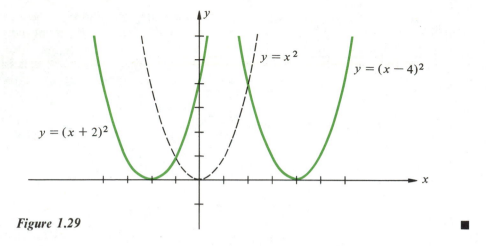

Figure 1.29   ■

To obtain the graph of $y = cf(x)$, we may *multiply* the ordinates of points on the graph of $y = f(x)$ by c. For example, if $y = 2f(x)$, we double ordinates, or if $y = \frac{1}{2}f(x)$, we multiply each ordinate by $1/2$. If $c > 0$ (and $c \neq 1$), we shall refer to this procedure as **stretching** the graph of $y = f(x)$.

Example 7   Sketch the graph of $y = cx^2$ if (a) $c = 4$; (b) $c = 1/4$.

Solution   To obtain the graph of $y = 4x^2$, we may refer to the graph of $y = x^2$ (see dashes in Figure 1.30) and multiply the ordinate of each point by 4. This gives us a narrower parabola which is sharper at the vertex, as illustrated in (i) of the figure. In order to get the correct position, several points such as $(0, 0)$, $(1/2, 1)$, and $(1, 4)$ should be plotted.

Similarly, for the graph of $y = (1/4)x^2$, we multiply ordinates of points on the graph of $y = x^2$ by $1/4$. This gives us a wider parabola which is flatter at the vertex, as shown in (ii) of Figure 1.30.

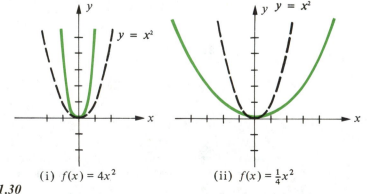

(i) $f(x) = 4x^2$ (ii) $f(x) = \frac{1}{4}x^2$

Figure 1.30   ■

The graph of $y = -f(x)$ may be obtained by multiplying the y-coordinate of each point on the graph of $y = f(x)$ by -1. In particular, every point (a, b) on the graph of $y = f(x)$ which lies above the x-axis determines a point $(a, -b)$ below the x-axis. Similarly, if (c, d) lies below the x-axis (that is, $d < 0$), then $(c, -d)$ lies above the x-axis. We call the graph of $y = -f(x)$ a **reflection** of the graph of $y = f(x)$ through the x-axis.

Example 8   Sketch the graph of $y = -x^2$.

Solution   The graph may be obtained by plotting points; however, since the graph of $y = x^2$ is well known, we sketch it with dashes, as in Figure 1.31, and then multiply ordinates of points by -1. This gives us the reflection through the x-axis indicated in the figure.

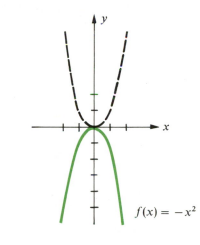

$f(x) = -x^2$

Figure 1.31

EXERCISES 1.5

In Exercises 1–20, sketch the graph of f and state where f is increasing, is decreasing, or is constant.

1 $f(x) = 5x$

2 $f(x) = -3x$

3 $f(x) = -4x + 2$

4 $f(x) = 4x - 2$

5 $f(x) = 3 - x^2$

6 $f(x) = 4x^2 + 1$

7 $f(x) = 2x^2 - 4$

8 $f(x) = \frac{1}{100}x^2$

9 $f(x) = \sqrt{x + 4}$

10 $f(x) = \sqrt{4 - x}$

11 $f(x) = \sqrt{x} + 2$

12 $f(x) = 2 - \sqrt{x}$

13 $f(x) = 4/x$

14 $f(x) = 1/x^2$

15 $f(x) = |x - 2|$

16 $f(x) = |x + 2|$

17 $f(x) = |x| - 2$

18 $f(x) = |x| + 2$

19 $f(x) = \dfrac{x}{|x|}$

20 $f(x) = x + |x|$

In Exercises 21–30, sketch on the same coordinate axes, the graph of f for the stated values of c. (Make use of results on vertical shifts, horizontal shifts, stretching, or reflection.)

21 $f(x) = 3x + c$; $c = 0, c = 2, c = -1$

22 $f(x) = -2x + c$; $c = 0, c = 1, c = -3$

23 $f(x) = x^3 + c$; $c = 0, c = 1, c = -2$

24 $f(x) = -x^3 + c$; $c = 0, c = 2, c = -1$

25 $f(x) = \sqrt{4 - x^2} + c;$ $c = 0, c = 4, c = -3$

26 $f(x) = c - |x|;$ $c = 0, c = 5, c = -2$

27 $f(x) = 3(x - c);$ $c = 0, c = 2, c = 3$

28 $f(x) = -2(x - c)^2;$ $c = 0, c = 3, c = 1$

29 $f(x) = (x + c)^3;$ $c = 0, c = 2, c = -2$

30 $f(x) = c\sqrt{9 - x^2};$ $c = 0, c = 2, c = 3$

1.6   REVIEW

Concepts

Define or discuss each of the following:

1 Rational and irrational numbers

2 A number a is greater than a number b

3 A number a is less than a number b

4 Absolute value of a real number

5 Variable

6 Domain of a variable

7 Solution of an equation

8 Identity

9 Equivalent equations

10 Coordinate line

11 Ordered pair

12 Rectangular coordinate system in a plane

13 Abscissa and ordinate of a point

14 The Distance Formula

15 The Midpoint Formula

16 Graph of an equation in x and y

17 Standard equation of a circle

18 Function

19 Domain of a function

20 Range of a function

21 One-to-one function

22 Graph of a function

23 Increasing function

24 Decreasing function

25 Even function

26 Odd function

27 Vertical shifts of graphs

28 Horizontal shifts of graphs

29 Stretching of graphs

30 Reflections of graphs

Exercises

1 Replace the symbol $\square$ with either $<, >,$ or $=$.
 (a) $-0.1 \,\square\, -0.01$ (b) $\sqrt{9} \,\square\, -3$
 (c) $1/6 \,\square\, 0.166$

2 Express in terms of inequalities:
 (a) x is negative.
 (b) a is between $1/2$ and $1/3$.
 (c) The absolute value of x is not greater than 4.

3 Rewrite without using the absolute value symbol:
 (a) $|-7|$ (b) $|-5|/(-5)$ (c) $|3^{-1} - 2^{-1}|$

4 If points A, B, and C on a coordinate line have coordinates $-8, 4,$ and -3, respectively, find the following:
 (a) $d(A, C)$ (b) $d(C, A)$ (c) $d(B, C)$

Solve the equations in Exercises 5–7.

5 $2x^2 + 5x - 12 = 0$

6 $3x^2 + 4x - 5 = 0$

7 $4x^4 - 33x^2 + 50 = 0$

8 Plot the points $A(3, 1)$, $B(-5, -3)$, $C(4, -1)$, and prove that they are vertices of a right triangle. What is the area of the triangle?

9 Describe the set of all points (x, y) in a coordinate plane such that $xy < 0$.

10 Find an equation of the circle with center $C(7, -4)$ and passing through the point $Q(-3, 3)$.

Sketch the graphs of the equations in Exercises 11–16.

11 $2y + 5x - 8 = 0$ **12** $x = 3y + 4$

13 $y = \sqrt{1 - x}$ **14** $x^2 = 10 - y^2$

15 $y + x^2 = 1$ **16** $y^2 + x = 1$

In each of Exercises 17–20, sketch the graph of f and determine where f is increasing or decreasing.

17 $f(x) = |x + 5|$ **18** $f(x) = \dfrac{1 - 3x}{2}$

19 $f(x) = 5$ **20** $f(x) = 1 - 4x^2$

In Exercises 21–22, determine if f is one-to-one.

21 $f(x) = 3x^2 + 1$ **22** $f(x) = 2x + 7$

23 Sketch the graphs of the following, using results on shifting, stretching, or reflecting.

(a) $y = \sqrt{x}$ (b) $y = \sqrt{x + 4}$

(c) $y = \sqrt{x} + 4$ (d) $y = 4\sqrt{x}$

(e) $y = \tfrac{1}{4}\sqrt{x}$ (f) $y = -\sqrt{x}$

24 Determine whether f is even, odd, or neither even nor odd.

(a) $f(x) = \sqrt[3]{x^3 + 4x}$

(b) $f(x) = \sqrt[3]{3x^2 - x^3}$

(c) $f(x) = \sqrt[3]{x^4 + 3x^2 + 5}$

2

THE TRIGONOMETRIC FUNCTIONS

Trigonometry originated over 2,000 years ago when the Greeks developed precise methods for measuring the angles and sides of triangles. Although such measurements are still important in certain branches of science and engineering, there are many modern applications of trigonometry in which the notion of angle either is secondary or does not enter into the picture. Of primary importance are properties of the so-called trigonometric functions, *whose domains are sets of real numbers. For this reason, these functions are introduced in Section 2.2 without reference to angles. However, since the classical techniques are also important, our modern definition is followed almost immediately, in Section 2.5, by a more traditional approach involving angles and ratios. As a consequence, we have available, very early in our work, two different, but equivalent, formulations of the trigonometric functions. The student should strive to become comfortable using both approaches, since each has certain advantages. Graphs involving the trigonometric functions are considered in Sections 2.7–2.9. The chapter concludes with some applications of trigonometry.*

2.1 THE UNIT CIRCLE *U*

If a and b are real numbers such that $a < b$, then the set of all real numbers between a and b is called the **open interval** from a to b. It is customary to use the ordered pair (a, b) to denote this interval. Although we also use ordered pairs to denote points in a coordinate plane, there is little chance for confusion, since it should always be clear from the discussion whether the symbol (a, b) represents an interval or a point. To reiterate, the open interval (a, b) is defined as follows.

Definition of Open Interval

$$(a, b) = \{x : a < x < b\}$$

We shall also employ **closed intervals**, denoted by $[a,b]$, and **half-open intervals**, denoted by $[a,b)$ or $(a,b]$. They are defined as follows.

Definitions of Closed and Half-Open Intervals

$$[a,b] = \{x : a \le x \le b\}$$
$$[a,b) = \{x : a \le x < b\}$$
$$(a,b] = \{x : a < x \le b\}$$

For example, the half-open interval $[0, 2\pi)$ consists of all real numbers between 0 and 2π, including 0 but not 2π. The interval $[2\pi, 4\pi)$ consists of all numbers between 2π and 4π, including 2π but not 4π. Similarly, $[4\pi, 6\pi) = \{x : 4\pi \le x < 6\pi\}$, etc. The set $\mathbb{R}$ of real numbers may be regarded as consisting of all such half-open intervals.

Let U be a unit circle, that is, a circle of radius 1, with center at the origin of a rectangular coordinate system. Thus U is the graph of the equation $x^2 + y^2 = 1$. If A is the point with coordinates $(1, 0)$ and P is any other point on U, then proceeding along U in a *counterclockwise direction* from A (see Figure 2.1), there is a unique positive real number t called the **length of the arc** $\overset{\frown}{AP}$. Since the circumference of U is 2π, we have $0 < t < 2\pi$. If we let $t = 0$ when $P = A$, then with each point P on U there is associated precisely one real number in the half-open interval $[0, 2\pi)$.

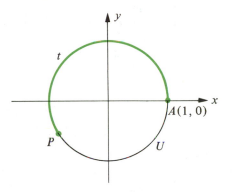

Figure 2.1

Conversely, it can be shown that for each real number t in the half-open interval $[0, 2\pi)$, there is one and only one point P on U such that the length of $\overset{\frown}{AP}$, obtained by proceeding in the counterclockwise direction from A to P, is t. This establishes a one-to-one correspondence between the real numbers in the interval $[0, 2\pi)$ and the points on U. Since the position of P depends on t, we shall use functional notation and denote it by $P(t)$. In certain applications, a (variable) point is regarded as moving along U, and we refer to the point as *traveling*, or *traversing*, *a distance t* from A to $P(t)$.

For most values of t it is very difficult to determine the rectangular coordinates of the point $P(t)$ on U. Three simple cases are illustrated in Figure 2.2. In Case (i) we note that since the circumference of the unit circle is 2π, the number $\pi/2$ is one-fourth the circumference, and hence, the point $P(\pi/2)$ has coordinates $(0, 1)$. Similarly, in Case (ii), π is one-half the circumference, and hence, $P(\pi)$ may be found by starting at A and traveling halfway around U to the point $(-1, 0)$. Finally, in Case (iii), $P(3\pi/2)$ can be

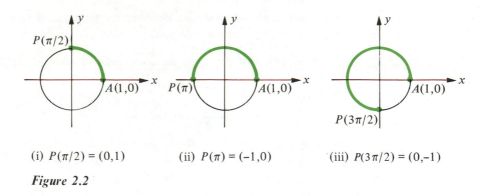

(i) $P(\pi/2) = (0,1)$ (ii) $P(\pi) = (-1,0)$ (iii) $P(3\pi/2) = (0,-1)$

Figure 2.2

located by traversing three-fourths of the circumference (in the counterclockwise direction) to the point $(0, -1)$.

Example 1   Find the rectangular coordinates of $P(\pi/4)$, $P(3\pi/4)$, $P(5\pi/4)$, and $P(7\pi/4)$.

Solution   The rectangular coordinates of the point $P(\pi/4)$ can be found by noting that $\pi/4$ is one-half of $\pi/2$, and consequently, $P(\pi/4)$ is in the first quadrant and bisects the circular arc from $(1,0)$ to $(0,1)$. It follows that $P(\pi/4)$ lies on the line $y = x$ and hence has coordinates (c, c) for some positive real number c (see Figure 2.3). Since (c, c) is a point on the unit circle $x^2 + y^2 = 1$, we must have $c^2 + c^2 = 1$, or $2c^2 = 1$. Thus $c = \sqrt{1/2} = \sqrt{2}/2$ and

$$P(\pi/4) = (\sqrt{2}/2, \sqrt{2}/2).$$

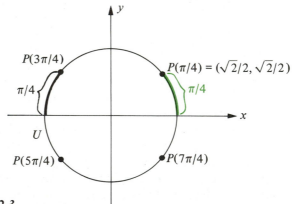

Figure 2.3

Since $3\pi/4 = \pi - (\pi/4)$, we see that $P(3\pi/4)$ and $P(\pi/4)$ are symmetric with respect to the y-axis, as illustrated in Figure 2.3. It follows that

$$P(3\pi/4) = (-\sqrt{2}/2, \sqrt{2}/2).$$

Again using symmetry, it is evident from the figure that

$$P\left(\frac{5\pi}{4}\right) = \left(-\frac{\sqrt{2}}{2}, -\frac{\sqrt{2}}{2}\right) \quad \text{and} \quad P\left(\frac{7\pi}{4}\right) = \left(\frac{\sqrt{2}}{2}, -\frac{\sqrt{2}}{2}\right).$$ ■

Example 2   Find the rectangular coordinates of (a) $P(\pi/6)$; (b) $P(\pi/3)$.

Solution

(a) Since $\pi/6 = (1/3)(\pi/2)$, the point $P(\pi/6)$ on *U* is in the first quadrant, one-third of the way from $A(1, 0)$ to $B(0, 1)$. If *P* has coordinates (c, d), then, as illustrated in (i) of Figure 2.4, the point $P'(c, -d)$ is also on *U*. Since the lengths of arcs $\overset{\frown}{P'P}$ and $\overset{\frown}{PB}$ are equal (both are $\pi/3$), it follows that the length $2d$ of chord $P'P$ is the same as the length of chord PB. Employing the Distance Formula of Section 1.2,

$$2d = \sqrt{(c - 0)^2 + (d - 1)^2}.$$

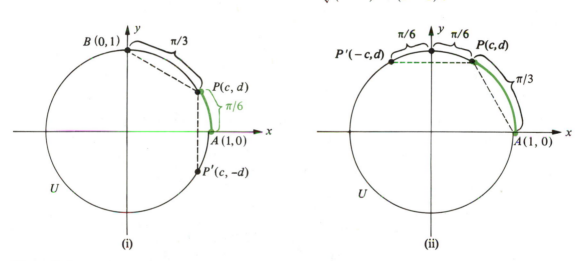

Figure 2.4

Squaring both sides of this equation, we obtain

$$4d^2 = c^2 + d^2 - 2d + 1.$$

Since (c, d) is a point on *U*, we must have $c^2 + d^2 = 1$, and hence,

$$4d^2 = 1 - 2d + 1, \quad \text{or} \quad 4d^2 + 2d - 2 = 0.$$

Factoring gives us

$$2(2d - 1)(d + 1) = 0.$$

Since *d* is positive, the last equation implies that $d = 1/2$. Consequently, since $c^2 + d^2 = 1$,

$$c = \sqrt{1 - d^2} = \sqrt{1 - (1/4)} = \sqrt{3/4} = \sqrt{3}/2$$

and therefore,

$$P(\pi/6) = (\sqrt{3}/2, 1/2).$$

(b) Since $\pi/3 = (2/3)(\pi/2)$, the point $P(\pi/3)$ on U is in the first quadrant, two-thirds of the way from $A(1,0)$ to $B(0,1)$. If P has coordinates (c, d), then by symmetry the point $P'(-c, d)$ is also on U. Moreover, referring to (ii) of Figure 2.4, the lengths of arcs $\overset{\frown}{PP'}$ and $\overset{\frown}{AP}$ both equal $\pi/3$, and hence, the length $2c$ of chord $P'P$ is the same as the length of chord AP. Applying the Distance Formula,

$$2c = \sqrt{(c - 1)^2 + d^2}$$

or, equivalently,

$$4c^2 = c^2 - 2c + 1 + d^2.$$

Proceeding as in part (a), we obtain $c = 1/2$ and $d = \sqrt{3}/2$. (Verify this fact!) Hence,

$$P(\pi/3) = (1/2, \sqrt{3}/2). \qquad \blacksquare$$

Using Example 2 and the symmetry of the unit circle U, we can find the rectangular coordinates of $P(t)$, where t is any integral multiple of $\pi/6$ that lies between 0 and 2π. The positions of these points are illustrated in Figure 2.5, and may be verified by noting that $2\pi/3 = \pi - \pi/3$, $5\pi/6 = \pi - \pi/6$, etc.

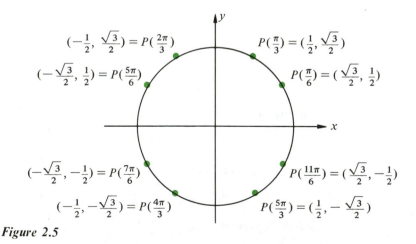

Figure 2.5

Although geometric arguments can be used to find the rectangular coordinates of special points on U, such as $P(\pi/4)$, $P(\pi/6)$, and $P(\pi/3)$, it is impossible for us to cope with values of t such as $2/3$, $\sqrt{5}$, 4.627, or for that matter, integer values such as 1, 2, 3, and 4. The reason for the difficulty is that techniques studied in calculus are required to handle all possibilities. Fortunately, in our future work it will be unnecessary to calculate the exact coordinates (x, y) of $P(t)$ for every value of t.

The preceding discussion can be extended so that to *every* real number there corresponds exactly one point on U. Specifically, to associate a point $P(t)$ with any *positive* real number t, we proceed along U in a counterclockwise direction from A, *making several revolutions*, if necessary. For example, if $t = 5\pi/2$, we first note that

$$\frac{5\pi}{2} = \frac{\pi}{2} + 2\pi.$$

Thus, the point $P(5\pi/2)$ may be found by first traversing the distance $\pi/2$ from A to the point $(0, 1)$, and then making one complete counterclockwise revolution through the distance 2π. Consequently, $P(5\pi/2) = (0, 1)$. Similarly, to locate $P(9\pi/2)$, we note that

$$\frac{9\pi}{2} = \frac{\pi}{2} + 4\pi$$

and hence, *two* complete revolutions should be made after reaching the point $(0, 1)$. This gives us $P(9\pi/2) = (0, 1)$. In general, if t_1 and t_2 are positive real numbers such that $t_2 = t_1 + 2\pi n$ for some positive integer n, then $P(t_2) = P(t_1)$, since the circumference of U is 2π.

To associate a point on U with each *negative* real number t, we start at A and proceed a distance $|t|$ in a *clockwise* direction along U. The three special cases $t = -\pi/2$, $t = -\pi$, and $t = -7\pi/4$ are illustrated in Figure 2.6. The reader should compare the third case with Example 1. Of course, for real numbers less than -2π, it is necessary to make more than one revolution (in the clockwise direction) along U.

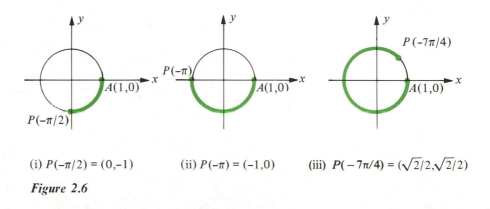

(i) $P(-\pi/2) = (0, -1)$ (ii) $P(-\pi) = (-1, 0)$ (iii) $P(-7\pi/4) = (\sqrt{2}/2, \sqrt{2}/2)$

Figure 2.6

We have demonstrated that to each real number t there is associated a unique point $P(t)$ on the unit circle U. We shall refer to $P(t)$ as **the point on U that corresponds to t**. Since the circumference of U is 2π, it follows that two real numbers t_1 and t_2 are associated with the same point if and only if $t_2 = t_1 + 2\pi n$ for some integer n. This gives us the important formula

$$P(t) = P(t + 2\pi n)$$

for every real number t and every integer n. Several uses of this formula are given in the next two examples.

Example 3   Find the rectangular coordinates of $P(27\pi/4)$.

Solution   Since $27/4 = 6 + (3/4)$, we see that

$$\frac{27\pi}{4} = 6\pi + \frac{3\pi}{4}.$$

Using the formula $P(t) = P(t + 2\pi n)$ (with $n = 3$),

$$P\left(\frac{27\pi}{4}\right) = P\left(\frac{3\pi}{4} + 6\pi\right) = P\left(\frac{3\pi}{4}\right).$$

Finally, referring to Example 1, we obtain $P(27\pi/4) = (-\sqrt{2}/2, \sqrt{2}/2)$.   ∎

Example 4   Find the quadrant that contains $P(21)$.

Solution   From the discussion in this section, $P(21) = P(21 + 2\pi n)$ for every integer n. By choosing n negative, we can find a number of the form $21 + 2\pi n$ which is the interval $[0, 2\pi)$. The quadrant may then be readily determined. In particular, if we let $n = -3$, then

$$21 - 6\pi \approx 21 - 18.85 = 2.15.$$

Since $\pi/2 < 2.15 < \pi$, we see that

$$\frac{\pi}{2} < 21 - 6\pi < \pi.$$

It follows that $P(21)$ is in the second quadrant.   ∎

EXERCISES 2.1

In Exercises 1–10, find the rectangular coordinates of the given points.

1 $P(5\pi)$
2 $P(-3\pi)$
3 $P(7\pi/2)$
4 $P(5\pi/2)$
5 $P(-6\pi)$
6 $P(11\pi/2)$
7 $P(37\pi)$
8 $P(99\pi)$
9 $P(-9\pi/2)$
10 $P(1000000\pi)$

Find the rectangular coordinates of the points in Exercises 11–22. (*Hint:* See Figures 2.3 and 2.5)

11 $P(-3\pi/4)$ **12** $P(-\pi/4)$

13 $P(-9\pi/4)$ **14** $P(-5\pi/4)$

15 $P(11\pi/4)$ **16** $P(9\pi/4)$

17 $P(-\pi/3)$ **18** $P(-\pi/6)$

19 $P(-5\pi/6)$ **20** $P(-4\pi/3)$

21 $P(8\pi/3)$ **22** $P(17\pi/6)$

If $P(t)$ has the rectangular coordinates given in each of Exercises 23–30, find (a) $P(t+\pi)$, (b) $P(t-\pi)$, (c) $P(-t)$, (d) $P(-t-\pi)$.

23 $(3/5, 4/5)$ **24** $(4/5, -3/5)$

25 $(-8/17, 15/17)$ **26** $(-15/17, 8/17)$

27 $(-1, 0)$ **28** $(0, -1)$

29 $(a/\sqrt{a^2+b^2}, b/\sqrt{a^2+b^2})$, where $a^2+b^2 \neq 0$

30 $(a, \sqrt{1-a^2})$

In each of Exercises 31–34, approximate the y-coordinate of $P(t)$ if $P(t)$ is in the indicated quadrant and has the given x-coordinate.

31 I, $x = 1/2$ **32** II, $x = -\sqrt{3}/2$

33 III, $x = -2/3$ **34** IV, $x = 0.1$

In each of Exercises 35–38, approximate the x-coordinate of $P(t)$ if $P(t)$ is in the indicated quadrant and has the given y-coordinate.

35 II, $y = \sqrt{3}/2$ **36** III, $y = -1/2$

37 IV, $y = -0.01$ **38** II, $y = 0.9$

CALCULATOR EXERCISES 2.1

Find the quadrants containing the points in Exercises 1–8.

1 $P(43)$ **2** $P(23.64)$

3 $P(-28)$ **4** $P(3.141591)$

5 $P(1776)$ **6** $P(-2001)$

7 $P(\sqrt[4]{782\pi})$ **8** $P(6\sqrt{2}+5\sqrt{7})$

9 Approximate the y-coordinate of $P(t)$ if $P(t)$ is in the fourth quadrant and has x-coordinate 0.9703.

10 Approximate the x-coordinate of $P(t)$ if $P(t)$ is in the third quadrant and has y-coordinate -0.6561.

2.2 THE TRIGONOMETRIC FUNCTIONS

In the preceding section we introduced a technique for associating with each real number t a unique point $P(t)$ on the unit circle U. The rectangular coordinates (x, y) of $P(t)$ can be used to define the six **trigonometric** or **(circular) functions**. These functions are referred to as the **sine, cosine, tangent, cotangent, secant,** and **cosecant functions**, and are designated by the symbols **sin, cos, tan, cot, sec,** and **csc**, respectively. If t is a real number, then the real number that the sine function associates with t will be denoted by either sin (t) or sin t, and similarly for the other five functions.

**Definition
of the
Trigonometric
Functions**

For any real number t, let $P(t)$ be the point on the unit circle U that corresponds to t. If the rectangular coordinates of $P(t)$ are (x, y), then

$$\sin t = y \qquad\qquad \csc t = \frac{1}{y} \quad (\text{if } y \neq 0)$$

$$\cos t = x \qquad\qquad \sec t = \frac{1}{x} \quad (\text{if } x \neq 0)$$

$$\tan t = \frac{y}{x} \quad (\text{if } x \neq 0) \qquad \cot t = \frac{x}{y} \quad (\text{if } y \neq 0).$$

In order to use this definition to find the values of trigonometric functions, it is necessary to determine the rectangular coordinates (x, y) of the point $P(t)$ on U and then substitute for x and y in the appropriate formulas. In later sections we shall introduce other techniques for finding functional values. The domains and ranges of the trigonometric functions will be discussed in Section 2.3.

Example 1   Find the values of the trigonometric functions corresponding to the number $t = \pi/4$.

Solution   Referring to Figure 2.3, we see that $P(\pi/4) = (\sqrt{2}/2, \sqrt{2}/2)$. Letting $x = \sqrt{2}/2$ and $y = \sqrt{2}/2$ in the last definition gives us

$$\sin\frac{\pi}{4} = \frac{\sqrt{2}}{2} \qquad\qquad \csc\frac{\pi}{4} = \frac{2}{\sqrt{2}} = \sqrt{2}$$

$$\cos\frac{\pi}{4} = \frac{\sqrt{2}}{2} \qquad\qquad \sec\frac{\pi}{4} = \frac{2}{\sqrt{2}} = \sqrt{2}$$

$$\tan\frac{\pi}{4} = \frac{\sqrt{2}/2}{\sqrt{2}/2} = 1 \qquad\qquad \cot\frac{\pi}{4} = \frac{\sqrt{2}/2}{\sqrt{2}/2} = 1.$$

Example 2   Find the values of the trigonometric functions at $t = \pi/6$.

Solution   From Figure 2.5, $P(\pi/6) = (\sqrt{3}/2, 1/2)$. Using the definition with $x = \sqrt{3}/2$ and $y = 1/2$, we obtain

$$\sin\frac{\pi}{6} = \frac{1}{2} \qquad\qquad \csc\frac{\pi}{6} = \frac{1}{(1/2)} = 2$$

$$\cos\frac{\pi}{6} = \frac{\sqrt{3}}{2} \qquad\qquad \sec\frac{\pi}{6} = \frac{1}{(\sqrt{3}/2)} = \frac{2}{\sqrt{3}} = \frac{2\sqrt{3}}{3}$$

$$\tan\frac{\pi}{6} = \frac{(1/2)}{(\sqrt{3}/2)} = \frac{1}{\sqrt{3}} = \frac{\sqrt{3}}{3} \qquad\qquad \cot\frac{\pi}{6} = \frac{(\sqrt{3}/2)}{(1/2)} = \sqrt{3}.$$

Before considering additional functional values, we shall discuss several important relationships that exist among the trigonometric functions. The formulas listed in the next box are, without doubt, the most important identities in trigonometry, because they may be used to simplify and unify many different aspects of the subject. Since the formulas are true for every allowable value of t, and are part of the foundation for work in trigonometry, they are called the *Fundamental Identities*. These identities should be memorized before proceeding to the next section of this text.

Three of the Fundamental Identities involve squares, such as $(\sin t)^2$ and $(\cos t)^2$. In general, if n is an integer different from -1, then powers such as $(\cos t)^n$ are written in the form $\cos^n t$. The symbols $\sin^{-1} t$ and $\cos^{-1} t$ are reserved for inverse trigonometric functions, to be discussed in the next chapter. With this agreement on notation we have, for example,

$$\cos^2 t = (\cos t)^2 = (\cos t)(\cos t)$$
$$\tan^3 t = (\tan t)^3 = (\tan t)(\tan t)(\tan t)$$
$$\sec^4 t = (\sec t)^4 = (\sec t)(\sec t)(\sec t)(\sec t).$$

Let us first list all the Fundamental Identities and then discuss the proofs. The formulas to follow are true for all values of t in the domains of the indicated functions.

The Fundamental Identities

$$\csc t = \frac{1}{\sin t}, \qquad \sec t = \frac{1}{\cos t}, \qquad \cot t = \frac{1}{\tan t}$$

$$\tan t = \frac{\sin t}{\cos t}, \qquad \cot t = \frac{\cos t}{\sin t}$$

$$\sin^2 t + \cos^2 t = 1, \qquad 1 + \tan^2 t = \sec^2 t, \qquad 1 + \cot^2 t = \csc^2 t$$

The proofs follow directly from the definition of the trigonometric functions. Thus,

$$\csc t = \frac{1}{y} = \frac{1}{\sin t}, \quad \sec t = \frac{1}{x} = \frac{1}{\cos t}, \quad \cot t = \frac{x}{y} = \frac{1}{(y/x)} = \frac{1}{\tan t},$$

$$\tan t = \frac{y}{x} = \frac{\sin t}{\cos t}, \quad \cot t = \frac{x}{y} = \frac{\cos t}{\sin t}$$

where we assume that no denominator is zero.

If (x, y) is a point on the unit circle U, then

$$y^2 + x^2 = 1.$$

Since $y = \sin t$ and $x = \cos t$, this gives us

$$(\sin t)^2 + (\cos t)^2 = 1$$

or, equivalently,

$$\sin^2 t + \cos^2 t = 1.$$

If $\cos t \neq 0$, then, dividing both sides of the last equation by $\cos^2 t$, we obtain

$$\frac{\sin^2 t}{\cos^2 t} + 1 = \frac{1}{\cos^2 t}$$

or

$$\left(\frac{\sin t}{\cos t}\right)^2 + 1 = \left(\frac{1}{\cos t}\right)^2.$$

Since $\tan t = \sin t / \cos t$ and $\sec t = 1/\cos t$, we see that

$$\tan^2 t + 1 = \sec^2 t.$$

The final Fundamental Identity is left as an exercise.

Example 3   Find the values of the trigonometric functions at the number t if
(a) $t = 0$ (b) $t = \pi/2$.

Solution

(a) The rectangular coordinates of the point $P(0)$ on the unit circle are $(1,0)$, and hence, we take $x = 1$ and $y = 0$ in the definition of the trigonometric functions. This gives us

$$\sin 0 = 0 \quad \text{and} \quad \cos 0 = 1.$$

Next, using two Fundamental Identities,

$$\tan 0 = \frac{\sin 0}{\cos 0} = \frac{0}{1} = 0, \quad \sec 0 = \frac{1}{\cos 0} = \frac{1}{1} = 1.$$

Of course, we could also find $\tan 0$ and $\sec 0$ by direct substitution for x and y in the definition. The cosecant and cotangent functions are undefined at $t = 0$, since 0 appears in a denominator in the definitions of these functions.

(b) As shown in Figure 2.2, $P(\pi/2) = (0,1)$, and hence, we let $x = 0$ and $y = 1$ in the definition of the trigonometric functions, obtaining

$$\sin(\pi/2) = 1 \quad \text{and} \quad \cos(\pi/2) = 0.$$

Next, applying appropriate Fundamental Identities,

$$\csc(\pi/2) = \frac{1}{\sin(\pi/2)} = \frac{1}{1} = 1$$

$$\cot(\pi/2) = \frac{\cos(\pi/2)}{\sin(\pi/2)} = \frac{0}{1} = 0.$$

The tangent and secant functions are undefined. (Why?)   ∎

It is not difficult to determine the signs of the functional values of the trigonometric functions when $P(t)$ is in various quadrants. For example, if $P(t) = (x,y)$ is in quadrant

II, then y is positive, x is negative, and we see from the definition that $\sin t$ and $\csc t$ are positive, whereas the other four functions are negative. The reader should check the remaining quadrants. The table below indicates the signs in all four quadrants.

Signs of the Trigonometric Functions

Quadrant containing $P(t) = (x, y)$	Positive functions	Negative functions
I	All	None
II	sin, csc	cos, sec, tan, cot
III	tan, cot	sin, csc, cos, sec
IV	cos, sec	sin, csc, tan, cot

Example 4   Find the quadrant containing $P(t)$ if both $\sin t < 0$ and $\cos t > 0$.

Solution   Referring to the preceding table, we see that $\sin t < 0$ if $P(t)$ is in quadrant III or IV, and $\cos t > 0$ if $P(t)$ is in quadrant I or IV. Hence, for both conditions to be satisfied, $P(t)$ must be in quadrant IV.   ∎

Example 5   If $\sin t = \sqrt{3}/2$ and $\sec t = -2$, find the following:
(a) $\csc t$ (b) $\cos t$ (c) $\tan t$.

Solution
(a)   Using a Fundamental Identity,

$$\csc t = \frac{1}{\sin t} = \frac{1}{(\sqrt{3}/2)} = \frac{2}{\sqrt{3}} = \frac{2\sqrt{3}}{3}.$$

(b)   Since $\sec t = 1/\cos t$, we also have $(\cos t)(\sec t) = 1$, and hence,

$$\cos t = \frac{1}{\sec t} = \frac{1}{-2} = -\frac{1}{2}.$$

(c)   Since $\sin t = \sqrt{3}/2$ and $\cos t = -1/2$,

$$\tan t = \frac{\sin t}{\cos t} = \frac{\sqrt{3}/2}{-1/2} = -\sqrt{3}.$$ ∎

The identity $\sin^2 t + \cos^2 t = 1$ can be used to express $\sin t$ in terms of $\cos t$, or vice versa. For example, since

$$\sin^2 t = 1 - \cos^2 t$$

we have

$$\sin t = \pm\sqrt{1 - \cos^2 t}$$

where the " +" sign is used if $P(t)$ is in quadrant I or II, and the "—" sign is used if $P(t)$ is in quadrant III or IV. Similarly,

$$\cos t = \pm\sqrt{1 - \sin^2 t}$$

where " +" is used if $P(t)$ is in quadrant I or IV and "—" is used if $P(t)$ is in quadrant II or III. The formulas $1 + \tan^2 t = \sec^2 t$ and $1 + \cot^2 t = \csc^2 t$ can be used in like manner.

Example 6   If $\sin t = 3/5$ and $P(t)$ is in quadrant II, find the values of the other trigonometric functions.

Solution   Since $\cos t$ is negative in quadrant II,

$$\cos t = -\sqrt{1 - \sin^2 t} = -\sqrt{1 - (3/5)^2} = -\sqrt{16/25} = -4/5.$$

Next, we see that

$$\tan t = \frac{\sin t}{\cos t} = \frac{3/5}{-4/5} = -\frac{3}{4}.$$

Finally, applying the first three Fundamental Identities gives us

$$\csc t = \frac{5}{3}, \quad \sec t = -\frac{5}{4}, \quad \cot t = -\frac{4}{3}. \qquad \blacksquare$$

EXERCISES 2.2

1 Prove that $1 + \cot^2 t = \csc^2 t$.

2 Prove that $\sin t = 1/\csc t$.

In Exercises 3–6, use Fundamental Identities to find the values of $\csc t$, $\sec t$, $\tan t$, and $\cot t$.

3 $\sin t = -3/5$, $\cos t = 4/5$

4 $\sin t = 8/17$, $\cos t = -15/17$

5 $\sin t = a/\sqrt{a^2 + b^2}$, $\cos t = b/\sqrt{a^2 + b^2}$, where $a^2 + b^2 \neq 0$

6 $\sin t = \sqrt{5}/5$, $\sec t = \sqrt{5}/2$

In Exercises 7–24, find the values of the trigonometric functions corresponding to the number t. (Refer to Figure 2.3 or 2.5 if necessary.)

7 $t = -3\pi/2$

8 $t = -\pi/2$

9 $t = 3\pi/4$

10 $t = -3\pi/4$

11 $t = -\pi$

12 $t = 5\pi$

13 $t = 7\pi/2$

14 $t = 9\pi/2$

15 $t = 200\pi$

16 $t = 375\pi$

17 $t = -5\pi/4$

18 $t = 29\pi/4$

19 $t = \pi/3$

20 $t = -\pi/6$

21 $t = 5\pi/6$

22 $t = 4\pi/3$

23 $t = -2\pi/3$

24 $t = -11\pi/6$

In each of Exercises 25–34, find the quadrant containing $P(t)$ if the given conditions are true.

25 $\cos t > 0$ and $\sin t < 0$

26 $\tan t < 0$ and $\cos t > 0$

27 $\sin t < 0$ and $\cot t > 0$

28 $\sec t > 0$ and $\tan t < 0$

29 $\csc t > 0$ and $\sec t < 0$

30 $\csc t > 0$ and $\cot t < 0$

31 $\sec t < 0$ and $\tan t > 0$

32 $\sin t < 0$ and $\sec t > 0$

33 $\cos t > 0$ and $\tan t > 0$

34 $\cos t < 0$ and $\csc t < 0$

In Exercises 35–43, use Fundamental Identities to find the values of all six trigonometric functions if the given conditions are true.

35 $\tan t = -\frac{3}{4}$ and $\sin t > 0$

36 $\cot t = \frac{3}{4}$ and $\cos t < 0$

37 $\sin t = -\frac{5}{13}$ and $\sec t > 0$

38 $\cos t = \frac{1}{2}$ and $\sin t < 0$

39 $\cos t = -\frac{1}{3}$ and $\sin t < 0$

40 $\csc t = 5$ and $\cot t < 0$

41 $\sec t = -4$ and $\csc t > 0$

42 $\sin t = \frac{2}{5}$ and $\cos t < 0$

43 Is there a real number t such that $7\sin t = 9$? Explain.

44 Is there a real number t such that $3\csc t = 1$? Explain.

45 If $f(t) = \cos t$ and $g(t) = t/4$, find the following.
(a) $f(g(\pi))$ (b) $g(f(\pi))$

46 If $f(t) = \tan t$ and $g(t) = t/4$, find the following.
(a) $f(g(\pi))$ (b) $g(f(\pi))$

47 Show that if $P(t)$ is not on the y-axis, then $(\cos t)(\sec t) = 1$.

48 Show that if $P(t)$ is not on a coordinate axis, then $(\tan t)(\cot t) = 1$.

CALCULATOR EXERCISES 2.2

In each of Exercises 1–6, use Fundamental Identities to approximate the values of all six trigonometric functions to four significant figures if the two given conditions are true.

1 $\sin t = 0.3145$, $\cos t = -0.9492$

2 $\cos t = 0.7314$, $\sin t = 0.6820$

3 $\cos t = 0.8910$, $\tan t = 0.5095$

4 $\sin t = 0.9744$, $\cot t = 0.2309$

5 $\cos t = -0.1219$, $\csc t > 0$

6 $\sin t = 0.9063$, $\tan t < 0$

2.3 THE VARIATION OF THE TRIGONOMETRIC FUNCTIONS

In this section we shall discuss the domains and ranges of each trigonometric function and make some preliminary observations about the variation of $\sin t$ and $\cos t$ as t varies through the set of real numbers.

The domain of each trigonometric function can be determined by referring to the definition in Section 2.2. If $P(t)$ has coordinates (x, y), then the sine and cosine functions always exist, and therefore, each has domain $\mathbb{R}$. In the definitions of the tangent and secant functions, x appears in the denominator, and hence, we must exclude values of t for which x is 0, that is, the values of t corresponding to the points $(0, 1)$ and $(0, -1)$ on the unit circle U. It follows that the domain of the tangent and secant functions consists of all numbers *except* those of the form $(\pi/2) + n\pi$, where n is an integer. In particular, we exclude $\pm\pi/2$, $\pm 3\pi/2$, $\pm 5\pi/2$, etc.

Since $\cot t = x/y$ and $\csc t = 1/y$, the domain of the cotangent and cosecant functions is the set of all real numbers except those numbers t for which the y-coordinate of $P(t)$ is 0. These include the numbers 0, $\pm\pi$, $\pm 2\pi$, $\pm 3\pi$, and, in general, all numbers of the form $n\pi$, where n is an integer. In the future, when we work with $\tan t$, $\cot t$, $\sec t$, and $\csc t$, we will always assume that t is in the appropriate domain, even though this fact will not always be mentioned explicitly.

It was pointed out in Section 2.1 that, except for special values of t, the determination of the point $P(t)$ on U (and hence the values of the trigonometric functions) requires techniques studied in calculus. We can, however, make some general observations. For the time being, let us concentrate on the sine function. Referring to the unit circle in Figure 2.7, we see that if t varies from 0 to $\pi/2$, then the coordinates (x, y) of $P(t)$ vary from $(1, 0)$ to $(0, 1)$. In particular, the y-coordinate, that is, the value of the sine function, increases from 0 to 1. Moreover, this function takes on *all* values between 0 and 1. If we let t vary from $\pi/2$ to π, then the coordinates (x, y) of $P(t)$ vary from $(0, 1)$ to $(-1, 0)$, and hence, the sine function, that is, the ordinate y of $P(t)$, decreases from 1 to 0. In similar fashion, we see that if t varies from π to $3\pi/2$, then $\sin t$ decreases from 0 to -1; and as t varies from $3\pi/2$ to 2π, $\sin t$ increases from -1 to 0.

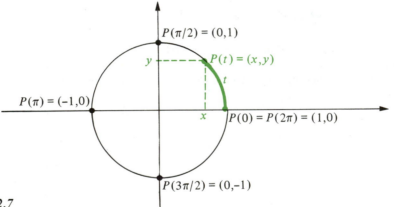

Figure 2.7

The following table partially indicates this behavior of $\sin t$ in the interval $[0, 2\pi]$. For a more complete description we would have to insert many more values of t and $\sin t$.

t	0	$\dfrac{\pi}{2}$	π	$\dfrac{3\pi}{2}$	2π
$\sin t$	0	1	0	-1	0

If we let t vary through the interval $[2\pi, 4\pi]$, then $P(t)$ traces the circle again and the identical pattern for $\sin t$ is repeated, that is,

$$\sin(t + 2\pi) = \sin t$$

for every t in $[0, 2\pi]$. The same is true for other intervals of length 2π. Indeed,

$$\sin(t + 2\pi n) = \sin t$$

since, as we observed in Section 2.1, $P(t) = P(t + 2\pi n)$ for every t and for every integer n. According to the next definition, this repetitive behavior is specified by saying that the sine function is *periodic*.

Definition

A function f is **periodic** if there exists a positive real number k such that

$$f(t + k) = f(t)$$

for every t in the domain of f. The least such positive real number k, if it exists, is called the **period** of f.

The period of the sine function is 2π (see Exercise 3).

The variation of the cosine function in the interval $[0, 2\pi]$ can be determined by observing the behavior of the x-coordinate of the point $P(t)$ on U as t varies from 0 to 2π. Again referring to Figure 2.7, we see that the cosine function (that is, x) decreases from 1 to 0 in the interval $[0, \pi/2]$, decreases from 0 to -1 in $[\pi/2, \pi]$, increases from -1 to 0 in $[\pi, 3\pi/2]$, and increases from 0 to 1 in $[3\pi/2, 2\pi]$. The pattern is then repeated in successive intervals of length 2π. It follows that the cosine function is periodic with period 2π.

The preceding discussion suggests that the graphs of the sine and cosine functions may have the appearance of those in Figures 2.8 and 2.9, respectively. In the figures we

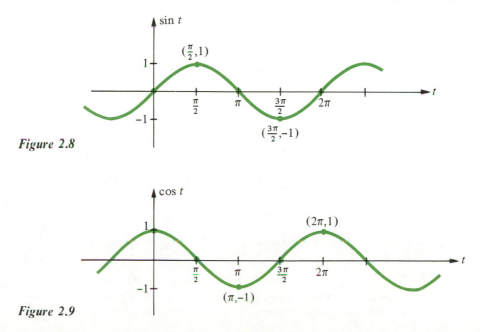

Figure 2.8

Figure 2.9

have plotted several points of the form $(t, \sin t)$ and $(t, \cos t)$, using the functional values mentioned earlier. Since each function has period 2π, each graph repeats itself every 2π units along the horizontal axis. These sketches should be considered as very rough approximations, since we have not yet developed techniques for obtaining many intermediate points. Note, however, that we could use Example 1 of the preceding section to get the points $(\pi/4, \sin \pi/4)$ and $(\pi/4, \cos \pi/4)$, that is, $(\pi/4, \sqrt{2}/2)$. Similarly, Example 2 in Section 2.2 gives us the point $(\pi/6, 1/2)$ on the sine graph, and $(\pi/6, \sqrt{3}/2)$ on the cosine graph. We will study the graphs of the trigonometric functions more carefully in Section 2.7.

It can be shown that the secant and cosecant functions are also periodic with period 2π (see Exercise 6). The variations of these functions will be discussed in Section 2.7. At that time we shall see that the tangent and cotangent functions are periodic with period π.

Finally, let us briefly discuss the range of each trigonometric function. Since the pair (x, y) in the definition of the trigonometric functions gives the coordinates of a point on the unit circle U, we have

$$-1 \le x \le 1 \quad \text{and} \quad -1 \le y \le 1.$$

Since $\sin t = y$ and $\cos t = x$, it follows that the range of both the sine and cosine functions is the set of all numbers in the closed interval $[-1, 1]$.

If x is a nonzero real number such that $-1 \le x \le 1$, then $|x| \le 1$. Multiplying both sides of the last inequality by $1/|x|$, we obtain $1 \le 1/|x|$. Since $\sec t = 1/x$, we see that $1 \le |\sec t|$ for every real number t, and therefore, the range of the secant function consists of all real numbers having absolute value greater than or equal to 1. The same is true for the range of the cosecant function.

It can be shown that $\tan t$ and $\cot t$ take on all real values (see Exercise 5). That will also become apparent in Section 2.7, when we study the graphs of the trigonometric functions.

EXERCISES 2.3

In each of Exercises 1 and 2, plot the points $(a, 0)$ on the x-axis if a satisfies both of the given conditions.

1 (a) The tangent and secant functions are undefined at a.

   (b) $-4\pi \le a \le 4\pi$

2 (a) The cotangent and cosecant functions are undefined at a.

   (b) $-4\pi \le a \le 4\pi$

3 Prove that the sine function has period 2π. (*Hint:* Assume that there is a positive real number k less

than 2π such that $\sin(t + k) = \sin t$ for all t. Arrive at contradiction by letting $t = 0$.)

4 Prove that the cosine function has period 2π.

5 Prove that the range of the tangent function is $\mathbb{R}$ by showing that if a is any real number, then there is a point $P(t)$ on U such that $\tan t = a$. (*Hint:* If $P(t) = (x, y)$ is on U, consider the equation $\tan t = y/x = a$, where $x^2 + y^2 = 1$.)

6 Prove that the cosecant and secant functions each have period 2π. (*Hint:* Use Exercises 3 and 4 and two fundamental identities.)

2.4 ANGLES

The definitions of the trigonometric functions can also be based on the notion of angles. This more traditional approach is quite common in applications of mathematics and hence should not be obscured by the definitions stated in Section 2.2. Indeed, for a thorough appreciation of the trigonometric functions, it is best to blend the two ideas. In this section we restrict our discussion to angles and their measurement. In Section 2.5 we shall demonstrate how angles can be used to find values of the trigonometric functions.

An angle is often regarded as the set of all points on two rays or half-lines, l_1 and l_2, having the same initial point O. If A and B are points on l_1 and l_2, respectively (see Figure 2.10), then we may refer to **angle AOB.** The same is true for finite line segments with a common endpoint. For trigonometric purposes it is convenient to regard angle AOB as generated by starting with the fixed ray l_1 with endpoint O and rotating it about O, in a plane, to a position specified by ray l_2. We call l_1 the **initial side,** l_2 the **terminal side,** and O the **vertex** of the angle. The amount or direction of rotation is not restricted in any way. Thus we might let l_1 make several revolutions in either direction about O before coming to the position l_2.

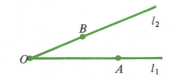

Figure 2.10

If a rectangular coordinate system is introduced, then the **standard position** of an angle is obtained by taking the vertex at the origin and letting l_1 coincide with the positive x-axis. If l_1 is rotated in a counterclockwise direction to position l_2, then the angle is considered **positive,** whereas if l_1 is rotated in a clockwise direction, the angle is **negative.** We often denote angles by lower-case Greek letters and specify the direction of rotation by means of a circular arc or spiral with an arrow attached. Figure 2.11 contains sketches of two positive angles α and β and a negative angle γ. If the terminal side of an angle is in a certain quadrant, we speak of the angle as being in that quadrant. In Figure 2.11, α is in quadrant II, β is in quadrant I, and γ is in quadrant III. If the terminal side coincides with a coordinate axis, then the angle is referred to as a

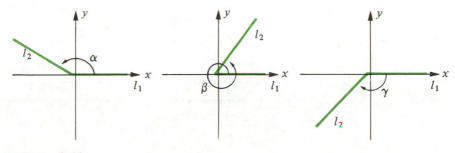

Figure 2.11

quadrantal angle. It is important to observe that there are many different angles in standard position which have the same terminal side. Any two such angles are called **coterminal**.

We shall next consider the problem of assigning a measure to a given angle. Let U be a unit circle with the center at the origin O of a rectangular coordinate system, and let θ be an angle in standard position. We regard θ as generated by rotating the positive x-axis about O. As the axis rotates to its terminal position, its point of intersection with U travels a certain distance t before arriving at its final position P, as illustrated in Figure 2.12. If t is considered positive for a counterclockwise rotation and negative for a clockwise rotation, then P is precisely the point on U that corresponds to the real number t. A natural way of assigning a measure to θ is to use the number t. When this is done, we say that **θ is an angle of t radians** and we write $\theta = t$ or $\theta = t\,radians$. In particular, if $\theta = 1$, then θ is an angle that subtends an arc of unit length on the unit circle U. The notation $\theta = -7.5$ means that θ is the angle generated by a clockwise rotation in which the point of intersection of the terminal side of θ with the unit circle U travels 7.5 units. Several angles, measured in radians, are sketched in Figure 2.13.

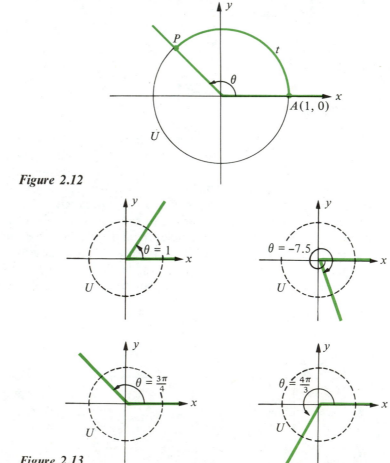

Figure 2.12

Figure 2.13

The radian measure of an angle can be found by using a circle of *any* radius. In the following discussion, the terminology **central angle** of a circle refers to an angle whose vertex is at the center of the circle. Thus, suppose that θ is a central angle of a circle of radius r and θ subtends an arc of length s, where $0 \le s < 2\pi r$. To find the radian measure of θ, let us place θ in standard position on a rectangular coordinate system and superimpose a unit circle U, as shown in Figure 2.14. If t is the length of arc subtended by θ on U, then by definition we may write $\theta = t$. From plane geometry, the ratio of the arcs in Figure 2.14 is the same as the ratio of the radii; that is,

$$\frac{t}{s} = \frac{1}{r} \quad \text{or} \quad t = \frac{s}{r}.$$

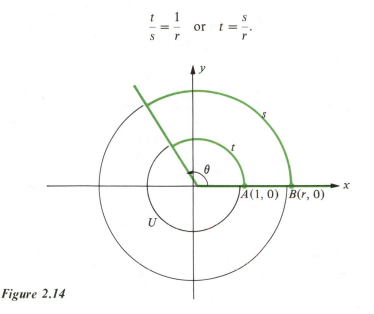

Figure 2.14

Substituting θ for t gives us the following result.

Theorem

> If a central angle θ of a circle of radius r subtends an arc of length s, then the radian measure of θ is given by
>
> $$\theta = \frac{s}{r}.$$

Example 1   A central angle θ subtends an arc 10 cm long on a circle of radius 4 cm. Find the radian measure of θ.

Solution   Substituting in the formula $\theta = s/r$ gives us the radian measure

$$\theta = \frac{10}{4} = 2.5.$$ ∎

The formula $\theta = s/r$ indicates that the radian measure of an angle is independent of the size of the circle. For example, if the radius of the circle is $r = 4$ cm and the arc subtended by a central angle θ is 8 cm, then the radian measure is

$$\theta = \frac{8 \text{ cm}}{4 \text{ cm}} = 2.$$

If the radius of the circle is 5 km and the subtended arc is 10 km, then

$$\theta = \frac{10 \text{ km}}{5 \text{ km}} = 2.$$

These calculations indicate that the radian measure of an angle is dimensionless and hence may be regarded as a real number. Indeed, it is for this reason that we usually employ the notation $\theta = t$ instead of $\theta = t$ radians.

Another unit of measurement for angles is the **degree**. If the angle is placed in standard position on a rectangular coordinate system, then an angle of 1 degree is, by definition, the measure of the angle formed by 1/360 of a complete revolution in the counterclockwise direction. The symbol "°" is used to denote the degrees in the measure of an angle. In Figure 2.15, several angles measured in degrees are shown in standard position on a rectangular coordinate system. It is customary to refer to an angle of measure 90° as a **right angle**. An angle is **acute** if its degree measure is between 0° and 90°. If its measure is between 90° and 180° an angle is **obtuse**.

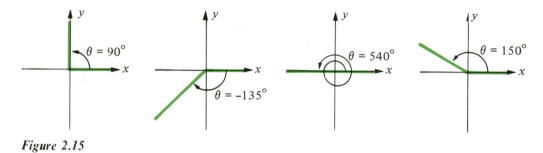

Figure 2.15

If smaller measurements than those afforded by the degree or radian are required, we can use tenths, hundredths, or thousandths of radians or degrees. If degrees are used, then another method is to divide each degree into 60 equal parts called **minutes** (denoted by ′) and each minute into 60 equal parts called **seconds** (denoted by ″). Thus 1′ is 1/60 of 1°, and 1″ is 1/60 of 1′. A notation such as $\theta = 73°56'18''$ refers to an angle θ of measure 73 degrees, 56 minutes, and 18 seconds.

It is not difficult to transform angular measure from one system to another. If we consider the angle θ, in standard position, generated by one-half of a complete counterclockwise rotation, then $\theta = 180°$. Using the formula $\theta = s/r$, we see that the radian measure of θ is π. This gives us the following:

Relationships between Degrees and Radians

$$180° = \pi \text{ radians}, \qquad 1° = \frac{\pi}{180} \text{ radians}, \qquad 1 \text{ radian} = \left(\frac{180}{\pi}\right)°.$$

If we use the approximation $\pi \approx 3.14159$ to calculate $\pi/180$ and $180/\pi$, we obtain

$$1° \approx 0.01745 \text{ radians} \quad \text{and} \quad 1 \text{ radian} \approx 57.296°.$$

Example 2
(a) Find the radian measure of θ if $\theta = 150°$ and if $\theta = 225°$.
(b) Find the degree measure of θ if $\theta = 7\pi/4$ and if $\theta = \pi/3$.

Solution
(a) Since there are $\pi/180$ radians in each degree, the number of radians in $150°$ can be found by multiplying 150 by $\pi/180$. Thus,

$$150° = 150\left(\frac{\pi}{180}\right) = \frac{5\pi}{6} \text{ radians.}$$

Similarly, $\qquad 225° = 225\left(\frac{\pi}{180}\right) = \frac{5\pi}{4} \text{ radians.}$

(b) The number of degrees in 1 radian is $180/\pi$. Consequently, to find the number of degrees in $7\pi/4$ radians, we multiply by $180/\pi$, obtaining

$$\frac{7\pi}{4} \text{ radians} = \frac{7\pi}{4}\left(\frac{180}{\pi}\right) = 315°.$$

In like manner, $\qquad \frac{\pi}{3} \text{ radians} = \frac{\pi}{3}\left(\frac{180}{\pi}\right) = 60°.$ ■

Example 3 If the measure of an angle θ is 3 radians, find the approximate measure of θ in terms of degrees, minutes, and seconds.

Solution Since 1 radian $\approx 57.296°$, we have

$$3 \text{ radians} \approx 171.888° = 171° + 0.888°.$$

Since there are $60'$ in each degree, the number of minutes in $0.888°$ is $60(0.888)$, or $53.28'$. Hence,

$$3 \text{ radians} \approx 171°53.28'.$$

Finally, $0.28' = (0.28)60'' \approx 17''$. Therefore,

$$3 \text{ radians} \approx 171°53'17''.$$ ■

Many hand-held calculators have a key that will automatically convert the degree measure of an angle to radians, and vice versa. The owner of a calculator should refer to the user's guide for information. Since entries are made in the decimal system, angles that are expressed in terms of degrees and minutes must be converted to decimal form before they are entered into the calculator. For example,

$$67°30' = 67.5° \quad \text{since} \quad 30' = (30/60)° = 0.5°$$
$$123°45' = 123.75° \quad \text{since} \quad 45' = (45/60)° = 0.75°$$
$$8°13' \approx 8.21667° \quad \text{since} \quad 13' = (13/60)° \approx 0.21667°.$$

If seconds are involved, another appropriate decimal must be calculated. To illustrate, since there are 3,600 seconds in each degree, $18'' = (18/3600)° = 0.005'$, and hence,

$$67°30'18'' = 67.505°.$$

EXERCISES 2.4

In each of Exercises 1–12, place the angle with the indicated measure in standard position on a rectangular coordinate system, and find the measure of two positive angles and two negative angles that are coterminal with the given angle.

1 120°   2 240°
3 135°   4 315°
5 −30°   6 −150°
7 620°   8 570°
9 $5\pi/6$ 10 $2\pi/3$
11 $-\pi/4$ 12 $-5\pi/4$

In Exercises 13–24, find the radian measure that corresponds to the given degree measure.

13 150°   14 120°
15 −60°   16 −135°
17 225°   18 210°
19 450°   20 630°
21 72°   22 54°
23 100°   24 95°

In Exercises 25–36, find the degree measure that corresponds to the given radian measure.

25 $2\pi/3$ 26 $5\pi/6$
27 $11\pi/6$ 28 $4\pi/3$
29 $3\pi/4$ 30 $11\pi/4$
31 $-7\pi/2$ 32 $-5\pi/2$
33 7π 34 9π
35 $\pi/9$ 36 $\pi/16$

In Exercises 37–40, find the approximate measure of θ in terms of degrees, minutes, and seconds.

37 $\theta = 2$ 38 $\theta = 1.5$
39 $\theta = 5$ 40 $\theta = 4$

41 A central angle θ subtends an arc 7 cm long on a circle of radius 4 cm. Approximate the measure of θ in (a) radians; (b) degrees.

42 A central angle θ subtends an arc 3 feet long on a circle of radius 20 inches. Approximate the measure of θ in (a) radians; (b) degrees.

43 Approximate the length of an arc subtended by a central angle of measure 50° on a circle of radius 8 meters.

44 Approximate the length of an arc subtended by a central angle of 2.2 radians on a circle of radius 60 cm.

45 If a central angle θ of measure 20° subtends a circular arc of length 3 km, find the radius of the circle.

46 If a central angle θ of radian measure 4 subtends a circular arc 10 cm long, find the radius of the circle.

47 The distance between two points A and B on the earth is measured along a circle having center C at the center of the earth and radius equal to the distance from C to the surface. If the diameter of the earth is approximately 8,000 miles, approximate the distance between A and B if angle ACB has measure (a) 60°; (b) 45°; (c) 30°; (d) 10°; (e) 1°.

48 Refer to Exercise 47. If angle ACB has measure 1′, then the distance between A and B is called a **nautical mile**. Approximate the number of ordinary (**statute**) miles in a nautical mile.

49 Refer to Exercise 47. If two points A and B are 500 miles apart, find angle ACB in both degree measure and radian measure.

50 The **angular speed** of a wheel that is rotating at a constant rate is the angle generated by a line segment from the center of the wheel to the circumference, per unit of time. If a wheel of diameter 3 feet is rotating at a rate of 2,400 rpm (revolutions per minute), find the angular speed.

CALCULATOR EXERCISES 2.4

In Exercises 1–6, approximate, to four decimal places, the radian measure that corresponds to the given degree measure of θ, or the degree measure that corresponds to the given radian measure.

1 $\theta = 73°24'$ **2** $\theta = 261°37'$

3 $\theta = 482°16'43''$ **4** $\theta = \sqrt{317} + \pi$

5 $\theta = \ln(13.6521)$ **6** $\theta = e^{\sqrt{\pi}}$

7–9 The diameter of the earth at the equator is estimated as 7,926.41 miles. Rework Exercises 47–49 using that measurement, assuming that points A and B are on the equator.

10 Refer to Exercise 50. If a wheel of diameter 1.683 meters is rotating at a rate of 2,875 rpm, find the angular speed.

2.5 TRIGONOMETRIC FUNCTIONS OF ANGLES

For certain applications it is convenient to change the domain of the trigonometric functions from a set of real numbers to a set of angles. This is very easy to do. If θ is an angle, we merely agree on the values $\sin \theta$, $\cos \theta$, and so on. The usual way of assigning such values is to use the radian measure of θ, as in the following definition.

Definition of Trigonometric Functions of Angles

> If θ is an angle, and if the radian measure of θ is t, then the value of each trigonometric function at θ is its value at the real number t.

We see from the preceding definition that if t is the radian measure of θ, then

$$\sin \theta = \sin t, \quad \cos \theta = \cos t, \quad \tan \theta = \tan t,$$

and likewise for the other functions. For convenience we shall use the terminology *trigonometric functions* regardless of whether angles or real numbers are employed for the domain. To make the unit of angular measure clear, we shall use the degree symbol and write sin 65°, tan 150°, etc., whenever the angle is measured in degrees. Numerals without any symbol attached, such as cos 3 and csc $(\pi/6)$, will indicate that radian measure is being used. This is not in conflict with our previous work, where, for example, cos 3 meant the value of the cosine function at the real number 3, since by definition the cosine of an angle of measure 3 radians is identical with the cosine of the real number 3.

Example 1   Find sin 90°, cos 45°, and tan 720°.

Solution   The angles are shown in standard position in Figure 2.16. The radian measures of the angles may be found as follows:

$$90° = 90\left(\frac{\pi}{180}\right) = \frac{\pi}{2}, \quad 45° = 45\left(\frac{\pi}{180}\right) = \frac{\pi}{4}, \quad 720° = 720\left(\frac{\pi}{180}\right) = 4\pi.$$

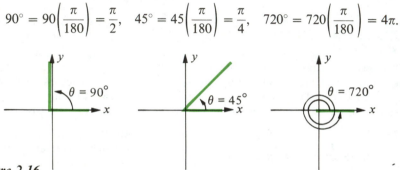

Figure 2.16

Using the definition of trigonometric functions of angles and Examples 1 and 2 of Section 2.2, we obtain

$$\sin 90° = \sin (\pi/2) = 1$$
$$\cos 45° = \cos (\pi/4) = \sqrt{2}/2$$
$$\tan 720° = \tan 4\pi = \tan 0 = 0.$$ ∎

In the next section we shall introduce techniques for approximating trigonometric functional values corresponding to *any* angle θ.

The values of the trigonometric functions at an angle θ may be determined by means of an arbitrary point on the terminal side of θ. To prove this, let θ be an angle in standard position and let $Q(a, b)$ be any point on the terminal side of θ, where $d(O, Q) = r > 0$. Figure 2.17 illustrates the case in which the terminal side lies in quadrant III; however, our discussion applies to any angle.

The point $Q(a, b)$ is not necessarily a point on the unit circle U, since r may be different from 1. Let $P(x, y)$ be the point on the terminal side of θ such that $d(O, P) = 1$. Hence, $P(x, y)$ is on the unit circle U. If t is the radian measure of θ, then by definition we have

$$\sin \theta = \sin t = y$$
$$\cos \theta = \cos t = x.$$

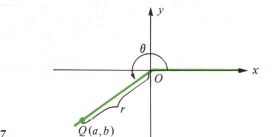

Figure 2.17

As in Figure 2.18, let us consider vertical lines through Q and P intersecting the x-axis at $Q'(a,0)$ and $P'(x,0)$, respectively. Since triangles OQQ' and OPP' are similar, we have

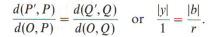

$$\frac{d(P',P)}{d(O,P)} = \frac{d(Q',Q)}{d(O,Q)} \quad \text{or} \quad \frac{|y|}{1} = \frac{|b|}{r}.$$

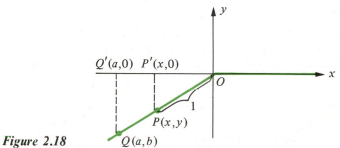

Figure 2.18

Since b and y always have the same sign, this gives us

$$y = \frac{b}{r} \quad \text{and hence} \quad \sin\theta = y = \frac{b}{r}.$$

In similar fashion, we obtain

$$\cos\theta = \frac{a}{r}.$$

Using a fundamental identity,

$$\tan\theta = \frac{\sin\theta}{\cos\theta} = \frac{(b/r)}{(a/r)} = \frac{b}{a}.$$

The remaining three functions may be obtained by taking reciprocals. This gives us the following theorem.

Theorem on Trigonometric Functions as Ratios

Let θ be an angle in standard position on a rectangular coordinate system and let $Q(a,b)$ be any point other than O on the terminal side of θ. If $d(O,Q) = r$, then

$$\sin \theta = \frac{b}{r} \qquad\qquad \csc \theta = \frac{r}{b} \quad \text{(if } b \neq 0)$$

$$\cos \theta = \frac{a}{r} \qquad\qquad \sec \theta = \frac{r}{a} \quad \text{(if } a \neq 0)$$

$$\tan \theta = \frac{b}{a} \quad \text{(if } a \neq 0) \qquad \cot \theta = \frac{a}{b} \quad \text{(if } b \neq 0).$$

It can be shown, by using similar triangles, that the formulas given in this theorem are independent of the point $Q(a,b)$ that is chosen on the terminal side of θ. Note that if $r = 1$, then the formulas reduce to the definition of the trigonometric functions given in Section 2.2, with $a = x$ and $b = y$. This theorem has many applications in trigonometry. In Section 2.10 we shall use it to solve problems concerned with right triangles. Another reason for its importance is that it can often be used to obtain values of trigonometric functions. Indeed, note that it is sufficient to find *one* point (other than O) on the terminal side of an angle, provided the angle is in standard position on a rectangular coordinate system.

Example 2   If θ is an angle in standard position on a rectangular coordinate system, and if the point $Q(-15,8)$ is on the terminal side of θ, find the values of the trigonometric functions of θ.

Solution   By the Distance Formula, the distance r from the origin O to any point $Q(a,b)$ is $r = \sqrt{(a-0)^2 + (b-0)^2} = \sqrt{a^2 + b^2}$. Hence, for $Q(-15,8)$ we have

$$r = \sqrt{(-15)^2 + 8^2} = \sqrt{225 + 64} = \sqrt{289} = 17.$$

Applying the last theorem with $a = -15$, $b = 8$, and $r = 17$, we obtain

$$\sin \theta = \frac{8}{17} \qquad \csc \theta = \frac{17}{8}$$

$$\cos \theta = -\frac{15}{17} \qquad \sec \theta = -\frac{17}{15}$$

$$\tan \theta = -\frac{8}{15} \qquad \cot \theta = -\frac{15}{8}. \qquad\blacksquare$$

Example 3   An angle θ is in standard position on a rectangular coordinate system. If its terminal side is in quadrant III and it lies on the line $y = 3x$, find the values of the trigonometric functions of θ.

Solution   The graph of $y = 3x$ is sketched in Figure 2.19, together with the initial and terminal sides of θ (in color). We begin by choosing a convenient point, say $Q(-1, -3)$, on the terminal side. The distance r from the origin to Q is

$$r = d(O, Q) = \sqrt{(-1)^2 + (-3)^2} = \sqrt{10}.$$

Applying the Theorem on Trigonometric Functions as Ratios with $a = -1$, $b = -3$, and $r = \sqrt{10}$ gives us

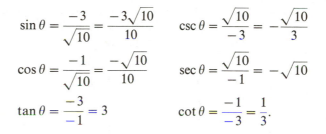

$$\sin \theta = \frac{-3}{\sqrt{10}} = \frac{-3\sqrt{10}}{10} \qquad \csc \theta = \frac{\sqrt{10}}{-3} = -\frac{\sqrt{10}}{3}$$

$$\cos \theta = \frac{-1}{\sqrt{10}} = \frac{-\sqrt{10}}{10} \qquad \sec \theta = \frac{\sqrt{10}}{-1} = -\sqrt{10}$$

$$\tan \theta = \frac{-3}{-1} = 3 \qquad \cot \theta = \frac{-1}{-3} = \frac{1}{3}.$$

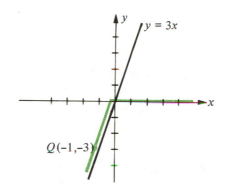

Figure 2.19

In the proof of the Theorem on Trigonometric Functions as Ratios we considered θ as a nonquadrantal angle; however, the formulas we derived are also true if the terminal side of θ lies on either the x- or y-axis. This is illustrated by the next example.

Example 4   Find the values of the trigonometric functions of θ if $\theta = 270°$.

Solution   If we place θ in standard position, then the terminal side coincides with the negative y-axis. We next choose any point Q on the terminal side of θ. For simplicity we consider $Q(0, -1)$. In this case $r = 1$, $a = 0$, $b = -1$, and hence

$$\sin \theta = \frac{-1}{1} = -1 \qquad \csc \theta = \frac{1}{-1} = -1$$

$$\cos \theta = \frac{0}{1} = 0 \qquad \cot \theta = \frac{0}{-1} = 0.$$

The tangent and secant functions are undefined, since the meaningless expressions $\tan\theta = (-1)/0$ and $\sec\theta = 1/0$ arise when we substitute in the appropriate formulas. ■

We shall conclude this section by showing that for acute angles, values of the trigonometric functions can be interpreted as ratios of the lengths of the sides of a right triangle. Recall that a triangle is called a **right triangle** if one of its angles is a right angle. If θ is an acute angle, then it can be regarded as an angle of a right triangle and we may refer to the lengths of the **hypotenuse**, the **opposite side**, and the **adjacent side** in the usual way. For convenience, we shall use **hyp**, **opp**, and **adj**, respectively, to denote these numbers. Introducing a rectangular coordinate system as in Figure 2.20, we see that the

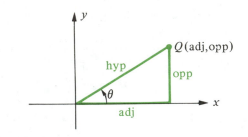

Figure 2.20

lengths of the adjacent side and the opposite side for θ are the abscissa and ordinate, respectively, of a point Q on the terminal side of θ. By the Theorem on Trigonometric Functions as Ratios, we have

$$\sin\theta = \frac{\text{opp}}{\text{hyp}} \qquad \csc\theta = \frac{\text{hyp}}{\text{opp}}$$

$$\cos\theta = \frac{\text{adj}}{\text{hyp}} \qquad \sec\theta = \frac{\text{hyp}}{\text{adj}}$$

$$\tan\theta = \frac{\text{opp}}{\text{adj}} \qquad \cot\theta = \frac{\text{adj}}{\text{opp}}$$

These formulas are very important in work with right triangles and should be memorized. The next example illustrates how they may be used.

Example 5   Find the values of $\sin\theta$, $\cos\theta$, and $\tan\theta$ for the following values of θ:
  (a) $\theta = 60°$;   (b) $\theta = 30°$;   (c) $\theta = 45°$.

Solution   Let us consider an equilateral triangle having sides of length 2. The median from one vertex to the opposite side bisects the angle at that vertex, as illustrated in (i) of Figure 2.21. By the Pythagorean Theorem, the length of this median is $\sqrt{3}$. Using the colored triangle, we obtain the following.

(a) $\sin 60° = \dfrac{\sqrt{3}}{2}, \quad \cos 60° = \dfrac{1}{2}, \quad \tan 60° = \dfrac{\sqrt{3}}{1} = \sqrt{3}$

(b) $\sin 30° = \dfrac{1}{2}, \quad \cos 30° = \dfrac{\sqrt{3}}{2}, \quad \tan 30° = \dfrac{1}{\sqrt{3}} = \dfrac{\sqrt{3}}{3}$

(c) To find the functional values for $\theta = 45°$, let us consider an isosceles right triangle whose two equal sides have length 1, as illustrated in (ii) of Figure 2.21. Thus,

$$\sin 45° = \frac{1}{\sqrt{2}} = \frac{\sqrt{2}}{2} = \cos 45°, \quad \tan 45° = \frac{1}{1} = 1.$$

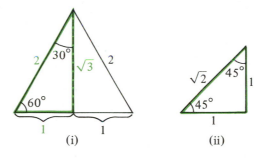

(i)   (ii)

Figure 2.21   ■

The radian measures corresponding to 30°, 45°, and 60° are $\pi/6$, $\pi/4$, and $\pi/3$, respectively. Since the values of the trigonometric functions at a real number t are the same as those at an angle of t radians, Example 5 provides a convenient method for obtaining these special values. For convenience, they are listed in tabular form in Table A on page 68, together with the values at 0 and $\pi/2$. The reader should check each entry (see Exercise 19). A dash indicates that the function is undefined. Two reasons for stressing these special values are (1) they are exact, and (2) they arise frequently in work involving trigonometry. It is a good idea either to memorize Table A or to be able to find the values quickly, using triangles and points on the coordinate axes.

We have now discussed two different approaches to the trigonometric functions. The definition introduced in Section 2.2 emphasizes the fact that the trigonometric functions have domains consisting of real numbers. Such functions are the building blocks for the subject of calculus. In addition, we shall see later that the unit circle approach is useful for discussing graphs and deriving various trigonometric identities. The development in terms of angles and ratios considered in this section has many applications in the sciences and engineering. Students should strive to become proficient in the use of both formulations of the trigonometric functions, since each will reinforce the other and make it easier to master more advanced aspects of trigonometry.

Table A. Special Values of the Trigonometric Functions

t number, radians	t degrees	$\sin t$	$\cos t$	$\tan t$	$\cot t$	$\sec t$	$\csc t$
0	$0°$	0	1	0	—	1	—
$\dfrac{\pi}{6}$	$30°$	$\dfrac{1}{2}$	$\dfrac{\sqrt{3}}{2}$	$\dfrac{\sqrt{3}}{3}$	$\sqrt{3}$	$\dfrac{2\sqrt{3}}{3}$	2
$\dfrac{\pi}{4}$	$45°$	$\dfrac{\sqrt{2}}{2}$	$\dfrac{\sqrt{2}}{2}$	1	1	$\sqrt{2}$	$\sqrt{2}$
$\dfrac{\pi}{3}$	$60°$	$\dfrac{\sqrt{3}}{2}$	$\dfrac{1}{2}$	$\sqrt{3}$	$\dfrac{\sqrt{3}}{3}$	2	$\dfrac{2\sqrt{3}}{3}$
$\dfrac{\pi}{2}$	$90°$	1	0	—	0	—	1

EXERCISES 2.5

In Exercises 1–18, use the Theorem on Trigonometric Functions as Ratios to find the values of the six trigonometric functions of θ if θ is in standard position and satisfies the given condition.

1 The point $P(4, -3)$ is on the terminal side of θ.

2 The point $P(-8, -15)$ is on the terminal side of θ.

3 The point $P(-2, -5)$ is on the terminal side of θ.

4 The point $P(-1, 2)$ is on the terminal side of θ.

5 The terminal side of θ is in quadrant II and lies on the line $y = -4x$.

6 The terminal side of θ is in quadrant IV and lies on the line $3y + 5x = 0$.

7 The terminal side of θ is in quadrant III and lies on the line $2y - 7x = 0$.

8 The terminal side of θ is in quadrant II and lies on the line $2y + 6x = 0$.

9 The terminal side of θ bisects the second quadrant.

10 The terminal side of θ bisects the third quadrant.

11 $\theta = 450°$ **12** $\theta = 180°$

13 $\theta = 135°$ **14** $\theta = 225°$

15 $\theta = -45°$ **16** $\theta = 405°$

17 $\theta = 360°$ **18** $\theta = 630°$

19 Check each entry in Table A.

20 Prove geometrically that the formulas given in the Theorem on Trigonometric Functions as Ratios are independent of the point $Q(a, b)$ that is chosen on the terminal side of θ.

In Exercises 21–30, find the values of the trigonometric functions of θ if θ is the angle of the pictured right triangle.

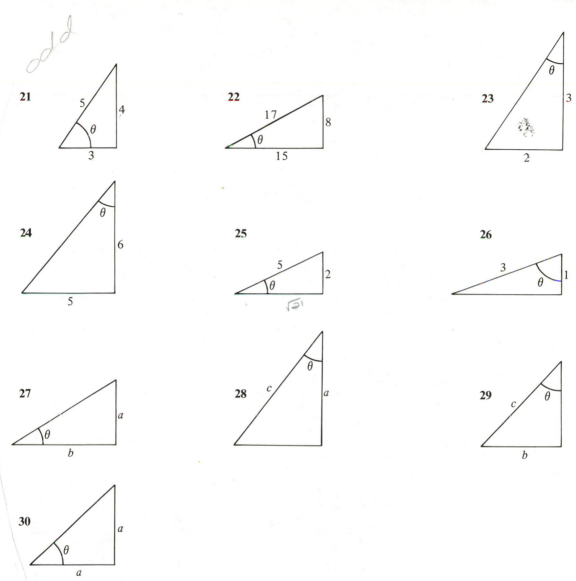

CALCULATOR EXERCISES 2.5

1 Use a calculator to find the values of the sine, cosine, and tangent functions at $30°, 45°$, and $60°$, and compare your answers with the entries in Table A. How do you account for any discrepancies?

2 Find the values of the six trigonometric functions of θ to two-decimal-place accuracy if θ is in standard position and the point $P(\ln 4.37, \sqrt{9.61} \, e^{1.35})$ is on the terminal side.

3 Find the values of the trigonometric functions of θ to three-decimal-place accuracy if θ is the angle of the right triangle on page 70.

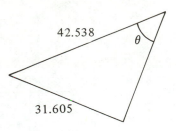

2.6 VALUES OF THE TRIGONOMETRIC FUNCTIONS

Several special values of the trigonometric functions were calculated in previous sections. Let us now turn to the problem of finding *all* values. Since the sine function has period 2π, it is sufficient to know the values of $\sin t$ for $0 \le t \le 2\pi$, because these values are repeated in every t-interval of length 2π. The same is true for the other trigonometric functions. As a matter of fact, the values of any trigonometric function can be determined if its values in the t-interval $[0, \pi/2]$ are known. In order to prove this, suppose that t is any real number and let $P(t)$ be the point on the unit circle U that corresponds to t. We shall make use of the following concept.

Definition

> The shortest arc length t' between $P(t)$ and the x-axis, on the unit circle U, is called the **reference number** associated with t.

Figure 2.22 illustrates arcs of length t' for positions of $P(t)$ in various quadrants. Note that $0 \le t' < \pi/2$ for all values of t.

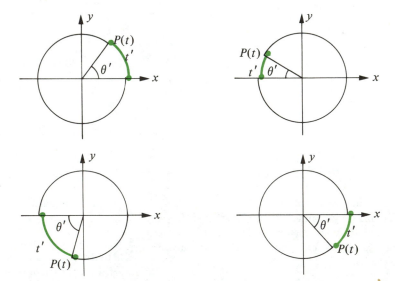

Figure 2.22

If we let θ' denote the angle with vertex O which subtends the arc of length t', as illustrated in Figure 2.22, then θ' is called *the reference angle associated with* $P(t)$, or with *any angle* θ *whose terminal side contains* $P(t)$. Thus, if θ is an angle in standard position and θ is not a quadrantal angle, we have the following definition.

Definition

> The **reference angle** associated with θ is the acute angle θ' that the terminal side of θ makes with the positive or negative x-axis.

Referring to Figure 2.22 and using the definition of trigonometric functions of angles stated in Section 2.5, we see that

$$\sin \theta' = \sin t', \quad \cos \theta' = \cos t', \quad \tan \theta = \tan t'.$$

In the remainder of our work we shall use the approximation $\pi \approx 3.1416$ for estimating reference numbers and angles.

Example 1 Approximate the reference number t' if
  (a) $t = 2$ (b) $t = 4$ (c) $t = 7\pi/4$ (d) $t = -2\pi/3$.

Solution   Each point $P(t)$ on the unit circle U, and the magnitude of its reference number t', are indicated in Figure 2.33. Referring to the figure, we see that

  (a) $t' = \pi - 2 \approx 3.1416 - 2 = 1.1416$
  (b) $t' = 4 - \pi \approx 4 - 3.1416 = 0.8584$
  (c) $t' = 2\pi - (7\pi/4) = \pi/4$
  (d) $t' = \pi - (2\pi/3) = \pi/3$.

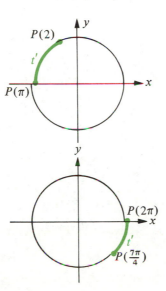
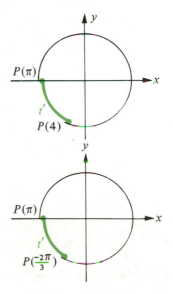

Figure 2.23

Example 2   Sketch the reference angle θ' for each of the following and express the measure of θ' in terms of both radians and degrees.

(a) $\theta = 5\pi/6$ (b) $\theta = 315°$ (c) $\theta = -240°$

Solution   Each angle θ and its reference angle θ' are sketched in Figure 2.24. Evidently,

(a) $\theta' = \pi/6 = 30°$
(b) $\theta' = 45° = \pi/4$
(c) $\theta' = 60° = \pi/3$.

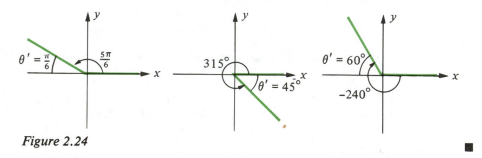

Figure 2.24

Let us now demonstrate how reference numbers or reference angles can be used to find values of the trigonometric functions. If the point $P(t)$ is not on a coordinate axis and t' is the reference number for t, then $0 < t' < \pi/2$. Suppose that $P(t)$ has rectangular coordinates (x, y), so that $P(t) = P(x, y)$. Consider the point $A(1, 0)$, and let $P'(x', y')$ be the point on U in quadrant I such that $\overset{\frown}{AP'} = t'$. Illustrations in which $P(x, y)$ lies in quadrants II, III, and IV are given in Figure 2 25.

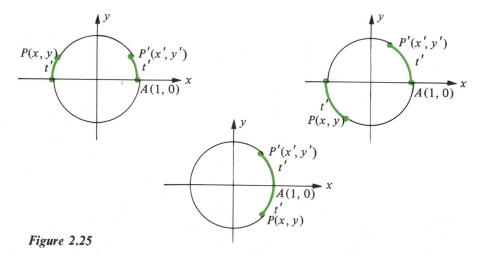

Figure 2.25

We see that in all cases

$$x' = |x| \quad \text{and} \quad y' = |y|$$

and hence, we have
$$|\cos t| = |x| = x' = \cos t'$$
$$|\sin t| = |y| = y' = \sin t'.$$

It is easy to show that the absolute value of *every* trigonometric function at t is the same as its value at t'. For example,

$$|\tan t| = \left|\frac{y}{x}\right| = \frac{|y|}{|x|} = \frac{y'}{x'} = \tan t'.$$

In terms of angles, if θ' is the reference angle of θ, then

$$|\sin \theta| = \sin \theta', \quad |\cos \theta| = \cos \theta',$$

and similarly for the other trigonometric functions. We may, therefore, state the following rules.

Rules for Finding Values of the Trigonometric Functions

(i)   To find the value of a trigonometric function at a number t, determine its value for the reference number t' associated with t and prefix the appropriate sign.

(ii) To find the value of a trigonometric function at an angle θ, determine its value for the reference angle θ' associated with θ and prefix the appropriate sign.

The "appropriate sign" can be determined from the table of signs in Section 2.2.

Example 3   Find $\sin (7\pi/4)$ and $\sec (-7\pi/6)$.

Solution   As indicated in Figure 2.26, the reference numbers of $7\pi/4$ and $-7\pi/6$ are $\pi/4$ and $\pi/6$, respectively. Hence, by the preceding rules and Table A of Section 2.5,

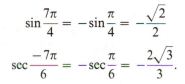

$$\sin \frac{7\pi}{4} = -\sin \frac{\pi}{4} = -\frac{\sqrt{2}}{2}$$

$$\sec \frac{-7\pi}{6} = -\sec \frac{\pi}{6} = -\frac{2\sqrt{3}}{3}.$$

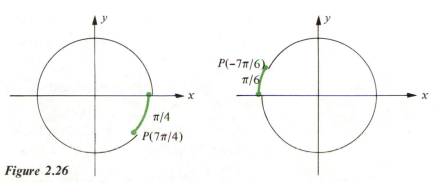

Figure 2.26

Example 4   Find each of the following:

    (a) $\sin 150°$ (b) $\tan 315°$ (c) $\sec(-240°)$

Solution   The angles and their reference angles are shown in Figure 2.27. Using the rules for finding functional values, together with Table A of Section 2.5, gives us

    (a) $\sin 150° = \sin 30° = 1/2$

    (b) $\tan 315° = -\tan 45° = -1$

    (c) $\sec(-240°) = -\sec 60° = -2$.

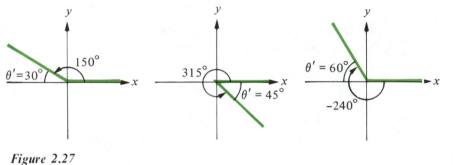

Figure 2.27

By employing advanced techniques it is possible to compute, to any degree of accuracy, all the values of the trigonometric functions in the t-interval $[0, \pi/2]$, or, equivalently, in the degree interval $[0°, 90°]$. Table 2, part of which is reproduced on the next page, gives approximations to such values.

The domain of t in Table 2 is from 0 to 1.5708. The last number is a four-decimal-place approximation to $\pi/2$. Table 2 is arranged so that functional values which correspond to angles in degree measure may be found directly. Angular measures are given in 10′ intervals from 0° to 90°. The inclusion of the degree columns is the reason that t varies at intervals of approximately 0.0029, since $10′ \approx 0.0029$ radians.

To find values of trigonometric functions at a real number t, whenever $0 \le t \le 0.7854 \approx \pi/4$ or $0° \le \theta \le 45°$, the labels at the *top* of the columns in Table 2 should be used. For example,

$$\sin(0.5003) \approx 0.4797 \qquad \tan 28°30′ \approx 0.5430$$
$$\cos(0.4945) \approx 0.8802 \qquad \sec 29°00′ \approx 1.143$$
$$\cot(0.5120) \approx 1.780 \qquad \csc 29°40′ \approx 2.020.$$

However, if $0.7854 \le t \le 1.5708$, or if $45° \le \theta \le 90°$, then the labels at the *bottom* of the columns should be employed. For example,

$$\sin(1.0705) \approx 0.8774 \qquad \csc 62°00′ \approx 1.133$$
$$\cos(1.0530) \approx 0.4950 \qquad \cot 61°10′ \approx 0.5505$$
$$\tan(1.0821) \approx 1.881 \qquad \sec 60°30′ \approx 2.031.$$

Part of Table 2

t	t degrees	$\sin t$	$\cos t$	$\tan t$	$\cot t$	$\sec t$	$\csc t$		
.4887	**28°00′**	.4695	.8829	.5317	1.881	1.133	2.130	**62°00′**	1.0821
.4916	10	.4720	.8816	.5354	1.868	1.134	2.118	50	1.0792
.4945	20	.4746	.8802	.5392	1.855	1.136	2.107	40	1.0763
.4974	30	.4772	.8788	.5430	1.842	1.138	2.096	30	1.0734
.5003	40	.4797	.8774	.5467	1.829	1.140	2.085	20	1.0705
.5032	50	.4823	.8760	.5505	1.816	1.142	2.074	10	1.0676
.5061	**29°00′**	.4848	.8746	.5543	1.804	1.143	2.063	**61°00′**	1.0647
.5091	10	.4874	.8732	.5581	1.792	1.145	2.052	50	1.0617
.5120	20	.4899	.8718	.5619	1.780	1.147	2.041	40	1.0588
.5149	30	.4924	.8704	.5658	1.767	1.149	2.031	30	1.0599
.5178	40	.4950	.8689	.5696	1.756	1.151	2.020	20	1.0530
.5207	50	.4975	.8675	.5735	1.744	1.153	2.010	10	1.0501
.5236	**30°00′**	.5000	.8660	.5774	1.732	1.155	2.000	**60°00′**	1.0472
⋮	⋮	⋮	⋮	⋮	⋮	⋮	⋮	⋮	⋮
		$\cos t$	$\sin t$	$\cot t$	$\tan t$	$\csc t$	$\sec t$	t degrees	t

The reason that the table can be so arranged follows from the fact, to be proved later, that

$$\sin t = \cos\left(\frac{\pi}{2} - t\right), \quad \cot t = \tan\left(\frac{\pi}{2} - t\right), \quad \csc t = \sec\left(\frac{\pi}{2} - t\right)$$

or, equivalently,

$$\sin \theta = \cos(90° - \theta), \quad \cot \theta = \tan(90° - \theta), \quad \csc \theta = \sec(90° - \theta).$$

In particular,

$$\sin 29° = \cos(90° - 29°) = \cos 61°$$
$$\cot 28°20′ = \tan(90° - 28°20′) = \tan 61°40′$$

as shown in the table.

If t is greater than 1.5708, we use the reference number t' associated with t, as illustrated in the following example.

Example 5 Approximate $\tan(2.3824)$.

Solution Since $P(2.3824)$ is in quadrant II, the reference number t' is $\pi - 2.3824$, or

$$t' \approx 3.1416 - 2.3824 = 0.7592.$$

Using the rules for finding functional values stated in this section, together with Table 2, we obtain

$$\tan(2.3824) \approx -\tan(0.7592) \approx -0.9490.\ \blacksquare$$

If it is necessary to find trigonometric functional values when t lies *between* numbers given in the table, the method of **linear interpolation** may be employed. This method is based on the premise that for small changes in t, the corresponding changes in the value of each trigonometric function are approximately proportional to the changes in t. We shall illustrate the method by means of examples.

Example 6   Approximate sin (0.6065).

Solution   Consulting Table 2, we see that

$$\sin(0.6050) \approx 0.5688$$
$$\sin(0.6080) \approx 0.5712.$$

Since 0.6065 is one-half the way from 0.6050 to 0.6080, it follows that sin (0.6065) is (approximately) one-half the way from 0.5688 to 0.5712. Computing the difference in the latter two numbers, we obtain $0.5712 - 0.5688 = 0.0024$. Hence,

$$\sin(0.6065) \approx 0.5688 + \tfrac{1}{2}(0.0024)$$
$$\approx 0.5688 + 0.0012 = 0.5700.$$

In order to systematize the process of linear interpolation, we shall usually arrange our work as follows:

$$0.0030 \left\{ 0.0015 \left\{ \begin{matrix} \sin(0.6050) \approx 0.5688 \\ \sin(0.6065) = \quad ? \end{matrix} \right\} d \right\} 0.0024$$
$$\sin(0.6080) \approx 0.5712$$

where we have indicated differences between values of t and functional values by appropriate symbols beside the braces. Assuming that changes in functional values are proportional to changes in t gives us the following proportion:

$$\frac{0.0015}{0.0030} = \frac{d}{0.0024} \quad \text{or} \quad d = \frac{15}{30}(0.0024) = 0.0012.$$

Hence,

$$\sin(0.6065) \approx 0.5688 + 0.0012 = 0.5700.\ \blacksquare$$

Example 7   Approximate cos (0.7).

Solution   To find cos (0.7), we locate the number 0.7000 between successive values of t in Table 2 and interpolate as follows:

$$0.0029 \left\{ 0.0019 \begin{cases} \cos (0.6981) \approx 0.7660 \\ \cos (0.7000) \approx \quad ? \end{cases} d \\ \cos (0.7010) \approx 0.7642 \right\} 0.0018$$

$$\frac{0.0019}{0.0029} = \frac{d}{0.0018}$$

or

$$d = \frac{19}{29}(0.0018) \approx 0.0012.$$

Hence,

$$\cos (0.7000) \approx 0.7660 - 0.0012 = 0.7648.$$

Note that since the cosine function is decreasing in the given interval we must *subtract d* from 0.7660.   ■

As illustrated in Example 7, if interpolation is used, then answers should be rounded off to the same number of decimal places as appear in the table. This is done because the numbers in Table 2 are approximations which do not guarantee more than four-decimal-place accuracy.

The method of interpolation may also be used to approximate t if we are given the value of a trigonometric function at t, as illustrated in the next example.

Example 8   Approximate the smallest positive real number t such that $\sin t = 0.6635$.

Solution   We locate 0.6635 between successive entries in the sine column of Table 2 and interpolate as follows:

$$0.0029 \left\{ d \begin{cases} \sin (0.7243) \approx 0.6626 \\ \sin t \qquad = 0.6635 \end{cases} 0.0009 \\ \sin (0.7272) = 0.6648 \right\} 0.0022$$

$$\frac{d}{0.0029} = \frac{0.0009}{0.0022}$$

or

$$d = \frac{9}{22}(0.0029) \approx 0.0012.$$

Hence,

$$t \approx 0.7243 + 0.0012 = 0.7255.$$ ■

Example 9   Approximate tan 155°44′.

Solution   Since the angle is in quadrant II, the reference angle is $180° - 155°44' = 24°16'$, and hence, $\tan 155°44' = -\tan 24°16'$. (Why?) We now consult Table 2 and interpolate as follows:

$$10'\left\{6'\left\{\begin{array}{l}\tan 24°10' \approx 0.4487\\ \tan 24°16' = \quad?\\ \tan 24°20' \approx 0.4522\end{array}\right\}d\right\}0.0035$$

$$\frac{d}{0.0035} = \frac{6}{10} \quad\text{or}\quad d = \frac{6}{10}(0.0035) \approx 0.0021$$

$$\tan 24°16' \approx 0.4487 + 0.0021 = 0.4508$$

$$\tan 155°44' \approx -0.4508. \qquad\blacksquare$$

Example 10 Approximate $\cos(-117°47')$.

Solution   The angle is in quadrant III. The reader should check that the reference angle is $62°13'$. Consequently, $\cos(-117°47') = -\cos 62°13'$. Interpolating, we have

$$10'\left\{3'\left\{\begin{array}{l}\cos 62°10' \approx 0.4669\\ \cos 62°13' = \quad?\\ \cos 62°20' \approx 0.4643\end{array}\right\}d\right\}0.0026$$

$$\frac{d}{0.0026} = \frac{3}{10} \quad\text{or}\quad d \approx 0.0008.$$

Since the cosine function is decreasing, we have

$$\cos 62°13' \approx 0.4669 - 0.0008 = 0.4661.$$

Hence, $\cos(-117°47') \approx -0.4661.$ $\qquad\blacksquare$

Example 11 If $\sin\theta = -0.7963$, approximate the degree measure of all angles θ that are in the interval $[0°, 360°]$.

Solution   Let θ' be the reference angle, so that $\sin\theta' = 0.7963$. Interpolating in Table 2,

$$10'\left\{d\left\{\begin{array}{l}\sin 52°40' \approx 0.7951\\ \sin\theta' \quad= 0.7963\\ \sin 52°50' \approx 0.7969\end{array}\right\}0.0012\right\}0.0018$$

$$\frac{d}{10} = \frac{0.0012}{0.0018} \quad\text{or}\quad d \approx 7'$$

$$\theta' \approx 52°47'.$$

Since $\sin\theta$ is negative, θ lies in quadrant III or IV. Using the reference angle $52°47'$, we have

$$\theta \approx 180° + 52°47' = 232°47'$$
$$\theta \approx 360° - 52°47' = 307°13'. \qquad \blacksquare$$

Table 3 can be used to find functional values of t if t is a two-decimal-place approximation of a real number or the radian measure of an angle, and $0 \leq t \leq 1.57$. For example, referring to the table, we see that

$$\sin(0.95) \approx 0.8134$$
$$\cos(1.48) \approx 0.0907$$
$$\cot(0.50) \approx 1.830.$$

Interpolation can be used if t is given to three decimal places. We shall not include exercises that require the use of Table 3, but instead leave it to the discretion of the teacher and student to determine what use should be made of that table.

EXERCISES 2.6

In Exercises 1–6, find the reference number t' if t has the given value.

1 (a) $3\pi/4$ (b) $4\pi/3$ (c) $-\pi/6$

2 (a) $5\pi/6$ (b) $2\pi/3$ (c) $-3\pi/4$

3 (a) $9\pi/4$ (b) $7\pi/6$ (c) $-2\pi/3$

4 (a) $8\pi/3$ (b) $7\pi/4$ (c) $-7\pi/6$

5 (a) 1.5 (b) 5

6 (a) 3.5 (b) -4

In Exercises 7–10, find the reference angle θ' if θ has the given measure.

7 (a) $240°$ (b) $340°$ (c) $-110°$

8 (a) $165°$ (b) $275°$ (c) $-202°$

9 (a) $130°40'$ (b) $-405°$ (c) $-260°35'$

10 (a) $335°20'$ (b) $-620°$ (c) $-185°40'$

In Exercises 11–16, find the exact values without the use of tables or calculators.

11 (a) $\sin 2\pi/3$ (b) $\sin 4\pi/3$

12 (a) $\cos 5\pi/6$ (b) $\cos 7\pi/6$

13 (a) $\tan(-5\pi/4)$ (b) $\cot 315°$

14 (a) $\sin 210°$ (b) $\csc(-150°)$

15 (a) $\csc 300°$ (b) $\sec(-120°)$

16 (a) $\tan(-135°)$ (b) $\sec 225°$

In Exercises 17–30, use Table 2 to approximate the given numbers.

17 $\sin(0.2676)$ 18 $\cos(0.3258)$

19 $\tan(0.9948)$ 20 $\sec(0.8988)$

21 $\csc(0.7738)$ 22 $\cot(0.7883)$

23 $\cos 38°30'$ 24 $\sin 73°20'$

25 $\cot 9°10'$ 26 $\csc 43°40'$

27 $\sec 168°50'$ 28 $\tan 207°10'$

29 $\sin 342°20'$ 30 $\cos 432°40'$

In Exercises 31–42, use interpolation in Table 2 to approximate the given numbers. If a suitable calculator is available, compare your approximations with those obtained by means of the calculator.

31 $\sin(0.46)$ 32 $\cos(0.82)$

33 $\tan 3$ 34 $\cot 6$

35 $\sec(1/4)$ 36 $\csc(1.54)$

37	$\cos 37°43'$	38	$\sin 22°34'$
39	$\cot 62°27'$	40	$\tan 57°16'$
41	$\csc 16°55'$	42	$\sec 9°12'$

In Exercises 43–48, use interpolation to approximate the smallest positive number t for which the equality is true.

43	$\cos t = 0.8620$	44	$\sin t = 0.6612$
45	$\tan t = 4.501$	46	$\sec t = 3.641$
47	$\csc t = 1.436$	48	$\cot t = 1.165$

In Exercises 49–56, use interpolation in Table 2 to approximate, to the nearest minute, the degree measure of all angles θ that lie in the interval $[0°, 360°]$.

49	$\sin \theta = 0.3672$	50	$\cos \theta = 0.8426$
51	$\tan \theta = 0.5042$	52	$\cot \theta = 1.348$
53	$\cos \theta = 0.3465$	54	$\csc \theta = 1.219$
55	$\sec \theta = 1.385$	56	$\sin \theta = 0.7534$

2.7 GRAPHS OF THE TRIGONOMETRIC FUNCTIONS

In our previous work with graphs of functions, we used the symbols x and y as labels for the coordinate axes. In this chapter x has been used primarily for the abscissa of a point on the unit circle U, and hence, in this section we shall use the symbol t for the horizontal axis. However, we shall continue to use y to denote the vertical axis. In the ty-coordinate system, the graph of the sine function is the same as the graph of the equation $y = \sin t$.

It is not difficult to sketch the graphs of the trigonometric functions. For example, since $-1 \le \sin t \le 1$ for every real number t, the graph of the sine function lies between the horizontal lines $y = 1$ and $y = -1$. Moreover, the sine function is periodic with period 2π, and therefore it is sufficient to determine the graph for $0 \le t \le 2\pi$, since the same pattern is repeated in intervals of length 2π along the t-axis. In Section 2.3 we discussed the behavior of $\sin t$ in the interval $[0, 2\pi]$ by concentrating on the ordinate y of the point $P(t)$ as $P(t)$ traversed the unit circle U once in the counterclockwise direction (see Figure 2.7). The manner in which $\sin t$ varies in $[0, 2\pi]$ may be briefly summarized as follows.

Variation of t	Variation of $\sin t$
0 to $\pi/2$	0 to 1
$\pi/2$ to π	1 to 0
π to $3\pi/2$	0 to -1
$3\pi/2$ to 2π	-1 to 0

Using these facts we conjectured that the graph of the sine function might look like the one in Figure 2.8. This guess may be further justified by calculating some intermediate values of $\sin t$, as indicated in the following table.

t	0	$\dfrac{\pi}{4}$	$\dfrac{\pi}{2}$	$\dfrac{3\pi}{4}$	π	$\dfrac{5\pi}{4}$	$\dfrac{3\pi}{2}$	$\dfrac{7\pi}{4}$	2π
$\sin t$	0	$\dfrac{\sqrt{2}}{2}$	1	$\dfrac{\sqrt{2}}{2}$	0	$\dfrac{-\sqrt{2}}{2}$	-1	$\dfrac{-\sqrt{2}}{2}$	0

To obtain a rough sketch, we may plot the points $(t, \sin t)$ given by this table, draw a smooth curve through them, and extend the configuration to the right and left in periodic fashion. This gives us the portion of the graph shown in Figure 2.28. Of course, the graph does not terminate, but continues indefinitely to the right and left. If greater accuracy is desired, additional points could be plotted using, for example, $\sin \pi/6 = 1/2$, $\sin \pi/3 = \sqrt{3}/2 \approx 0.86$, etc. We could also use Table 2 or a calculator to obtain many additional points on the graph. We refer to the part of the graph corresponding to the interval $[0, 2\pi]$ as a **sine wave**.

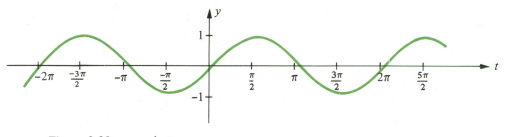

Figure 2.28 $y = \sin t$

The graph of the cosine function can be found in similar fashion, by studying the abscissa x of the point $P(t)$ in Figure 2.7 as $P(t)$ goes around U once in the counterclockwise direction. We may briefly summarize the behavior of $\cos t$ in the interval $[0, 2\pi]$ as follows.

Variation of t	Variation of $\cos t$
0 to $\pi/2$	1 to 0
$\pi/2$ to π	0 to -1
π to $3\pi/2$	-1 to 0
$3\pi/2$ to 2π	0 to 1

Using this information, together with the fact that the cosine function has period 2π, and plotting points as we did for the sine function, leads to the sketch in Figure 2.29. Note that the graph of $y = \cos t$ can be obtained by shifting the graph of $y = \sin t$ to the left a distance $\pi/2$.

Several values of the tangent function are given in the following table.

t	$-\dfrac{\pi}{3}$	$-\dfrac{\pi}{4}$	$-\dfrac{\pi}{6}$	0	$\dfrac{\pi}{6}$	$\dfrac{\pi}{4}$	$\dfrac{\pi}{3}$
$\tan t$	$-\sqrt{3}$	-1	$\dfrac{-\sqrt{3}}{3}$	0	$\dfrac{\sqrt{3}}{3}$	1	$\sqrt{3}$

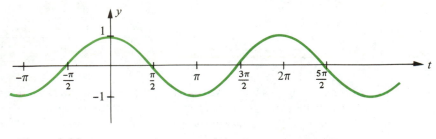

Figure 2.29 $y = \cos t$

The corresponding points are plotted in Figure 2.30. The values of tan t near $t = \pi/2$ demand special consideration. As t increases through positive values toward $\pi/2$, the point $P(t) = (x, y)$ on the unit circle U that corresponds to t approaches the point $(0, 1)$.

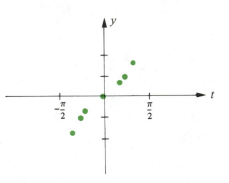

Figure 2.30

Since, by definition, $\tan t = y/x$, it follows that if y approaches 1 and x approaches 0 (through positive values), then tan t takes on large positive values. This can also be seen by referring to Table 2. First recall that $\pi/2 \approx \frac{1}{2}(3.1416) = 1.5708$. Next, we see from Table 2 that

$$\tan (1.5650) \approx 171.9$$
$$\tan (1.5679) \approx 343.8.$$

The following additional values were obtained using a hand-held calculator:

$$\tan (1.5700) \approx 1{,}255.8$$
$$\tan (1.5703) \approx 2{,}014.8$$
$$\tan (1.5706) \approx 5{,}093.5$$
$$\tan (1.5707) \approx 10{,}381.3$$
$$\tan (1.57079) \approx 158{,}057.9.$$

Notice how rapidly tan t increases as t gets close to $\pi/2$. Indeed, tan t can be made arbitrarily large by choosing t sufficiently close to $\pi/2$. We say that tan t *increases without bound as t approaches $\pi/2$ through values less than $\pi/2$.* Similarly, if t approaches

$-\pi/2$ through values greater than $-\pi/2$, than $\tan t$ *decreases without bound.* This behavior is illustrated in Figure 2.31. The lines $t = \pi/2$ and $t = -\pi/2$ are called **vertical asymptotes** for the graph. It is not difficult to show that the same pattern is repeated in the open intervals $(\pi/2, 3\pi/2)$, $(3\pi/2, 5\pi/2)$, and similar intervals of length π, as shown in Figure 2.31. Thus *the tangent function has period* π.

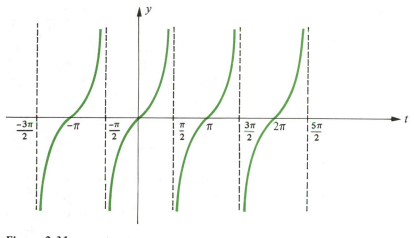

Figure 2.31 $\quad y = \tan t$

The graphs of the sine and tangent functions are symmetric with respect to the origin, whereas the graph of the cosine function is symmetric with respect to the y-axis. These facts are consequences of the following formulas, each of which holds for every real number t in the domain of the indicated function.

Formulas
for Negatives

$$\sin(-t) = -\sin t$$
$$\cos(-t) = \cos t$$
$$\tan(-t) = -\tan t$$

To establish these formulas, let us recall from Section 2.1 that if t ranges from 0 to 2π, the point $P(t)$ traces the unit circle U once in the counterclockwise direction, whereas, $P(-t)$ traces U once in the clockwise direction. Moreover, as illustrated in Figure 2.32, if $P(t)$ has coordinates (x, y), then $P(-t)$ has coordinates $(x, -y)$.

Applying the definition of the trigonometric functions (see Section 2.2) gives us

$$\sin(-t) = -y = -\sin t$$
$$\cos(-t) = \quad x = \cos t$$
$$\tan(-t) = \frac{-y}{x} = -\frac{y}{x} = -\tan t$$

which is what we wished to prove. According to the tests for symmetry stated in Section 1.3, these identities imply that the graphs of the sine and tangent functions are

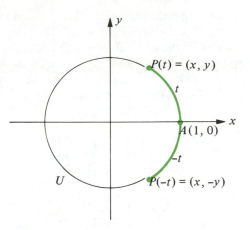

Figure 2.32

symmetric with respect to the origin, whereas that of the cosine function is symmetric with respect to the y-axis.

The graphs of the remaining three trigonometric functions can now be easily obtained. For example, since $\csc t = 1/\sin t$, we may find an ordinate of a point on the graph of the cosecant function by taking the reciprocal of the corresponding ordinate of the sine graph. This is possible except for $t = n\pi$, where n is an integer, for in this case $\sin t = 0$ and hence $1/\sin t$ is undefined. As an aid to sketching the graph of the cosecant function, it is convenient to sketch the graph of the sine function with dashes (see Figure 2.33) and then take reciprocals of ordinates to obtain points on the cosecant graph. Notice the manner in which the cosecant function increases or decreases without bound as t approaches $n\pi$, where n is an integer. The graph has vertical asymptotes as indicated in the figure.

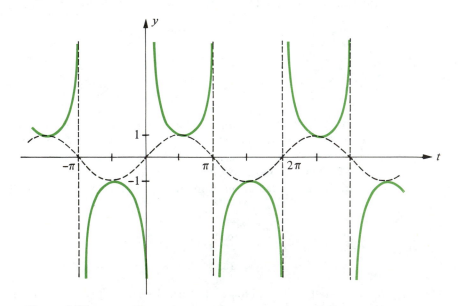

Figure 2.33 $y = \csc t$

Since $\sec t = 1/\cos t$ and $\cot t = 1/\tan t$, the graphs of the secant and cotangent functions may be obtained in similar fashion (see Figures 2.34 and 2.35). Their verifications are left as exercises.

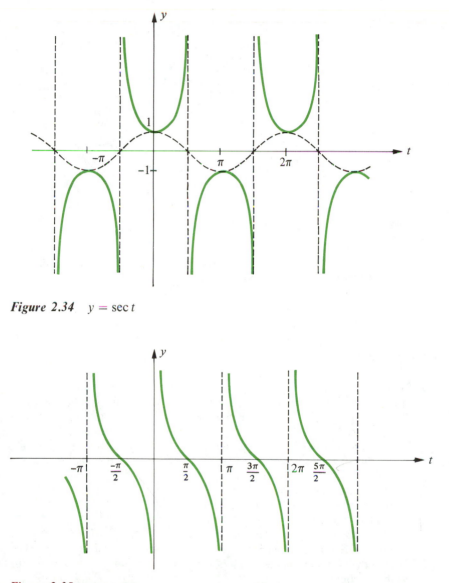

Figure 2.34 $y = \sec t$

Figure 2.35 $y = \cot t$

Example 1   Sketch the graph of the function f if $f(t) = 2 \sin t$.

Solution   Although the graph could be obtained by plotting points, note that for each abscissa t_1 the ordinate $f(t_1)$ is always twice that of the corresponding ordinate on the sine graph. A simple graphical technique is to sketch the graph of $y = \sin t$ with dashes and then double each ordinate to find points on the graph of $y = 2 \sin t$ (see Figure 2.36).

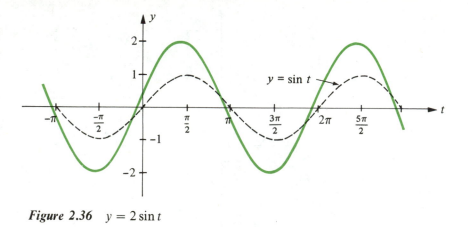

Figure 2.36 $y = 2 \sin t$ ∎

Graphs of the type given in the preceding example will be discussed more thoroughly in the next section.

EXERCISES 2.7

1 (a) Sketch the graph of the cosine function after plotting a sufficient number of points.
  (b) Sketch the graph of the secant function by taking reciprocals in part (a).
  (c) Describe the intervals between -2π and 2π in which the secant function is increasing.
  (d) Describe the intervals between -2π and 2π in which the secant function is decreasing.
  (e) With the aid of Table 2 or a calculator, discuss the behavior of $\sec t$ as t approaches $\pi/2$ through values less than $\pi/2$ and through values greater than $\pi/2$.
  (f) Discuss the symmetry of the graph of the secant function.

2 (a) Sketch the graph of the cotangent function after plotting a sufficient number of points.
  (b) In what intervals is the cotangent function increasing?
  (c) In what intervals is the cotangent function decreasing?

  (d) With the aid of Table 2 or a calculator, discuss the behavior of $\cot t$ as t approaches 0 through values greater than 0 and through values less than 0.
  (e) Discuss the symmetry of the graph of the cotangent function.

3 Establish the following identities.
  (a) $\csc(-t) = -\csc t$
  (b) $\sec(-t) = \sec t$
  (c) $\cot(-t) = -\cot t$

4 Prove that the graph of the cosecant function is symmetric with respect to the origin.

5 Practice sketching graphs of the sine, cosine, and tangent functions, taking different units of length on the horizontal and vertical axes. Continue this practice until you reach the stage at which if you were awakened from a sound sleep in the middle of the night and asked to sketch one of these graphs, you could do so in less than thirty seconds.

6 Repeat Exercise 5 for the cosecant, secant, and cotangent functions.

In Exercises 7–16, use the method illustrated in the Example of this section to sketch the graph of f.

7 $f(t) = 4 \sin t$

8 $f(t) = 3 \sin t$

9 $f(t) = \frac{1}{2} \sin t$

10 $f(t) = \frac{1}{4} \sin t$

11 $f(t) = 2 \cos t$

12 $f(t) = 4 \cos t$

13 $f(t) = \frac{1}{3} \cos t$

14 $f(t) = \frac{1}{2} \cos t$

15 $f(t) = -\sin t$

16 $f(t) = -\cos t$

CALCULATOR EXERCISES 2.7

If f is a function, the notation

$$f(t) \to L \quad \text{as} \quad t \to a^+$$

is sometimes used to express the fact that $f(t)$ gets very close to L as t gets close to a (through values greater than a). Use a calculator to support Exercises 1–6 by substituting the following values for t: $t = 0.1$, $t = 0.01$, $t = 0.001$, $t = 0.0001$.

1 $\dfrac{\sin t}{t} \to 1 \quad \text{as} \quad t \to 0^+$

2 $\dfrac{\tan t}{t} \to 1 \quad \text{as} \quad t \to 0^+$

3 $\dfrac{1 - \cos t}{t} \to 0 \quad \text{as} \quad t \to 0^+$

4 $\dfrac{\sin t}{1 + \cos t} \to 0 \quad \text{as} \quad t \to 0^+$

5 $t \cot t \to 1 \quad \text{as} \quad t \to 0^+$

6 $\dfrac{t + \tan t}{\sin t} \to 2 \quad \text{as} \quad t \to 0^+$

2.8 TRIGONOMETRIC GRAPHS

In this section we shall consider graphs of equations of the form

$$y = a \sin (bx + c)$$

where a, b, and c are real numbers. We shall also discuss graphs of similar equations that involve different trigonometric functions. Instead of using a ty-coordinate system as in Section 2.7, we shall now use the conventional xy-coordinate system. In this situation the letter x is used in place of t and hence is not to be regarded as the x used in the definition of the trigonometric functions. To sketch a graph, we could begin by plotting many points; however, it is generally easier to use information about the graphs of the trigonometric functions discussed in the preceding section. Let us consider the special case in which $c = 0$, $b = 1$, and $a > 0$. Thus, we wish to sketch the graph of the equation

$$y = a \sin x.$$

As in our discussion of stretching of graphs (see Section 1.5), we may find the ordinate of a point on the graph by multiplying the corresponding ordinate on the graph of $y = \sin x$ by a. Thus, if $y = 2 \sin x$, we multiply by 2; if $y = \frac{1}{2} \sin x$, we multiply by $\frac{1}{2}$; and so on. The graph of $y = 2 \sin x$ is sketched in Figure 2.36. The graph of $y = \frac{1}{2} \sin x$ is sketched in Figure 2.37, where for comparison we have indicated the graph of $y = \sin x$ with dashes.

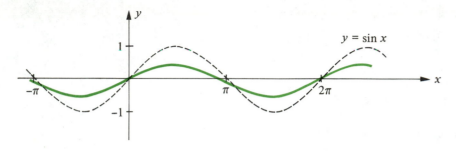

Figure 2.37 $y = \frac{1}{2} \sin x$

Example 1   Sketch the graph of the equation $y = 3 \cos x$.

Solution   The graph of the given equation may be obtained from the graph of $y = \cos x$ by multiplying ordinates of points by 3. We first sketch $y = \cos x$ with dashes, and then we triple the ordinates. This gives us the sketch in Figure 2.38.

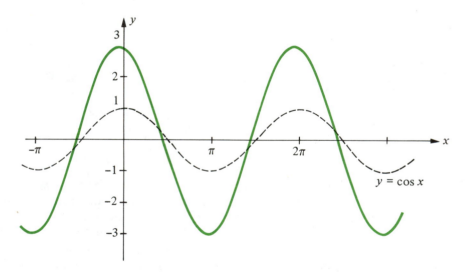

Figure 2.38 $y = 3 \cos x$ ■

If $a < 0$, then the ordinates of points on the graph of $y = a \sin x$ are negatives of the corresponding ordinates of points on the graph of $y = |a| \sin x$, as illustrated in the next example.

Example 2   Sketch the graph of $y = -2 \sin x$.

Solution As a guide we first sketch the graph of $y = \sin x$ with dashes, and then we multiply each ordinate by -2. This gives us the sketch shown in Figure 2.39. The sketch may also be obtained by multiplying ordinates of the graph of $y = 2 \sin x$ (see Figure 2.36) by -1. We sometimes refer to the graph of $y = -2 \sin x$ as a *reflection through the x-axis* of the graph of $y = 2 \sin x$.

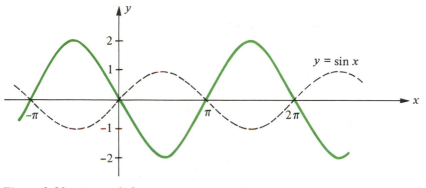

Figure 2.39 $y = -2 \sin x$

If $f(x) = a \sin(bx + c)$, then the **amplitude** of f (or of its graph) is defined as the largest ordinate of points on the graph. If $a > 0$, the largest ordinate occurs if $\sin(bx + c) = 1$, whereas if $a < 0$, we must take $\sin(bx + c) = -1$. In either case the amplitude is $|a|$. For example, if $f(x) = \frac{1}{2} \sin x$, then from Figure 2.37 we see that the amplitude is $\frac{1}{2}$. If $f(x) = -2 \sin x$, then from Figure 2.39 we see that the amplitude is 2. The same is true if f is given by $f(x) = a \cos(bx + c)$.

The next theorem provides some information about periods.

Theorem

> If $f(x) = \sin bx$, where $b \neq 0$, then the period of f is $2\pi/|b|$.

Proof

If $b > 0$, then as bx varies from 0 to 2π, we obtain exactly one sine wave for the graph of f. The conclusion of the theorem follows from the fact that bx ranges from 0 to 2π if and only if x ranges from 0 to $2\pi/b$. A similar proof may be given if $b < 0$. ∎

Example 3 Find the period and sketch the graph of f if

(a) $f(x) = \sin 2x$ (b) $f(x) = \sin \frac{1}{2}x$.

Solution Both functions have the form given in the preceding theorem. Hence, in part (a) the period is $2\pi/2 = \pi$, which means that there is exactly one sine wave of amplitude 1 corresponding to the interval $[0, \pi]$. The graph is sketched in Figure 2.40, where for convenience we have used different scales on the x- and y-axes. For part (b) the period is $2\pi(1/2) = 4\pi$, and hence, there is one sine wave of amplitude 1 corresponding to the interval $[0, 4\pi]$, as illustrated in Figure 2.41.

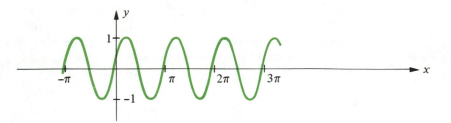

Figure 2.40 $y = \sin 2x$ ∎

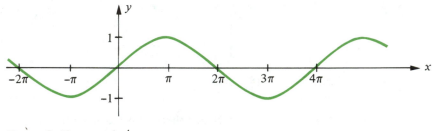

Figure 2.41 $y = \sin \frac{1}{2}x$

Given $f(x) = \sin bx$ where $b > 0$, then, roughly speaking, if b is large, $2\pi/b$ is small and the sine waves are close together. As a matter of fact, there are b sine waves in an interval of 2π units. However, if b is small, then $2\pi/b$ is large and the waves are shallow. For example, if $y = \sin (1/10)x$, then $1/10$ of a sine wave occurs in the interval $[0, 2\pi]$, and an interval 20π units long is required for one complete wave.

If $b < 0$, we can use the fact that $\sin(-t) = -\sin t$ to obtain the graph. To illustrate, the graph of $y = \sin(-2x)$ is the same as the graph of $y = -\sin 2x$.

By combining the above remarks, we can arrive at a technique for sketching the graph of a function f defined by $f(x) = a \sin bx$. The graph has the basic sine wave pattern. However, the amplitude is $|a|$ and the period is $2\pi/|b|$. If $a < 0$ or $b < 0$, we make adjustments on the signs of ordinates, as discussed earlier.

Example 4   Sketch the graph of f if $f(x) = 3 \sin 2x$.

Solution   From the preceding discussion we see that the amplitude of f is 3 and the period is $2\pi/2 = \pi$. The graph is readily obtained by first sketching the graph of $y = \sin 2x$ with dashes and then multiplying the ordinates of each point by 3. This leads to the sketch in Figure 2.42.

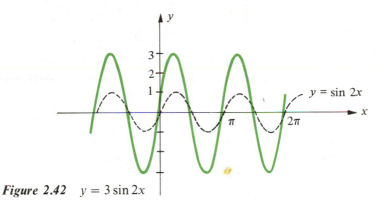

Figure 2.42 $y = 3 \sin 2x$ ■

Example 5   Sketch the graph of f if $f(x) = 2 \sin(-3x)$.

Solution   Since $f(x) = -2 \sin 3x$, we see that the amplitude is 2 and the period is $2\pi/3$. Thus, there is one sine wave in every interval of length $2\pi/3$. The minus sign indicates a reflection through the x-axis. If we consider the interval $[0, 2\pi/3]$ and sketch a sine wave of amplitude 2 (reflected through the x-axis), the shape of the graph is apparent. The configuration given in the interval $[0, 2\pi/3]$ is carried along periodically, as illustrated in Figure 2.43.

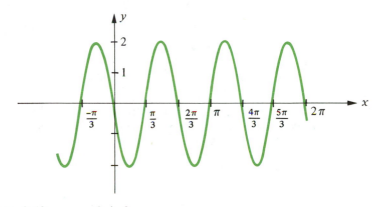

Figure 2.43 $y = -2 \sin 3x$ ■

Similar discussions can be given if f is defined by $f(x) = a \cos bx$ or by $f(x) = a \tan bx$. In the latter case the period is $\pi/|b|$, since the tangent function has period π. There is no largest ordinate for points on the graph of the tangent function, and hence, we do not refer to its amplitude; however, we may still use the process of multiplying tangent ordinates by a in order to obtain points on the graph of $y = a \tan bx$.

Let us conclude this section by considering the general situation

$$f(x) = a \sin (bx + c).$$

We have already observed that the amplitude is $|a|$. We also know that one sine wave for the graph of $y = \sin (bx + c)$ is obtained if $bx + c$ varies from 0 to 2π, that is, if bx ranges from $-c$ to $2\pi - c$. In turn, the latter variation is obtained by letting x range from $-c/b$ to $(2\pi - c)/b$. If $-c/b > 0$, this amounts graphically to *shifting* the graph of $y = a \sin bx$ to the right $-c/b$ units. If $-c/b < 0$, the shift is to the left. The number $-c/b$ is sometimes called the **phase shift** associated with the function. Similar remarks can be made for the other functions. It is unnecessary to remember a general formula for finding the phase shift. In any specific problem, the interval that contains one complete sine wave can be found by solving the two equations

$$bx + c = 0 \quad \text{and} \quad bx + c = 2\pi$$

for x, as illustrated in the next example.

Example 6   Sketch the graph of $f(x) = 3 \sin \left(2x - \dfrac{\pi}{2} \right)$.

Solution   The equation is of the form discussed in this section, with $a = 3$, $b = 2$, and $c = -\pi/2$. It follows from our discussion that the graph has the sine wave pattern with amplitude 3 and period $2\pi/2 = \pi$. In order to obtain an interval containing exactly one sine wave, we let $2x - (\pi/2)$ range from 0 to 2π. The endpoints of the interval can be found by solving the two equations

$$2x - \frac{\pi}{2} = 0 \quad \text{and} \quad 2x - \frac{\pi}{2} = 2\pi.$$

This gives us
$$x = \frac{\pi}{4} \quad \text{and} \quad x = \frac{5\pi}{4}.$$

Thus, one sine wave of amplitude 3 will occur in the interval $[\pi/4, 5\pi/4]$. Sketching that wave and then repeating it to the right and left gives us the graph in Figure 2.44.

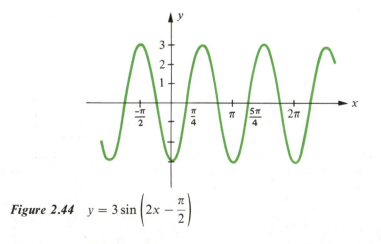

Figure 2.44 $y = 3 \sin \left(2x - \dfrac{\pi}{2} \right)$ ∎

EXERCISES 2.8

1 Without plotting many points, sketch the graph and determine the amplitude and period of each function f defined as follows:

(a) $f(x) = 4 \sin x$
(b) $f(x) = \sin 4x$
(c) $f(x) = \frac{1}{4} \sin x$
(d) $f(x) = \sin (x/4)$
(e) $f(x) = 2 \sin (x/4)$
(f) $f(x) = \frac{1}{2} \sin 4x$
(g) $f(x) = -4 \sin x$
(h) $f(x) = \sin (-4x)$

2 Sketch the graphs of the functions involving the cosine which are analogous to those defined in Exercise 1.

3 Without plotting many points, sketch the graph of each function f defined as follows, determining the amplitude and period in each case:

(a) $f(x) = 3 \cos x$
(b) $f(x) = \cos 3x$
(c) $f(x) = \frac{1}{3} \cos x$
(d) $f(x) = \cos (x/3)$
(e) $f(x) = 2 \cos (x/3)$
(f) $f(x) = \frac{1}{3} \cos (2x)$
(g) $f(x) = -3 \cos x$
(h) $f(x) = \cos (-3x)$

4 Sketch the graphs of the functions involving the sine which are analogous to those defined in Exercise 3.

Sketch the graphs of the equations in Exercises 5–44.

5 $y = \sin \left(x - \frac{\pi}{2} \right)$

6 $y = \cos \left(x + \frac{\pi}{4} \right)$

7 $y = 3 \sin \left(x - \frac{\pi}{2} \right)$

8 $y = 4 \cos \left(x + \frac{\pi}{4} \right)$

9 $y = \cos \left(x + \frac{\pi}{3} \right)$

10 $y = \sin \left(x - \frac{\pi}{3} \right)$

11 $y = 4 \cos \left(x + \frac{\pi}{3} \right)$

12 $y = 5 \sin \left(x - \frac{\pi}{3} \right)$

13 $y = \sin (3x + \pi)$

14 $y = \cos (3x - \pi)$

15 $y = -2 \sin (3x + \pi)$

16 $y = 6 \cos (3x - \pi)$

17 $y = 5 \sin \left(3x - \frac{\pi}{2} \right)$

18 $y = -4 \cos \left(2x + \frac{\pi}{3} \right)$

19 $y = 6 \sin \pi x$

20 $y = 3 \cos \frac{1}{2} \pi x$

21 $y = 2 \cos \frac{\pi}{2} x$

22 $y = 4 \sin 3 \pi x$

23 $y = \frac{1}{2} \sin 2 \pi x$

24 $y = \frac{1}{2} \cos \frac{\pi}{2} x$

25 $y = \frac{1}{2} \sec x$

26 $y = \frac{1}{4} \csc x$

27 $y = -2 \csc x$

28 $y = -3 \sec x$

29 $y = \sec 2x$

30 $y = \csc 3x$

31 $y = \csc \left(x - \frac{\pi}{4} \right)$

32 $y = \sec \left(x + \frac{\pi}{3} \right)$

33 $y = \tan (x/2)$

34 $y = \cot 2x$

35 $y = \tan \left(x + \frac{\pi}{2} \right)$

36 $y = \cot \left(x - \frac{\pi}{4} \right)$

37 $y = \frac{1}{2} \cot x$

38 $y = -2 \tan x$

39 $y = \tan (-x)$

40 $y = -\cot x$

41 $y = 2 \sin \left(x - \frac{\pi}{2} \right)$

42 $y = \cos \left(x - \frac{\pi}{2} \right)$

43 $y = \sin \left(x + \frac{\pi}{2} \right)$

44 $y = \cos \left(x + \frac{\pi}{2} \right)$

CALCULATOR EXERCISES 2.8

1–6 The graphs in Examples 1–6 of this section were obtained *qualitatively*, in the sense that we determined the general shape by referring to other graphs and not by plotting points. Verify them *quantitatively*, by calculating the coordinates of many points on the graphs.

2.9 ADDITIONAL GRAPHICAL TECHNIQUES

In mathematical applications it is common to encounter functions that are defined in terms of sums and products of expressions, such as

$$f(x) = \sin 2x + \cos x \quad \text{or} \quad f(x) = 2^{-x} \sin x.$$

When working with sums, the graphical technique called **addition of ordinates** is useful. The method applies not only to trigonometric expressions but to arbitrary expressions as well. If f is a sum of two functions g and h having the same domain X, then

$$f(x) = g(x) + h(x)$$

for every x in X. A sketch of the graph of f may be obtained from the graphs of g and h as follows. We begin by sketching the graphs of the equations $y = g(x)$ and $y = h(x)$ on the same coordinate axes, as illustrated by the dashes in Figure 2.45.

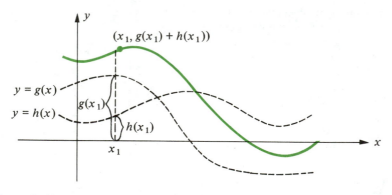

Figure 2.45 $y = g(x) + h(x)$

Since $f(x_1) = g(x_1) + h(x_1)$ for every x_1 in X, the ordinate of the point on the graph of $y = g(x) + h(x)$ with abscissa x_1 is the *sum* of the corresponding ordinates of points on the graphs of g and h. If we draw a vertical line at the point with coordinates $(x_1, 0)$, then the ordinates $g(x_1)$ and $h(x_1)$ may be added geometrically by means of a compass or ruler, as is illustrated in Figure 2.45. If either $g(x_1)$ or $h(x_1)$ is negative, then a *subtraction* of ordinates may be employed. By using this technique a sufficient number of times, we obtain a sketch of the graph of f.

Example 1   If $f(x) = \cos x + \sin x$, use the method of addition of ordinates to sketch the graph of f.

Solution   We begin by sketching (with dashes) the graphs of the equations $y = \cos x$ and $y = \sin x$. Next, for various numbers x_1, we add ordinates geometrically. After a sufficient number of ordinates are added and a pattern emerges, we draw a smooth curve through the points, as indicated by the sketch in Figure 2.46. As a check, it would be worthwhile to plot some points on the graph by substituting numbers for x. We shall leave such verifications to the reader. It can be seen from the graph that the function f is periodic with period 2π.

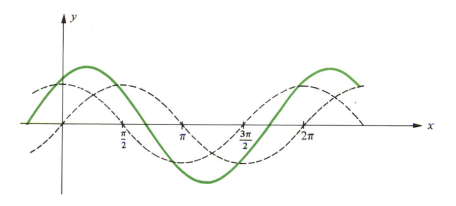

Figure 2.46 $\quad y = \cos x + \sin x$ ■

Example 2   Sketch the graph of the equation $y = \cos x + \sin 2x$.

Solution   We sketch (with dashes) the graphs of the equations $y = \cos x$ and $y = \sin 2x$ on the same coordinate axes and use the method of addition of ordinates. The graph is illustrated in Figure 2.47. Evidently f is periodic with period 2π.

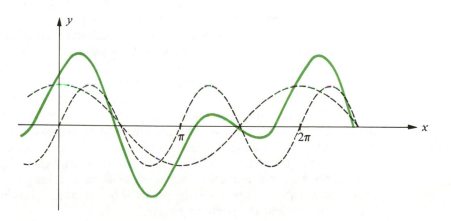

Figure 2.47 $\quad y = \cos x + \sin 2x$ ■

EXERCISES 2.9

Use addition of ordinates to sketch the graphs of the equations in Exercises 1–20.

1 $y = \cos x + 3 \sin x$

2 $y = \sin x + 3 \cos x$

3 $y = 2 \cos x + 3 \sin x$

4 $y = 2 \sin x + 3 \cos x$

5 $y = \sin x + \cos 2x$

6 $y = 2 \cos x + \sin 2x$

7 $y = \cos x - \sin x$

8 $y = 2 \sin x - \cos x$

9 $y = 2 \cos x - \frac{1}{2} \sin 2x$

10 $y = 2 \cos x + \cos \frac{1}{2} x$

11 $y = 1 + \sin x$

12 $y = 2 + \tan x$

13 $y = \frac{1}{2} x + \sin x$

14 $y = 1 + \cos x$

15 $y = 2^x + \sin x$

16 $y = \csc x - 1$

17 $y = 2 + \sec x$

18 $y = x - \sin x$

19 $y = \cos x - 1$

20 $y = |x + 1| + \cos 2x$

CALCULATOR EXERCISES 2.9

Verify some of the graphs in this section quantitatively, by calculating the coordinates of many points.

2.10 APPLICATIONS INVOLVING RIGHT TRIANGLES

The early development of trigonometry was concerned with measurements of angles and finding lengths of sides of triangles. Solving problems of that type is no longer the most important application; however, trigonometric techniques are still used to answer questions about triangles which arise in physical situations. We shall restrict our discussion in this section to right triangles. Triangles that do not contain a right angle will be considered in the next chapter.

In this section and in Chapter Four we shall often use the following notation. The vertices of a triangle will be denoted by A, B, and C. The angles of the triangle at A, B, and C will be denoted by α, β, and γ, respectively, and the lengths of the sides opposite these angles by a, b, and c, respectively. The triangle itself will often be referred to as *triangle ABC*. To *solve* a triangle means to find all of its parts, that is, the lengths of the three sides and the measure of the three angles. If the triangle is a right triangle and if one of the acute angles and a side are known, or if two sides are given, then the formulas in Section 2.5 which express the trigonometric functions as ratios of sides of a triangle may be used to find the remaining parts.

Example 1 If, in triangle ABC, $\gamma = 90°$, $\alpha = 34°$, and $b = 10.5$, approximate the remaining parts of the triangle.

Solution   Since the sum of the angles is 180°, it follows that $\beta = 56°$. Referring to Figure 2.48 and using the fact that the tangent equals opp/adj, we have

$$\tan 34° = \frac{a}{10.5} \quad \text{or} \quad a = (10.5)\tan 34°.$$

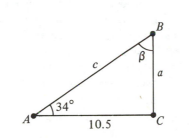

Figure 2.48

Substituting from Table 2, we obtain

$$a \approx (10.5)(0.6745) \approx 7.1.$$

Side c can be found using either the cosine or secant function. Since the cosine equals adj/hyp, we may write

$$\cos 34° = \frac{10.5}{c} \quad \text{or} \quad c = \frac{10.5}{\cos 34°}.$$

Using Table 2 and dividing, we obtain

$$c \approx \frac{10.5}{0.8290} \approx 12.7.$$

The division involved in finding c could have been avoided through the use of the secant, which equals hyp/adj. Thus,

$$\sec 34° = \frac{c}{10.5} \quad \text{or} \quad c = (10.5)\sec 34°.$$

Referring to Table 2 and multiplying gives us

$$c \approx (10.5)(1.2062) = 12.6651 \approx 12.7. \qquad\blacksquare$$

As illustrated in Example 1, when working with triangles we shall round off answers. One reason for doing this is that in applications, the lengths of sides of triangles and measures of angles are usually found by mechanical devices, and hence are only approximations to the exact values. Consequently, a number such as 10.5 in Example 1 is assumed to have been rounded off to the nearest tenth. One cannot expect more accuracy in the calculated values for the remaining sides, and, therefore, they should also be rounded off to the nearest tenth.

In some problems, a large number of digits, such as 13,647.29, may be given for a number. If Table 2 is used, a number of this type should be rounded off to four significant figures and written as 13,650 before calculations are begun. Since the values of the trigonometric functions given in Table 2 have been rounded off to four significant figures, we cannot expect more than four-figure accuracy in our computations.

Answers should also be rounded off when Table 2 is used to find angles. In general, we shall use the following rules: if the sides of a triangle are known to four significant figures, then measures of angles calculated from Table 2 should be rounded off to the nearest minute; if the sides are known to three significant figures, then calculated measures of angles should be rounded off to the nearest multiple of ten minutes; and if the sides are known to only two significant figures, then calculations should be rounded off to the nearest degree. In order to justify these rules, we would have to make a much deeper analysis of problems involving approximate data.

Example 2 If, in triangle ABC, $\gamma = 90°$, $a = 12.3$, and $b = 31.6$, find the remaining parts.

Solution   Referring to the triangle illustrated in Figure 2.49, we have

$$\tan \alpha = \frac{12.3}{31.6} \approx 0.3892.$$

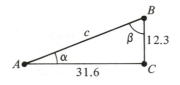

Figure 2.49

By the rule stated in the preceding paragraph, α should be rounded off to the nearest multiple of 10′. From Table 2, we see that $\alpha \approx 21°20′$. Consequently,

$$\beta \approx 90° - 21°20′ = 68°40′.$$

Again referring to Figure 2.49,

$$\sec \alpha = \frac{c}{31.6} \quad \text{or} \quad c = (31.6)\sec \alpha$$

and hence, $c \approx (31.6)\sec 21°20′ \approx (31.6)(1.0736) \approx 33.9.$

Side c can also be found using the cosine. Referring to Figure 2.49, we see that

$$\cos \alpha = \frac{31.6}{c}$$

and hence, $c = \dfrac{31.6}{\cos 21°20′} \approx \dfrac{31.6}{0.9315} \approx 33.9.$ ∎

Right angles are useful in solving various types of applied problems. The following examples give two illustrations; others will be found in the exercises.

Example 3   From a point on level ground 135 feet from the foot of a tower, the angle of elevation of the top of the tower is 57°20′. Find the height of the tower.

Solution   The **angle of elevation** is the angle that the line of sight makes with the horizontal. If we let d denote the height of the tower, then the given facts are represented by the triangle in Figure 2.50. Referring to the figure, we see that

$$\tan 57°20' = \frac{d}{135} \quad \text{or} \quad d = (135)\tan 57°20'.$$

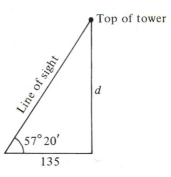

• Top of tower

Line of sight

d

57°20′

135

Figure 2.50

Substituting from Table 2 gives us

$$d = (135)(1.560) = 210.6 \approx 211.$$ ■

Example 4   From the top of a building that overlooks the ocean, a man sees a boat sailing directly toward him. If the man is 100 feet above sea level and if the angle of depression of the boat changes from 25° to 40° during the period of observation, find the approximate distance the boat travels during that time.

Solution   The **angle of depression** is the angle between the line of sight and the horizontal. Let A and B be the positions of the boat which correspond to the 25° and 40° angles, respectively. Suppose that the man is at point D, and let C be the point 100 feet directly below him. Let d denote the distance the boat travels, and let g denote the distance from B to C. This gives us the drawing in Figure 2.51, where α and β denote angles DAC and DBC, respectively. It follows that $\alpha = 25°$ and $\beta = 40°$. (Why?)

From triangle BCD we have

$$\cot \beta = \frac{g}{100} \quad \text{or} \quad g = 100 \cot \beta.$$

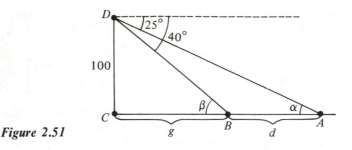

Figure 2.51

From triangle DAC we have

$$\cot \alpha = \frac{d + g}{100} \quad \text{or} \quad d + g = 100 \cot \alpha.$$

Consequently,

$$\begin{aligned}
d &= 100 \cot \alpha - g \\
&= 100 \cot \alpha - 100 \cot \beta \\
&= 100 \left(\cot \alpha - \cot \beta \right) \\
&= 100 \left(\cot 25° - \cot 40° \right) \\
&\approx 100(2.145 - 1.192) \\
&= 100(0.953) = 95.3.
\end{aligned}$$

Hence, $d \approx 95$ feet. ∎

    In certain navigation and surveying problems, the **direction**, or **bearing**, from a point P to a point Q is often specified by stating the acute angle through which the half-line from P through Q varies to the east or west of the north-south line. Figure 2.52 illustrates four such lines. The north-south and east-west lines are labeled NS and WE, respectively. The bearing from P to Q_1 is 25° east of north and is denoted by N25°E. We also refer to the *direction* N25°E, meaning the direction from P to Q_1. The bearings from P to Q_2, Q_3, and Q_4 are represented in a similar manner in the figure.

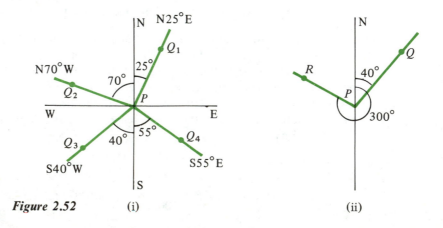

Figure 2.52   (i)   (ii)

In air navigation, directions and bearings are specified by measuring from the north in a clockwise direction. In this particular situation a positive measure is assigned to the angle instead of the negative measure to which we are accustomed for clockwise rotations. Thus, referring to (ii) of Figure 2.52, we see that the direction of PQ is 40°, whereas the direction of PR is 300°.

We shall use these notations in Exercises 35–37.

EXERCISES 2.10

Given the indicated parts of triangle ABC with $\gamma = 90°$, approximate the remaining parts of each triangle in Exercises 1–16.

1 $\alpha = 30°$, $b = 20$ **2** $\beta = 45°$, $b = 35$

3 $\beta = 52°$, $a = 15$ **4** $\alpha = 37°$, $b = 24$

5 $\alpha = 17°40'$, $a = 4.50$ **6** $\beta = 64°20'$, $a = 20.1$

7 $\beta = 71°51'$, $b = 240.0$ **8** $\alpha = 31°10'$, $a = 510$

9 $a = 25$, $b = 45$ **10** $a = 31$, $b = 9.0$

11 $c = 5.8$, $b = 2.1$ **12** $a = 0.42$, $c = 0.68$

13 $\alpha = 37°46'$, $b = 512.0$ **14** $\beta = 10°17'$, $b = 68.40$

15 $a = 614$, $c = 806$ **16** $c = 37.4$, $b = 21.6$

17 Approximate the angle of elevation of the sun if a boy 5.0 feet tall casts a shadow 4.0 feet long on level ground.

18 From a point 15 meters above level ground, an observer measures the angle of depression of an object on the ground as 68°. Approximately how far is the object from the point on the ground directly beneath the observer?

19 The string on a kite is taut and makes an angle of 54°20' with the horizontal. Find the approximate height of the kite above level ground if 85.0 meters of string are out and the end of the string is held 1.50 meters above the ground.

20 The side of a regular pentagon is 24.0 cm long. Approximate the radius of the circumscribed circle.

21 From a point P on level ground, the angle of elevation of the top of a tower is 26°50'. From a point 25.0 meters closer to the tower and on the same line with P and the base of the tower, the angle of elevation of the top is 53°30'. Approximate the height of the tower.

22 A ladder 20 feet long leans against the side of a building. If the angle between the ladder and the building is 22° approximately how far is the bottom of the ladder from the building? If the distance from the bottom of the ladder to the building is increased by 3.0 feet, approximately how far does the top of the ladder move down the building?

23 As a weather balloon rises vertically, its angle of elevation from a point P on the level ground 110 km from the point Q directly underneath the balloon changes from 19°20' to 31°50'. Approximately how far does the balloon rise during this period?

24 From a point A, 8.20 meters above level ground, the angle of elevation of the top of a building is 31°20' and the angle of depression of the base of the building is 12°50'. Approximate the height of the building.

25 In order to find the distance d between two points P and Q on opposite shores of a lake, a surveyor locates a point R which is 50.0 meters from P and such that RP is perpendicular to PQ. Next, using a transit, angle PRQ is found to measure 72°40'. What is d?

26 A guy wire is attached to the top of a radio antenna and to a point on horizontal ground which is 40.0 meters from the base of the antenna. If the wire makes an angle of 58°20' with the ground, approximately how long is the wire?

27 An octagon is inscribed in a circle of radius 12.0 cm. Approximate the perimeter of the octagon.

28 A builder wishes to construct a ramp 24 feet long which rises to a height of 5.0 feet above level ground. Approximate the angle that the ramp should make with the horizontal.

29 A rocket is fired at sea level and climbs at a constant angle of 75° through a distance of 10,000 feet. Approximate its altitude to the nearest foot.

30 A CB antenna is located on the top of a garage 16 feet tall. From a point on level ground which is 100 feet from a point directly below the antenna, the antenna subtends an angle of 12°. Approximate the length of the antenna.

31 An airplane flying at an altitude of 10,000 feet passes directly over a fixed object on the ground. One minute later the angle of depression of the object is 42°. Approximate the speed of the airplane to the nearest mph.

32 A motorist is traveling along a level highway at a speed of 60 km per hour directly toward a distant mountain. She observes that between 1:00 P.M. and 1:10 P.M. the angle of elevation of the top of the mountain changes from 10° to 70°. Approximate the height of the mountain.

33 An airplane pilot wishes to make his approach to an airstrip at an angle of 10° with the horizontal. If he is flying at an altitude of 5,000 feet, approximately how far from the airstrip should he begin his descent? (Give answer to the nearest 100 feet.)

34 In order to measure the height h of a cloud cover, a spotlight is directed vertically upward from the ground. From a point on level ground which is d meters from the spotlight, the angle of elevation θ of the light image on the clouds is then measured. Find a formula that expresses h in terms of d and θ. As a special case, approximate h if $d = 1000$ meters and $\theta = 59°0'$.

35 A ship leaves port at 1:00 P.M. and sails in the direction N34°W at a rate of 24 miles per hour. Another ship leaves port at 1:30 P.M. and sails in the direction N56°E at a rate of 18 miles per hour. Approximately how far apart are the ships at 3:00 P.M.?

36 From an observation point A, a forest ranger sights a fire in the direction S48°20'W. From a point B, 5 miles due west of A, another ranger sights the same fire in the direction S54°10'E. Approximate, to the nearest mile, the distance of the fire from A.

37 An airplane flying at a speed of 360 miles per hour flies from a point A in the direction 137° for 30 minutes and then flies in the direction 227° for 45 minutes. Approximate, to the nearest mile, the distance from the airplane to A.

38 Generalize Exercise 19 to the case where the angle is α, the number of meters of string out is d, and the end of the string is held c meters above the ground. Express the height h of the kite in terms of α, d, and c.

39 Generalize Exercise 23 to the case where the distance from P to Q is d km and the angle of elevation changes from α to β.

40 Generalize Exercise 24 to the case where point A is d meters above ground and the angles of elevation and depression are α and β, respectively. Express the height h of the building in terms of d, α, and β.

CALCULATOR EXERCISES 2.10

Given the indicated parts of triangle ABC with $\gamma = 90°$, approximate the remaining parts of each triangle in Exercises 1–10. Round off answers to four significant figures.

1 $\alpha = 41.27°$, $a = 314.6$

2 $\beta = 24.96°$, $b = 209.3$

3 $\beta = 37.06°$, $a = 0.4613$

4 $\alpha = 17.69$, $b = 1.307$

5 $\beta = 2.71$, $b = 7149$

6 $\alpha = 84.07°$, $a = 0.1024$

7 $a = 46.87$, $b = 13.12$

8 $a = 6.948$, $b = 8.371$

9 $b = 2,462$, $c = 5,074$

10 $a = 88.12$, $c = 94.06$

2.11   HARMONIC MOTION

Trigonometric functions are important in the investigation of vibratory or oscillatory motion, such as the motion of a particle in a vibrating guitar string, or in a spring that has been compressed or elongated and then released to oscillate back and forth. The fundamental type of particle displacement inherent in these illustrations is termed *harmonic motion*. As an aid to introducing this concept, let us consider a point P moving at a constant rate around a circle of radius a with center at the origin O of a rectangular coordinate system. Suppose the initial position of P is $A(a, 0)$ and θ is the angle generated by the ray OP after t units of time (see Figure 2.53).

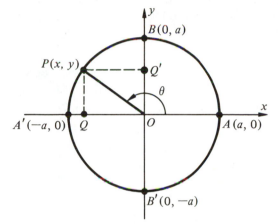

Figure 2.53

The **angular speed** ω of OP is, by definition, the rate at which the measure of θ changes per unit time. To state that P moves around the circle at a constant rate is equivalent to stating that the angular speed ω is constant. If ω is constant, then $\theta = \omega t$. To illustrate, if $\omega = \pi/6$ radians per second, then $\theta = (\pi/6)t$. In this case, at $t = 1$ second, $\theta = (\pi/6)(1) = \pi/6$, and P is one-third of the way from $A(a, 0)$ to $B(0, a)$. At $t = 2$ seconds, $\theta = (\pi/6)(2) = \pi/3$, and P is two-thirds of the way from A to B. At $t = 6$ seconds, $\theta = (\pi/6)(6) = \pi$ and P is at $A'(-a, 0)$, etc.

If the coordinates of P are (x, y), then $\sin \theta = y/a$ and $\cos \theta = x/a$. Multiplying both sides of these equations by a and using the fact that $\theta = \omega t$ gives us

$$x = a \cos \omega t, \quad y = a \sin \omega t.$$

The last two equations specify the position (x, y) of P at any time t. Let us next consider the point $Q(x, 0)$, which is called the **projection** of P on the x-axis. The position of Q is given by $x = a \cos \omega t$. As P moves around the circle several times, the point Q oscillates back and forth between $A(a, 0)$ and $A'(-a, 0)$. Similarly, the point $Q'(0, y)$ is called the **projection** of P on the y-axis, and its position is given by $y = a \sin \omega t$. As P moves around the circle, Q' oscillates between $B'(0, -a)$ and $B(0, a)$. The motions of Q and Q' are of the type described in the next definition.

Definition

> A point that moves on a coordinate line such that its distance d from the origin at time t is given by either $d = a \cos \omega t$ or $d = a \sin \omega t$, where a and ω are real numbers, is said to be in **simple harmonic motion**.

In the preceding definition, the **amplitude** of the motion is the maximum displacement $|a|$ of the point from the origin. The **period** is the time $2\pi/\omega$ required for one complete oscillation. The **frequency** $\omega/2\pi$ is the number of oscillations per unit of time.

A physical interpretation of simple harmonic motion can be obtained by considering a spring with an attached weight, which is oscillating vertically relative to a coordinate line, as illustrated in Figure 2.54. The number d represents the coordinate of a fixed point Q in the weight, and we assume that the amplitude a of the motion is constant. In this case, there is no frictional force retarding the motion. If friction is present, then the amplitude decreases with time, and the motion is said to be damped.

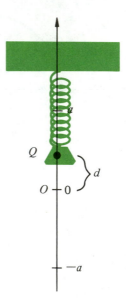

Figure 2.54

Example 1 Suppose the weight shown in Figure 2.54 is oscillating according to the law:

$$d = 10 \cos\left(\frac{\pi}{6}t\right)$$

where t is measured in seconds and d in centimeters. Discuss the motion of the weight.

Solution   By definition, the motion is simple harmonic. The amplitude is $a = 10$ cm. Since $\omega = \pi/6$, the period is $2\pi/\omega = 2\pi/(\pi/6) = 12$. Thus, it requires 12 seconds for one complete oscillation. The frequency is $\omega/2\pi = (\pi/6)/2\pi = 1/12$, that is, 1/12 of an oscillation takes place each second. The following table indicates the position of Q at various times.

t	0	1	2	3	4	5	6
$(\pi/6)t$	0	$\pi/6$	$\pi/3$	$\pi/2$	$2\pi/3$	$5\pi/6$	π
d	10	$5\sqrt{3} \approx 8.7$	5	0	-5	$-5\sqrt{3} \approx -8.7$	-10

Note that the initial position of Q is 10 cm above the origin O. It then moves downward, gaining speed until it reaches O. In particular, Q travels approximately 1.3 cm during the first second, 3.7 cm during the next second, and 5 cm during the third second. It then slows down until it reaches a point 10 cm below O at the end of 6 seconds. It is left to the reader to verify that the direction of motion is then reversed, and the weight moves upward, gaining speed until it reaches O, after which it slows down until it returns to its original position at the end of 12 seconds. The direction of motion is then reversed again, and the same pattern is repeated indefinitely. ■

The preceding example is typical of simple harmonic motion. If the initial angle AOP in Figure 2.53 is ϕ at $t = 0$, then the position (x, y) of P on the circle is given by

$$x = a \cos (\omega t + \phi), \quad y = a \sin (\omega t + \phi).$$

Points that vary on a coordinate line according to either of these formulas are also said to be in simple harmonic motion.

Simple harmonic motion takes place in many different types of wave motion, such as water waves, sound waves, radio waves, light waves, and distortional waves which are present in vibrating bodies. As a specific example, consider the waves made by holding one end of a long rope, as in Figure 2.55, and then causing it to vibrate by raising and lowering the hand in simple harmonic motion. Waves appear to move along the rope, traveling away from the hand. By placing a fixed vertical measuring device a distance c from the end, as shown in the figure, one may study the upward and downward motion of a specific particle P in the rope. If a suitable horizontal axis is chosen, it can be shown that P is in simple harmonic motion, as if it were attached to a spring. A similar motion takes place in water ripples on a large pond.

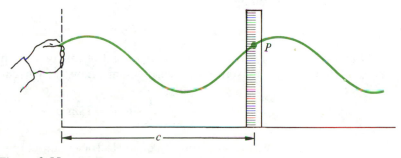

Figure 2.55

The definition of simple harmonic motion is usually extended to include situations where d is *any* mathematical or physical quantity (not necessarily a distance). In the next illustration d is itself an angle.

Historically, the first type of harmonic motion to be scientifically investigated involved pendulums. Figure 2.56 illustrates a *simple pendulum* consisting of a bob of mass m attached to one end of a string, with the other end of the string attached to a fixed point P. In the ideal case, it is assumed that the string is weightless, that there is no air resistance, and that the only force acting on the bob is gravity. If the bob is displaced sideways and released, the pendulum oscillates back and forth in a vertical plane. Let α denote the *angular displacement* at time t (see Figure 2.56). If the bob moves through a small arc (say $|\alpha| < 5°$), then it can be shown, by using physical laws, that

$$\alpha = \beta \cos (\omega t + \alpha_0)$$

where α_0 is the initial displacement, ω is the frequency of oscillation of the angle α, and β is the (angular) amplitude of oscillation. This means that the *angle* α is in simple harmonic motion, and hence, we refer to the motion as *angular* simple harmonic motion.

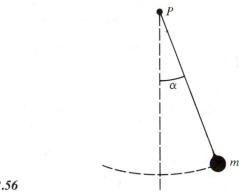

Figure 2.56

As a final illustration, in electric circuits an alternating electromotive force (emf) and the current may vary harmonically. For example, the emf e (measured in volts) at time t may be given by

$$e = E \sin \omega t$$

where E is the maximum value of e. If an emf of this type is impressed on a circuit containing only a resistance R, then by Ohm's Law, the current i at time t is

$$i = \frac{e}{R} = \frac{E}{R} \sin \omega t = I \sin \omega t$$

where $I = E/R$. A schematic drawing of an electric circuit of this type is illustrated in Figure 2.57.

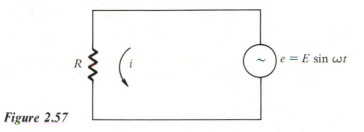

Figure 2.57

In this case, the maximum value I of i occurs at the same time as the maximum value E of e. In other situations, these maximum values may occur at different times, in which case we say there is a **phase difference** between e and i. For example, if $e = E \sin \omega t$, we could have either

$$\text{(a)} \quad i = I \sin(\omega t - \phi) \quad \text{or} \quad \text{(b)} \quad i = I \sin(\omega t + \phi)$$

where $\phi > 0$. In case (a), the current is said to **lag** the emf by an amount ϕ/ω, and the graph of i can be obtained by shifting the graph of $i = I \sin \omega t$ and amount ϕ/ω to the *right*. In case (b), we shift the graph to the *left*, and the current is said to **lead** the emf by an amount ϕ/ω.

There are numerous other physical illustrations involving simple harmonic motion. Interested students may find further information in books on physics and engineering.

EXERCISES 2.11

1 A wheel of diameter 40 centimeters is rotating about an axle at a rate of 100 revolutions per minute. If a coordinate system is introduced as in Figure 2.53, where P is a point on the rim of the wheel, find
(a) the angular speed of OP.
(b) the position (x, y) of P after t minutes.

2 A wheel of radius 2 feet is rotating about an axle, and the angular speed of a ray from the center of the wheel to a point P on the rim is $5\pi/6$ radians per second.
(a) How many revolutions does the wheel make in 10 minutes?
(b) If a coordinate system is introduced as in Figure 2.53, find the position (x, y) of P after t seconds.

In each of Exercises 3–6, the given formula specifies the position of a point P moving harmonically on a vertical axis, where t is in seconds and d is in centimeters. Determine the amplitude, period, and frequency, and describe the motion of the point during one complete oscillation (starting at $t = 0$).

3 $d = 10 \sin 6\pi t$ **4** $d = \frac{1}{3} \cos \frac{\pi}{4} t$

5 $d = 4 \cos \frac{3\pi}{2} t$ **6** $d = 6 \sin \frac{2\pi}{3} t$

7 A point P in simple harmonic motion has a period of 3 seconds and an amplitude of 5 cm. Express the motion of P by means of an equation of the form $d = a \cos \omega t$.

8 A point P in simple harmonic motion has a frequency of 1/2 oscillation per minute and an amplitude of 4 feet. Express the motion of P by means of an equation of the form $d = a \sin \omega t$.

9 The electromotive force e and current i in a certain alternating current circuit are given by

$$e = 220 \sin 360\pi t$$

$$i = 20 \sin\left(360\pi t - \frac{\pi}{4}\right).$$

Sketch the graphs of e and i on the same coordinate axes, and determine the lag or lead.

10 Rework Exercise 9 if

$$e = 110 \sin 120\pi t$$

$$i = 15 \sin\left(120\pi t + \frac{\pi}{3}\right).$$

2.12   REVIEW

Concepts

Define or discuss each of the following.

1 Point $P(t)$ on the unit circle U

2 The trigonometric functions

3 The Fundamental Identities.

4 Domains and ranges of the trigonometric functions

5 Periodic function; period; periods of the trigonometric functions

6 Graphs of the trigonometric functions

7 Angles

8 Standard position of an angle

9 Initial and terminal sides

10 Coterminal angles

11 Positive and negative angles

12 Radian measure

13 Degree measure

14 Acute and obtuse angles

15 The relationship between radian measure and degree measure

16 Trigonometric functions of angles

17 Trigonometric functions as ratios

18 Reference numbers and angles

19 Finding values of trigonometric functions using reference numbers and angles

20 The graphs of $f(x) = a \sin(bx + c)$ and $f(x) = a \cos(bx + c)$

21 Addition of ordinates

22 Trigonometric solutions of right triangles

Exercises

In Exercises 1–3, $P(t)$ denotes the point on the unit circle U that corresponds to the real number t.

1 Find the rectangular coordinates of $P(7\pi)$, $P(-5\pi/2)$, $P(9\pi/2)$, $P(-3\pi/4)$, $P(18\pi)$, and $P(\pi/6)$.

2 If $P(t)$ has coordinates $(-3/5, -4/5)$, find the coordinates of $P(t + 3\pi)$, $P(t - \pi)$, $P(-t)$, and $P(2\pi - t)$.

3 Find the quadrant containing $P(t)$ if
   (a) $\sec t < 0$ and $\sin t > 0$
   (b) $\cot t > 0$ and $\csc t < 0$
   (c) $\cos t > 0$ and $\tan t < 0$.

4 Find the values of the remaining trigonometric functions if
   (a) $\sin t = -4/5$ and $\cos t = 3/5$
   (b) $\csc t = \sqrt{13}/2$ and $\cot t = -3/2$.

5 Without the use of tables, find the values of the trigonometric functions corresponding to each of the following real numbers.
(a) $9\pi/2$ (b) $-5\pi/4$
(c) 0 (d) $11\pi/6$

6 Find the radian measures that correspond to the following degree measures: $330°$, $405°$, $-150°$, $240°$, $36°$.

7 Find the degree measures that correspond to the following radian measures: $9\pi/2$, $-2\pi/3$, $7\pi/4$, 5π, $\pi/5$.

8 Find the reference number t' if t equals: $5\pi/4$, $-5\pi/6$, $9\pi/8$.

9 Find the reference angle θ' if θ has measure: $245°$, $137°10'$, $892°$.

10 A central angle θ subtends an arc 20 cm long on a circle of radius 2 meters. What is the radian measure of θ?

11 Find the values of the six trigonometric functions of θ if θ is in standard position and satisfies the stated condition.
(a) The point $(30, -40)$ is on the terminal side of θ.
(b) The terminal side of θ is in quadrant II and is on the line $2x + 3y = 0$.
(c) $\theta = -90°$.

12 Find each of the following without the use of tables or calculators.
(a) $\cos 225°$ (b) $\tan 150°$
(c) $\sin(-\pi/6)$ (d) $\sec(4\pi/3)$
(e) $\cot(7\pi/4)$ (f) $\csc(300°)$

13 Use interpolation in Table 2 to approximate the following.
(a) $\cos 31°47'$ (b) $\tan 71°24'$
(c) $\csc 64°3'$

14 Use interpolation to approximate, to the nearest minute, the degree measure of all angles θ which are in the interval $[0°, 360°]$ if
(a) $\sin\theta = 0.8237$
(b) $\cos\theta = -0.7281$
(c) $\cot\theta = 1.238$.

In each of Exercises 15–22, find the amplitude and period, and sketch the graph of f.

15 $f(x) = 5\cos x$ **16** $f(x) = \frac{2}{3}\sin x$

17 $f(x) = -\tan x$ **18** $f(x) = 4\sin 3x$

19 $f(x) = 3\cos 4x$ **20** $f(x) = -4\sin(x/3)$

21 $f(x) = 2\sec(x/2)$ **22** $f(x) = \frac{1}{2}\csc(2x)$

Sketch the graph of the equation in each of Exercises 23–29.

23 $y = 2\sin\left(x - \dfrac{2\pi}{3}\right)$ **24** $y = -4\cos\left(x + \dfrac{\pi}{6}\right)$

25 $y = 5\cos\left(2x + \dfrac{\pi}{2}\right)$ **26** $y = \tan\left(x - \dfrac{\pi}{4}\right)$

27 $y = 2\sin x + \sin 2x$ **28** $y = 1 + x + \cos x$

29 $y = 2 + \sin 2x$

30 Given the following parts of triangle ABC with $\gamma = 90°$, approximate the remaining parts.
(a) $\beta = 60°$, $b = 40$
(b) $\alpha = 54°40'$, $b = 220$
(c) $a = 62$, $b = 25$

ANALYTIC TRIGONOMETRY

In this chapter we shall examine various algebraic and geometric aspects of trigonometry. In Sections 3.1 through 3.6, the emphasis is on identities and equations. In Section 3.7, we consider inverse functions for the trigonometric functions. In the course of our work we shall derive many important trigonometric identities and formulas. For convenient reference they are listed on the inside covers of the text.

3.1 THE FUNDAMENTAL IDENTITIES

The Fundamental Identities were introduced in Section 2.2. At that time we were primarily interested in their numerical significance. In this chapter they will be employed in a more general fashion. In particular, we shall see how the Fundamental Identities may be used to help simplify complicated expressions, derive other important formulas, and solve equations that involve trigonometric functions. Let us begin by restating them and working two numerical examples of the type considered in the last chapter.

The Fundamental Identities

$$\csc t = \frac{1}{\sin t}, \qquad \sec t = \frac{1}{\cos t}, \qquad \cot t = \frac{1}{\tan t}$$

$$\tan t = \frac{\sin t}{\cos t}, \qquad \cot t = \frac{\cos t}{\sin t}$$

$$\sin^2 t + \cos^2 t = 1, \qquad 1 + \tan^2 t = \sec^2 t, \qquad 1 + \cot^2 t = \csc^2 t$$

Example 1   If $\sec \theta = 3$ and θ is a fourth quadrant angle, find $\tan \theta$.

Solution   Using the identity $1 + \tan^2 \theta = \sec^2 \theta$, we obtain

$$\tan \theta = \pm\sqrt{\sec^2 \theta - 1}.$$

110

Since θ is in quadrant IV, $\tan \theta$ is negative, and hence,

$$\tan \theta = -\sqrt{\sec^2 \theta - 1} = -\sqrt{(3)^2 - 1} = -\sqrt{8} = -2\sqrt{2}. \qquad \blacksquare$$

Example 2 If $\csc t = 3/2$ and $\tan t < 0$, use fundamental identities to find the values of the remaining trigonometric functions of t.

Solution   Since $\csc t = 1/\sin t$, it follows that

$$\sin t = \frac{1}{\csc t} = \frac{1}{(3/2)} = 2/3.$$

Since $\csc t > 0$ and $\tan t < 0$, the angle (or point on the unit circle) corresponding to t is in quadrant II. Thus, $\cos t$ is negative and we may write

$$\begin{aligned}
\cos t &= -\sqrt{1 - \sin^2 t} \\
&= -\sqrt{1 - (2/3)^2} \\
&= -\sqrt{1 - (4/9)} = -\sqrt{5/9} = -\sqrt{5}/3.
\end{aligned}$$

Consequently, $\sec t = \dfrac{1}{\cos t} = -\dfrac{3}{\sqrt{5}} = \dfrac{-3\sqrt{5}}{5}.$

Next we see that

$$\tan t = \frac{\sin t}{\cos t} = \frac{(2/3)}{(-\sqrt{5}/3)} = -\frac{2}{\sqrt{5}} = \frac{-2\sqrt{5}}{5}$$

and $\cot t = \dfrac{1}{\tan t} = -\dfrac{\sqrt{5}}{2}.$

This gives us all of the functional values.

There are other ways of arriving at the values. For example, we could have started with

$$\cot^2 t = \csc^2 t - 1$$

and, since t is in quadrant II,

$$\begin{aligned}
\cot t &= -\sqrt{\csc^2 t - 1} \\
&= -\sqrt{(3/2)^2 - 1} \\
&= -\sqrt{(9/4) - 1} \\
&= -\sqrt{5/4} = -\sqrt{5}/2.
\end{aligned}$$

Other identities could also have been employed. $\blacksquare$

The next example illustrates how fundamental identities may be used to express one of the trigonometric functions in terms of another. You are asked to provide similar illustrations in Exercises 33–38.

Example 3   Find a formula that expresses $\tan t$ in terms of $\cos t$.

Solution   We may write

$$\tan t = \frac{\sin t}{\cos t} = \frac{\pm\sqrt{1 - \cos^2 t}}{\cos t}$$

where the sign depends on the particular value of t.   ∎

The following example illustrates how fundamental identities may be used to simplify trigonometric expressions. In the next section much more will be done along these lines.

Example 4   Use fundamental identities to simplify the expression

$$\sec t - \sin t \tan t.$$

Solution   Give reasons for each of the following steps:

$$\sec t - \sin t \tan t = \frac{1}{\cos t} - \sin t \left(\frac{\sin t}{\cos t}\right)$$

$$= \frac{1}{\cos t} - \frac{\sin^2 t}{\cos t}$$

$$= \frac{1 - \sin^2 t}{\cos t}$$

$$= \frac{\cos^2 t}{\cos t}$$

$$= \cos t. \qquad ∎$$

Example 5   Use fundamental identities to transform

$$\frac{\sin^2 t}{1 + \cos t} \quad \text{into} \quad 1 - \cos t.$$

Solution   We may proceed as follows:

$$\frac{\sin^2 t}{1 + \cos t} = \frac{1 - \cos^2 t}{1 + \cos t}$$

$$= \frac{(1 + \cos t)(1 - \cos t)}{1 + \cos t}$$

$$= 1 - \cos t. \qquad ∎$$

EXERCISES 3.1

In each of Exercises 1–8, use fundamental identities to find the values of the remaining trigonometric functions of t.

1 $\cos t = 1/2, \quad \sin t = -\sqrt{3}/2$

2 $\cos t = -\sqrt{3}/2, \quad \csc t = 2$

3 $\sin t = \sqrt{2}/2, \quad \sec t = -\sqrt{2}$

4 $\cos t = 0, \quad \sin t = 1$

5 $\cot t = -\sqrt{3}, \quad \csc t = -2$

6 $\sec t = \sqrt{2}, \quad \csc t = -\sqrt{2}$

7 $\cos t = -1, \quad \sin t = 0$

8 $\cot t = -1, \quad \sec t = -\sqrt{2}$

In Exercises 9–16, use fundamental identities to find the values of all six trigonometric functions if the given conditions are true.

9 $\tan t = 3/4$ and $\sin t < 0$

10 $\cot t = -3/4$ and $\cos t > 0$

11 $\sec t = -13/5$ and $\tan t < 0$

12 $\cos t = -1/2$ and $\sin t > 0$

13 $\sin t = -2/3$ and $\sec t > 0$

14 $\sec t = -5$ and $\csc t < 0$

15 $\csc t = 8$ and $\cos t < 0$

16 $\cos t = 0$ and $\sin t = -1$

In Exercises 17–32, use fundamental identities to transform the first expression into the second.

17 $\cos t \csc t, \quad \cot t$

18 $\tan t \csc t, \quad \sec t$

19 $\tan x \cos x, \quad \sin x$

20 $\cot x \sin x, \quad \cos x$

21 $\dfrac{\sec \theta}{\tan \theta}, \quad \csc \theta$

22 $\dfrac{\cot \theta}{\csc \theta}, \quad \cos \theta$

23 $\dfrac{\cos \alpha}{\sec \alpha}, \quad \cos^2 \alpha$

24 $\dfrac{\sec t}{\csc t}, \quad \tan t$

25 $(1 + \cot^2 t)\tan^2 t, \quad \sec^2 t$

26 $(1 - \sin^2 \theta)\sec^2 \theta, \quad 1$

27 $\sin x (\csc x - \sin x), \quad \cos^2 x$

28 $(\sec t - \cos t)\cos t, \quad \sin^2 t$

29 $\dfrac{\sin^2 \theta}{1 - \sin^2 \theta}, \quad \tan^2 \theta$

30 $\dfrac{1 - \sin^2 \alpha}{1 - \cos^2 \alpha}, \quad \cot^2 \alpha$

31 $\dfrac{1 + \tan^2 x}{\tan^2 x}, \quad \csc^2 x$ **32** $\dfrac{\cos^2 t}{1 - \sin t}, \quad 1 + \sin t$

33 Express each trigonometric function in terms of $\sin t$.

34 Express each trigonometric function in terms of $\cos t$.

35 Express $\sin t$ in terms of $\tan t$.

36 Express $\cos t$ in terms of $\cot t$.

37 Express $\sec t$ in terms of $\csc t$.

38 Express $\csc t$ in terms of $\tan t$.

Exercises 39 and 40 require a knowledge of logarithms (see Chapter Six).

39 Prove that if $0 < t < \pi/2$, then

$$\log \csc t = -\log \sin t.$$

40 Prove that if θ is an acute angle, then

$$\log \tan \theta = \log \sin \theta - \log \cos \theta.$$

CALCULATOR EXERCISES 3.1

Use direct calculations to demonstrate that

$$\tan t = \frac{\sin t}{\cos t} \quad \text{and} \quad \sin^2 t + \cos^2 t = 1$$

for the values of t given in Exercises 1–8.

1 $1.62°$

2 $37°15'$

3 $\pi/20$

4 137.48

5 $\sin 2$

6 $\sqrt{\pi} + \log 9$

7 $e^{1.6}$

8 $\ln 13.42$

9 If a calculator has keys for sin, cos, and tan, but not for csc, sec, and cot, how are values for the latter functions calculated?

10 Calculate $(\cos 5)^a$, where $a = \log (\tan(\sin 2))$.

3.2 TRIGONOMETRIC IDENTITIES

Any mathematical expression that contains symbols such as $\sin x$, $\cos \beta$, $\tan v$, etc., where the letters x, β, and v are variables, is referred to as a **trigonometric expression**. Trigonometric expressions may be very simple or very complicated. Some examples are

$$x + \sin x, \quad \frac{\cos(3y + 1)}{x^2 + \tan^2(z - y^2)}, \quad \frac{\sqrt{\theta} + 2^{\sin \theta}}{\sec(\cot \theta)}.$$

As usual, we assume that the domain of each variable is the set of real numbers (or angles) for which the expressions are meaningful. As indicated in Section 3.1, many trigonometric expressions can be simplified or changed in form by employing fundamental identities. The next example is another illustration of how this may be accomplished.

Example 1   Simplify the expression $(\sec \theta + \tan \theta)(1 - \sin \theta)$.

Solution   Supply reasons for the following steps:

$$
\begin{aligned}
(\sec \theta + \tan \theta)(1 - \sin \theta) &= \left(\frac{1}{\cos \theta} + \frac{\sin \theta}{\cos \theta} \right)(1 - \sin \theta) \\
&= \left(\frac{1 + \sin \theta}{\cos \theta} \right)(1 - \sin \theta) \\
&= \frac{1 - \sin^2 \theta}{\cos \theta} \\
&= \frac{\cos^2 \theta}{\cos \theta} \\
&= \cos \theta. \qquad \blacksquare
\end{aligned}
$$

There are other ways to treat the expression in Example 1. We could begin by multiplying the two factors and then proceed to simplify and combine terms. The method we employed—of changing all expressions to expressions that involve only sines and cosines—is often worthwhile. However, that technique does not always lead to the shortest possible simplification.

A **trigonometric equation** is an equation that contains trigonometric expressions. When working with trigonometric equations, we may express solutions either in terms of real numbers or in terms of angles.

We encountered several trigonometric identities in our previous work. Some of them, such as the Fundamental Identities, are basic and should be memorized. Other identities are introduced merely to supply practice in manipulating trigonometric expressions and therefore should not be memorized. We shall take the latter point of view in this section. Thus the identities to be investigated are unimportant in their own right. The important thing is the manipulative practice that is gained. The ability to carry out trigonometric manipulations is essential for problems that are encountered in advanced courses in mathematics and science.

We often use the phrase "verify an identity" instead of "prove that an equation is an identity." When verifying an identity, we shall not use the definition of the trigonometric functions to return to the coordinates (x, y) of a point on the unit circle U. Although many of the identities could be proved in that way, it is not the type of practice we desire. Rather, we shall use fundamental identities and algebraic manipulations to change the form of trigonometric expressions in a manner similar to the method used in the solution of Example 1. The preferred method of showing that an equation is an identity is to transform one side into the other, as illustrated in the next three examples. The reader should supply reasons for all steps in the solutions.

Example 2 Verify the identity $\dfrac{\tan t + \cos t}{\sin t} = \sec t + \cot t$.

Solution We shall transform the left side into the right side. Thus,

$$\frac{\tan t + \cos t}{\sin t} = \frac{\tan t}{\sin t} + \frac{\cos t}{\sin t}$$

$$= \frac{\left(\dfrac{\sin t}{\cos t}\right)}{\sin t} + \cot t$$

$$= \frac{1}{\cos t} + \cot t$$

$$= \sec t + \cot t. \qquad \blacksquare$$

Example 3 Verify the identity $\sec \alpha - \cos \alpha = \sin \alpha \tan \alpha$.

Solution

$$\sec \alpha - \cos \alpha = \frac{1}{\cos \alpha} - \cos \alpha$$

$$= \frac{1 - \cos^2 \alpha}{\cos \alpha}$$

$$= \frac{\sin^2 \alpha}{\cos \alpha} = \sin \alpha \left(\frac{\sin \alpha}{\cos \alpha}\right)$$

$$= \sin \alpha \tan \alpha. \qquad \blacksquare$$

Example 4 Verify the identity $\dfrac{\cos x}{1 - \sin x} = \dfrac{1 + \sin x}{\cos x}$.

Solution   We begin by multiplying the numerator and denominator of the fraction on the left by $1 + \sin x$. Thus,

$$\frac{\cos x}{1 - \sin x} = \frac{\cos x}{1 - \sin x} \cdot \frac{1 + \sin x}{1 + \sin x}$$

$$= \frac{\cos x(1 + \sin x)}{1 - \sin^2 x}$$

$$= \frac{\cos x(1 + \sin x)}{\cos^2 x}$$

$$= \frac{1 + \sin x}{\cos x}.$$ ∎

In another technique for showing that an equation $p = q$ is an identity, we begin by transforming the left side p into another expression s, making sure that each step is *reversible* in the sense that it is possible to transform s back into p by reversing the procedure that has been used. In this case, the equation $p = s$ is an identity. Next, as a *separate* exercise, it is shown that the right side q can also be transformed to the expression s by means of reversible steps and hence that $q = s$ is an identity. It then follows that $p = q$ is an identity. This method is illustrated in the next example.

Example 5   Verify the identity $(\tan \theta - \sec \theta)^2 = \dfrac{1 - \sin \theta}{1 + \sin \theta}.$

Solution   We shall verify the identity by showing that each side of the equation can be transformed into the same expression. Starting with the left side, we may write

$$(\tan \theta - \sec \theta)^2 = \tan^2 \theta - 2 \tan \theta \sec \theta + \sec^2 \theta$$

$$= \frac{\sin^2 \theta}{\cos^2 \theta} - \frac{2 \sin \theta}{\cos^2 \theta} + \frac{1}{\cos^2 \theta}$$

$$= \frac{\sin^2 \theta - 2 \sin \theta + 1}{\cos^2 \theta}.$$

The right side of the given equation may be changed by multiplying numerator and denominator by $1 - \sin \theta$. Thus,

$$\frac{1 - \sin \theta}{1 + \sin \theta} = \frac{1 - \sin \theta}{1 + \sin \theta} \cdot \frac{1 - \sin \theta}{1 - \sin \theta}$$

$$= \frac{1 - 2 \sin \theta + \sin^2 \theta}{1 - \sin^2 \theta}$$

$$= \frac{1 - 2 \sin \theta + \sin^2 \theta}{\cos^2 \theta}$$

which is the same expression as that obtained for $(\tan \theta - \sec \theta)^2$. Since all steps are reversible, it follows that the given equation is an identity.   ∎

EXERCISES 3.2

Verify the following identities.

1 $\cos\theta\sec\theta = 1$ **2** $\tan\alpha\cot\alpha = 1$

3 $\sin\theta\sec\theta = \tan\theta$ **4** $\sin\alpha\cot\alpha = \cos\alpha$

5 $\dfrac{\csc x}{\sec x} = \cot x$ **6** $\cot\beta\sec\beta = \csc\beta$

7 $(1+\cos\alpha)(1-\cos\alpha) = \sin^2\alpha$

8 $\cos^2 x(\sec^2 x - 1) = \sin^2 x$

9 $\cos^2 t - \sin^2 t = 2\cos^2 t - 1$

10 $(\tan\theta + \cot\theta)\tan\theta = \sec^2\theta$

11 $\dfrac{\sin t}{\csc t} + \dfrac{\cos t}{\sec t} = 1$

12 $1 - 2\sin^2 x = 2\cos^2 x - 1$

13 $(1+\sin\alpha)(1-\sin\alpha) = \dfrac{1}{\sec^2\alpha}$

14 $(1-\sin^2 t)(1+\tan^2 t) = 1$

15 $\sec\beta - \cos\beta = \tan\beta\sin\beta$

16 $\dfrac{\sin w + \cos w}{\cos w} = 1 + \tan w$

17 $\dfrac{\csc^2\theta}{1+\tan^2\theta} = \cot^2\theta$

18 $\sin x + \cos x\cot x = \csc x$

19 $\sin t(\csc t - \sin t) = \cos^2 t$

20 $\cot t + \tan t = \csc t\sec t$

21 $\csc\theta - \sin\theta = \cot\theta\cos\theta$

22 $\cos\theta(\tan\theta + \cot\theta) = \csc\theta$

23 $\dfrac{\sec^2 u - 1}{\sec^2 u} = \sin^2 u$

24 $(\tan u + \cot u)(\cos u + \sin u) = \sec u + \csc u$

25 $(\cos^2 x - 1)(\tan^2 x + 1) = 1 - \sec^2 x$

26 $(\cot\alpha + \csc\alpha)(\tan\alpha - \sin\alpha) = \sec\alpha - \cos\alpha$

27 $\sec t\csc t + \cot t = \tan t + 2\cos t\csc t$

28 $\dfrac{1+\cos^2 y}{\sin^2 y} = 2\csc^2 y - 1$

29 $\sec^2\theta\csc^2\theta = \sec^2\theta + \csc^2\theta$

30 $\dfrac{\sec x - \cos x}{\tan x} = \dfrac{\tan x}{\sec x}$

31 $\dfrac{1+\cos t}{\sin t} + \dfrac{\sin t}{1+\cos t} = 2\csc t$

32 $\tan^2\alpha - \sin^2\alpha = \tan^2\alpha\sin^2\alpha$

33 $\dfrac{1+\tan^2 v}{\tan^2 v} = \csc^2 v$

34 $\dfrac{\sec\theta + \csc\theta}{\sec\theta - \csc\theta} = \dfrac{\sin\theta + \cos\theta}{\sin\theta - \cos\theta}$

35 $\dfrac{1+\sin x}{1-\sin x} - \dfrac{1-\sin x}{1+\sin x} = 4\tan x\sec x$

36 $\dfrac{1}{1-\cos\gamma} + \dfrac{1}{1+\cos\gamma} = 2\csc^2\gamma$

37 $\dfrac{1+\csc\beta}{\sec\beta} - \cot\beta = \cos\beta$

38 $\dfrac{\cos x\cot x}{\cot x - \cos x} = \dfrac{\cot x + \cos x}{\cos x\cot x}$

39 $(\sec u - \tan u)(\csc u + 1) = \cot u$

40 $\dfrac{\cot\theta - \tan\theta}{\sin\theta + \cos\theta} = \csc\theta - \sec\theta$

41 $\dfrac{\cot\alpha - 1}{1-\tan\alpha} = \cot\alpha$

42 $\dfrac{1+\sec\beta}{\tan\beta + \sin\beta} = \csc\beta$

43 $\csc^4 t - \cot^4 t = \cot^2 t + \csc^2 t$

44 $\cos^4\theta + \sin^2\theta = \sin^4\theta + \cos^2\theta$

45 $\dfrac{\cos\beta}{1-\sin\beta} = \sec\beta + \tan\beta$

46 $\dfrac{1}{\csc y - \cot y} = \csc y + \cot y$

47 $\dfrac{\tan^2 x}{\sec x + 1} = \dfrac{1-\cos x}{\cos x}$

48 $\dfrac{\cot x}{\csc x + 1} = \dfrac{\csc x - 1}{\cot x}$

49 $\dfrac{\cot u - 1}{\cot u + 1} = \dfrac{1-\tan u}{1+\tan u}$

50 $\dfrac{1 + \sec x}{\sin x + \tan x} = \csc x$

51 $\sin^4 r - \cos^4 r = \sin^2 r - \cos^2 r$

52 $\sin^4 \theta + 2\sin^2 \theta \cos^2 \theta + \cos^4 \theta = 1$

53 $\tan^4 k - \sec^4 k = 1 - 2\sec^2 k$

54 $\sec^4 u - \sec^2 u = \tan^4 u + \tan^2 u$

55 $(\sec t + \tan t)^2 = \dfrac{1 + \sin t}{1 - \sin t}$

56 $\sec^2 \gamma + \tan^2 \gamma = (1 - \sin^4 \gamma)(\sec^4 \gamma)$

57 $(\sin^2 \theta + \cos^2 \theta)^3 = 1$

58 $\dfrac{\sin t}{1 - \cos t} = \csc t + \cot t$

59 $\dfrac{1 + \csc \beta}{\cot \beta + \cos \beta} = \sec \beta$

60 $\dfrac{\sin z \tan z}{\tan z - \sin z} = \dfrac{\tan z + \sin z}{\sin z \tan z}$

61 $\left(\dfrac{\sin^2 x}{\tan^4 x}\right)^3 \left(\dfrac{\csc^3 x}{\cot^6 x}\right)^2 = 1$

62 $\dfrac{\cos^3 x - \sin^3 x}{\cos x - \sin x} = 1 + \sin x \cos x$

63 $\dfrac{\sin \theta + \cos \theta}{\tan^2 \theta - 1} = \dfrac{\cos^2 \theta}{\sin \theta - \cos \theta}$

64 $(\csc t - \cot t)^4 (\csc t + \cot t)^4 = 1$

65 $(a\cos t - b\sin t)^2 + (a\sin t + b\cos t)^2$

        $= a^2 + b^2$

66 $\sin^6 v + \cos^6 v = 1 - 3\sin^2 v \cos^2 v$

67 $\dfrac{\sin \alpha \cos \beta + \cos \alpha \sin \beta}{\cos \alpha \cos \beta - \sin \alpha \sin \beta} = \dfrac{\tan \alpha + \tan \beta}{1 - \tan \alpha \tan \beta}$

68 $\dfrac{\tan u - \tan v}{1 + \tan u \tan v} = \dfrac{\cot v - \cot u}{1 + \cot u \cot v}$

69 $\sqrt{\dfrac{1 - \cos t}{1 + \cos t}} = \dfrac{1 - \cos t}{|\sin t|}$

70 $\sqrt{\dfrac{1 - \sin \theta}{1 + \sin \theta}} = \dfrac{|\cos \theta|}{1 + \sin \theta}$

71 $\dfrac{\sin \alpha}{1 + \cos \alpha} + \dfrac{1 + \cos \alpha}{\sin \alpha} = 2\csc \alpha$

72 $\dfrac{\csc x}{1 + \csc x} - \dfrac{\csc x}{1 - \csc x} = 2\sec^2 x$

73 $\dfrac{1}{\tan \beta + \cot \beta} = \sin \beta \cos \beta$

74 $\dfrac{\cot y - \tan y}{\sin y \cos y} = \csc^2 y - \sec^2 y$

75 $\sec \theta + \csc \theta - \cos \theta - \sin \theta$

        $= \sin \theta \tan \theta + \cos \theta \cot \theta$

76 $\sin^3 t + \cos^3 t = (1 - \sin t \cos t)(\sin t + \cos t)$

77 $(1 - \tan^2 \phi)^2 = \sec^4 \phi - 4\tan^2 \phi$

78 $\cos^4 w + 1 - \sin^4 w = 2\cos^2 w$

79 $\dfrac{\tan x}{1 - \cot x} + \dfrac{\cot x}{1 - \tan x} = 1 + \sec x \csc x$

80 $\dfrac{\cos \gamma}{1 - \tan \gamma} + \dfrac{\sin \gamma}{1 - \cot \gamma} = \cos \gamma + \sin \gamma$

81 $\sin(-t)\sec(-t) = -\tan t$

82 $\dfrac{\cot(-v)}{\csc(-v)} = \cos v$

Exercises 83–88 require a knowledge of logarithms.

83 $\log 10^{\tan t} = \tan t$

84 $10^{\log|\sin t|} = |\sin t|$

85 $\log \cot x = -\log \tan x$

86 $\log \sec \theta = -\log \cos \theta$

87 $-\log|\sec \theta - \tan \theta| = \log|\sec \theta + \tan \theta|$

88 $\log|\csc x - \cot x| = -\log|\csc x + \cot x|$

Show that the equations in Exercises 89–100 are not identities. (*Hint:* Find one number in the domain of t or θ for which the equation is false.)

89 $\cos t = \sqrt{1 - \sin^2 t}$

90 $\sqrt{\sin^2 t + \cos^2 t} = \sin t + \cos t$

91 $\sqrt{\sin^2 t} = \sin t$

92 $\sec t = \sqrt{\tan^2 t + 1}$

93 $(\sin \theta + \cos \theta)^2 = \sin^2 \theta + \cos^2 \theta$

94 $\sin(1/t) = 1/\sin t$

95 $\cos(-t) = -\cos t$	**96** $\sin(t + \pi) = \sin t$	**99** $\sin^2 t - 4\sin t - 5 = 0$	
97 $\cos(\sec t) = 1$	**98** $\cot(\tan \theta) = 1$	**100** $3\cos^2 \theta + \cos \theta - 2 = 0$	

3.3 TRIGONOMETRIC EQUATIONS

If a trigonometric equation is not an identity, then techniques similar to those used for algebraic equations may be employed to find the solutions. The main difference here is that we usually solve for $\sin x$, $\cos \theta$, and so on, and then find x and θ, as illustrated below.

Example 1   Solve the equation $\sin \theta \tan \theta = \sin \theta$.

Solution   Each of the following is equivalent to the given equation:

$$\sin \theta \tan \theta - \sin \theta = 0$$
$$(\sin \theta)(\tan \theta - 1) = 0.$$

To find the solutions, we set each factor on the left equal to zero, obtaining

$$\sin \theta = 0 \quad \text{and} \quad \tan \theta = 1.$$

The solutions of the equation $\sin \theta = 0$ consist of all multiples of π, that is, $\theta = n\pi$, where n is any integer.

Since the tangent function has period π, it is sufficient to find the solutions of the equation $\tan \theta = 1$ which are in the interval $[0, \pi)$, for once they are known, we may obtain all the others by adding multiples of π. The only solution of $\tan \theta = 1$ in $[0, \pi)$ is $\pi/4$, and hence, every solution has the form

$$\theta = \frac{\pi}{4} + n\pi$$

where n is an integer.

It follows that the solutions of the given equation consist of all numbers of the form

$$n\pi \quad \text{and} \quad \frac{\pi}{4} + n\pi$$

where n is any integer. Some particular solutions are 0, $\pm\pi$, $\pm 2\pi$, $\pm 3\pi$, $\pi/4$, $5\pi/4$, $-3\pi/4$, and $-7\pi/4$. ∎

Note that in Example 1 it would have been incorrect to begin by dividing both sides by $\sin \theta$, for this manipulation would lose the solutions of $\sin \theta = 0$.

Example 2   Solve the equation $2\sin^2 t - \cos t - 1 = 0$.

Solution   We first change the equation to an equation that involves only $\cos t$, and then we factor as follows:

$$2(1 - \cos^2 t) - \cos t - 1 = 0$$
$$-2\cos^2 t - \cos t + 1 = 0$$
$$2\cos^2 t + \cos t - 1 = 0$$
$$(2\cos t - 1)(\cos t + 1) = 0.$$

As in Example 1, the solutions of the last equation are the solutions of

$$2\cos t - 1 = 0 \quad \text{and} \quad \cos t + 1 = 0$$

or, equivalently, $\cos t = \tfrac{1}{2}$ and $\cos t = -1$.

It is sufficient to find the solutions that are in the interval $[0, 2\pi)$, for once they are known, all solutions may be found by adding multiples of 2π.

If $\cos t = \tfrac{1}{2}$, then the reference number (or reference angle) is $\pi/3$ (or $60°$). Since $\cos t$ is positive, the point $P(t)$ on U (or the angle t) lies in quadrant I or quadrant IV. Hence, in the interval $[0, 2\pi)$ we have

$$t = \frac{\pi}{3} \quad \text{or} \quad t = 2\pi - \frac{\pi}{3} = \frac{5\pi}{3}.$$

If $\cos t = -1$, then $t = \pi$.

It follows that the solutions of the given equation are

$$\frac{\pi}{3} + 2\pi n, \quad \frac{5\pi}{3} + 2\pi n, \quad \pi + 2\pi n$$

where n is any integer. If we wish to express the solutions in terms of degrees, we may write

$$60° + 360°n, \quad 300° + 360°n, \quad 180° + 360°n. \qquad \blacksquare$$

Example 3   Find the solutions of $4\sin^2 x \tan x - \tan x = 0$ which are in the interval $[0, 2\pi)$.

Solution   Factoring the left side, we obtain

$$(\tan x)(4\sin^2 x - 1) = 0.$$

Setting each factor equal to zero gives us

$$\tan x = 0 \quad \text{and} \quad \sin^2 x = \tfrac{1}{4}$$

or, equivalently,

$$\tan x = 0, \quad \sin x = \tfrac{1}{2}, \quad \text{and} \quad \sin x = -\tfrac{1}{2}.$$

The equation $\tan x = 0$ has solutions 0 and π in the interval $[0, 2\pi)$. The equation $\sin x = \tfrac{1}{2}$ has solutions $\pi/6$ and $5\pi/6$. The equation $\sin x = -\tfrac{1}{2}$ leads to the numbers between π and 2π which have reference number $\pi/6$. These are

$$\pi + \frac{\pi}{6} = \frac{7\pi}{6} \quad \text{and} \quad 2\pi - \frac{\pi}{6} = \frac{11\pi}{6}.$$

Hence, the solutions of the given equation in the interval $[0, 2\pi)$ are

$$0, \quad \pi, \quad \frac{\pi}{6}, \quad \frac{5\pi}{6}, \quad \frac{7\pi}{6}, \quad \frac{11\pi}{6}. \qquad \blacksquare$$

Example 4   Find the solutions of the equation $\csc^4 2u - 4 = 0$.

Solution   Factoring the left side, we obtain

$$(\csc^2 2u - 2)(\csc^2 2u + 2) = 0.$$

Setting each factor equal to 0 leads to

$$\csc^2 2u = 2 \quad \text{and} \quad \csc^2 2u = -2.$$

The equation $\csc^2 2u = -2$ has no solutions. (Why?) The solutions of $\csc^2 2u = 2$ consist of the solutions of the two equations

$$\csc 2u = \sqrt{2} \quad \text{and} \quad \csc 2u = -\sqrt{2}.$$

If $\csc 2u = \sqrt{2}$, then

$$2u = \frac{\pi}{4} + 2\pi n \quad \text{and} \quad 2u = \frac{3\pi}{4} + 2\pi n$$

where n is any integer. Dividing both sides of the last two equations by 2 gives us the solutions

$$u = \frac{\pi}{8} + \pi n \quad \text{and} \quad u = \frac{3\pi}{8} + \pi n.$$

Similarly, from $\csc 2u = -\sqrt{2}$ we obtain

$$2u = \frac{5\pi}{4} + 2\pi n \quad \text{and} \quad 2u = \frac{7\pi}{4} + 2\pi n$$

where n is any integer. Dividing both sides of the last two equations by 2 gives us

$$u = \frac{5\pi}{8} + \pi n \quad \text{and} \quad u = \frac{7\pi}{8} + \pi n.$$

Collecting the above information, we see that all solutions are given by the formula

$$u = \frac{\pi}{8} + \frac{\pi}{4}n,$$

where n is any integer. ■

Example 5 Approximate the solutions of the equation

$$5 \sin \theta \tan \theta - 10 \tan \theta + 3 \sin \theta - 6 = 0$$

in the degree interval $[0°, 360°)$.

Solution   The equation may be factored by grouping terms as follows:

$$5 \tan \theta (\sin \theta - 2) + 3 (\sin \theta - 2) = 0$$
$$(5 \tan \theta + 3)(\sin \theta - 2) = 0.$$

Since the equation $\sin \theta = 2$ has no solutions (Why?), the solutions of the given equation are the same as those of

$$\tan \theta = -\tfrac{3}{5} = -0.6000.$$

Approximations to θ may be found by interpolating in Table 2. We first approximate the reference angle θ' as follows:

$$10' \left\{ d \begin{cases} \tan 30°50' \approx 0.5969 \\ \tan \theta' \quad\;\; = 0.6000 \end{cases} 0.0031 \\ \quad\quad \tan 31°00' \approx 0.6009 \right\} 0.0040$$

$$\frac{d}{10} = \frac{31}{40} \quad \text{or} \quad d = \frac{31}{4} \approx 8'$$
$$\theta' \approx 30°58'.$$

Since θ lies in quadrant II or quadrant IV, this implies that

$$\theta \approx 180° - 30°58' = 149°2' \quad \text{or} \quad \theta \approx 360° - 30°58' = 329°2'. \quad ■$$

A technique for solving trigonometric equations with the aid of a calculator will be discussed later in the chapter, after inverse trigonometric functions have been introduced.

EXERCISES 3.3

In each of Exercises 1–16, find all solutions of the given equation.

1 $2 \cos t + 1 = 0$

2 $\cot \theta + 1 = 0$

3 $\tan^2 x = 1$

4 $4 \cos \theta - 2 = 0$

5 $(\cos \theta - 1)(\sin \theta + 1) = 0$

6 $2\cos x = \sqrt{3}$ **7** $\sec^2 \alpha - 4 = 0$

8 $3 - \tan^2 \beta = 0$ **9** $\sqrt{3} + 2\sin \beta = 0$

10 $4\sin^2 x - 3 = 0$ **11** $\cot^2 x - 3 = 0$

12 $(\sin t - 1)\cos t = 0$

13 $(2\sin \theta + 1)(2\cos \theta + 3) = 0$

14 $(2\sin u - 1)(\cos u - \sqrt{2}) = 0$

15 $\sin 2x(\csc 2x - 2) = 0$

16 $\tan \alpha + \tan^2 \alpha = 0$

In each of Exercises 17–36, find the solutions of the equation in the interval $[0, 2\pi)$ and also find the degree measure of each solution.

17 $2 - 8\cos^2 t = 0$ **18** $\cot^2 \theta - \cot \theta = 0$

19 $2\sin^2 u = 1 - \sin u$

20 $2\cos^2 t + 3\cos t + 1 = 0$

21 $\tan^2 x \sin x = \sin x$ **22** $\sec \beta \csc \beta = 2\csc \beta$

23 $2\cos^2 \gamma + \cos \gamma = 0$ **24** $\sin x - \cos x = 0$

25 $\sin^2 \theta + \sin \theta - 6 = 0$

26 $2\sin^2 u + \sin u - 6 = 0$

27 $1 - \sin t = \sqrt{3}\cos t$ **28** $\cos \theta - \sin \theta = 1$

29 $\cos \alpha + \sin \alpha = 1$ **30** $2\tan t - \sec^2 t = 0$

31 $\tan \theta + \sec \theta = 1$

32 $\cot \alpha + \tan \alpha = \csc \alpha \sec \alpha$

33 $2\sin^3 x + \sin^2 x - 2\sin x - 1 = 0$

34 $\sec^5 \theta = 4\sec \theta$

35 $2\tan t \csc t + 2\csc t + \tan t + 1 = 0$

36 $2\sin v \csc v - \csc v = 4\sin v - 2$

In each of Exercises 37–40, use Table 2 to approximate, to the nearest multiple of ten minutes, the solutions of the given equation in the interval $[0°, 360°)$.

37 $\sin^2 t - 4\sin t + 1 = 0$

38 $\tan^2 \theta + 3\tan \theta + 2 = 0$

39 $12\sin^2 u - 5\sin u - 2 = 0$

40 $5\cos^2 \alpha + 3\cos \alpha - 2 = 0$

3.4 THE ADDITION AND SUBTRACTION FORMULAS

In this section we shall derive formulas involving trigonometric functions of $u + v$ or $u - v$, where u and v represent any real numbers or angles. These formulas are known as **addition** or **subtraction** formulas, respectively.

Let t_1 and t_2 be any real numbers, and let $P(t_1)$ and $P(t_2)$ be the corresponding points on the unit circle U. We shall denote these points in terms of rectangular coordinates by $P_1(x_1, y_1)$ and $P_2(x_2, y_2)$, respectively. Let us next consider the real number $t_1 - t_2$ and denote the rectangular coordinates of $P(t_1 - t_2)$ by $P_3(x_3, y_3)$. Applying the definition of the trigonometric functions (Section 2.2), we have

(*)
$$\cos t_1 = x_1, \quad \cos t_2 = x_2, \quad \cos (t_1 - t_2) = x_3,$$
$$\sin t_1 = y_1, \quad \sin t_2 = y_2, \quad \sin (t_1 - t_2) = y_3,$$

where the symbol (*) has been used for later reference to these formulas. Our goal is to obtain a formula for $\cos (t_1 - t_2)$ in terms of functional values of t_1 and t_2. For convenience, let us assume that t_1 and t_2 are in the interval $[0, 2\pi]$ and $0 \le t_1 - t_2 < t_2$. In this case, $t_2 \le t_1$, and hence, if A is the point $(1, 0)$ on U, then the length t_1 of $\overparen{AP_1}$ is greater than or equal to the length t_2 of $\overparen{AP_2}$. Also, the length $t_1 - t_2$

of $\widehat{AP_3}$ is less than the length t_2 of $\widehat{AP_2}$. Figure 3.1 illustrates one arrangement of points P_1 and P_2 under these conditions.

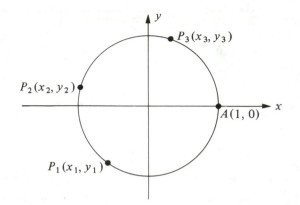

Figure 3.1

It is possible to extend our discussion to cover all values of t. Since the arc lengths of both $\widehat{P_2P_1}$ and $\widehat{AP_3}$ equal $t_1 - t_2$, the line segments P_2P_1 and AP_3 also have the same length; that is,

$$d(A, P_3) = d(P_1, P_2).$$

Using the Distance Formula in Section 1.2, the last equation may be written

$$\sqrt{(x_3 - 1)^2 + (y_3 - 0)^2} = \sqrt{(x_2 - x_1)^2 + (y_2 - y_1)^2}.$$

Squaring both sides and expanding the terms underneath the radical gives us

$$x_3^2 - 2x_3 + 1 + y_3^2 = x_2^2 - 2x_1x_2 + x_1^2 + y_2^2 - 2y_1y_2 + y_1^2.$$

Since P_1, P_2, and P_3 lie on U and since an equation for U is $x^2 + y^2 = 1$, we may substitute 1 for each of $x_1^2 + y_1^2$, $x_2^2 + y_2^2$, and $x_3^2 + y_3^2$. Doing this and simplifying, we obtain

$$2 - 2x_3 = 2 - 2x_1x_2 - 2y_1y_2$$

which reduces to $\qquad x_3 = x_1x_2 + y_1y_2.$

Substituting from the formulas stated in (*) at the beginning of this section gives us the desired formula, namely

$$\cos(t_1 - t_2) = \cos t_1 \cos t_2 + \sin t_1 \sin t_2.$$

In order to make the formula less cumbersome, we shall eliminate subscripts by changing the symbols for the variables from t_1 and t_2 to u and v, respectively. Our identity then takes on the following form.

**Subtraction Formula
for Cosine**

$$\boxed{\cos(u - v) = \cos u \cos v + \sin u \sin v.}$$

Example 1   Find the exact value of $\cos 15°$.

Solution   If we write $15° = 60° - 45°$, we may use the last formula with $u = 60°$ and $v = 45°$ as follows:

$$\cos 15° = \cos (60° - 45°)$$

$$= \cos 60° \cos 45° + \sin 60° \sin 45°$$

$$= \left(\frac{1}{2}\right)\left(\frac{\sqrt{2}}{2}\right) + \left(\frac{\sqrt{3}}{2}\right)\left(\frac{\sqrt{2}}{2}\right)$$

$$= \frac{\sqrt{2} + \sqrt{6}}{4}.$$ ∎

It is easy to obtain a formula for $\cos (u + v)$. We simply write $u + v = u - (-v)$ and employ the formula derived previously. Thus,

$$\cos (u + v) = \cos [u - (-v)]$$

$$= \cos u \cos (-v) + \sin u \sin (-v).$$

It was shown in Section 2.7 that $\cos (-v) = \cos v$ and $\sin (-v) = -\sin v$ for all v, and hence,

Addition Formula for Cosine

$$\boxed{\cos (u + v) = \cos u \cos v - \sin u \sin v.}$$

Example 2   Find $\cos (7\pi/12)$ by using $\pi/3$ and $\pi/4$.

Solution   Writing $7\pi/12 = (\pi/3) + (\pi/4)$ and using the formula for $\cos (u + v)$ gives us

$$\cos \frac{7\pi}{12} = \cos \left(\frac{\pi}{3} + \frac{\pi}{4}\right)$$

$$= \cos \frac{\pi}{3} \cos \frac{\pi}{4} - \sin \frac{\pi}{3} \sin \frac{\pi}{4}$$

$$= \frac{1}{2}\frac{\sqrt{2}}{2} - \frac{\sqrt{3}}{2}\frac{\sqrt{2}}{2}$$

$$= \frac{\sqrt{2} - \sqrt{6}}{4}.$$ ∎

Similar identities are true for the sine function. Let us first establish the following identities, which are of some interest in themselves.

$$\cos\left(\frac{\pi}{2} - u\right) = \sin u$$

$$\sin\left(\frac{\pi}{2} - u\right) = \cos u$$

$$\tan\left(\frac{\pi}{2} - u\right) = \cot u$$

The first of these identities may be proved as follows:

$$\cos\left(\frac{\pi}{2} - u\right) = \cos\frac{\pi}{2} \cdot \cos u + \sin\frac{\pi}{2} \cdot \sin u$$

$$= 0 \cdot \cos u + 1 \cdot \sin u$$

$$= \sin u.$$

To obtain the second identity, we substitute $(\pi/2) - v$ for u in the first identity, obtaining

$$\cos\left[\frac{\pi}{2} - \left(\frac{\pi}{2} - v\right)\right] = \sin\left(\frac{\pi}{2} - v\right)$$

or, equivalently,

$$\cos v = \sin\left(\frac{\pi}{2} - v\right).$$

The third identity may be established as follows:

$$\tan\left(\frac{\pi}{2} - u\right) = \frac{\sin\left(\dfrac{\pi}{2} - u\right)}{\cos\left(\dfrac{\pi}{2} - u\right)} = \frac{\cos u}{\sin u} = \cot u.$$

If θ denotes the degree measure of an angle, we may write

$$\sin(90° - \theta) = \cos\theta$$
$$\cos(90° - \theta) = \sin\theta$$
$$\tan(90° - \theta) = \cot\theta.$$

If θ is acute, then θ and $90° - \theta$ are **complementary**, since their sum is $90°$. It is customary to refer to the sine and cosine functions as **cofunctions** of one another. Similarly, the tangent and cotangent functions are cofunctions, as are the secant and cosecant. Consequently, the last three formulas constitute a partial description of the fact that *any functional value of θ equals the cofunction of the complementary angle $90° - \theta$.*

The following identities may now be established.

Addition and Subtraction Formulas for Sine and Tangent

$$\sin (u + v) = \sin u \cos v + \cos u \sin v$$
$$\sin (u - v) = \sin u \cos v - \cos u \sin v$$
$$\tan (u + v) = \frac{\tan u + \tan v}{1 - \tan u \tan v}$$
$$\tan (u - v) = \frac{\tan u - \tan v}{1 + \tan u \tan v}$$

Proof

We shall prove the first and third and leave the proofs of the remaining two as exercises. The reader should supply reasons for each of the following steps.

$$\sin (u + v) = \cos \left[\frac{\pi}{2} - (u + v) \right]$$

$$= \cos \left[\left(\frac{\pi}{2} - u \right) - v \right]$$

$$= \cos \left(\frac{\pi}{2} - u \right) \cos v + \sin \left(\frac{\pi}{2} - u \right) \sin v$$

$$= \sin u \cos v + \cos u \sin v.$$

To verify the formula for $\tan (u + v)$, we begin as follows:

$$\tan (u + v) = \frac{\sin (u + v)}{\cos (u + v)}$$

$$= \frac{\sin u \cos v + \cos u \sin v}{\cos u \cos v - \sin u \sin v}.$$

Next, dividing numerator and denominator by $\cos u \cos v$ (assuming, of course, that $\cos u \cos v \neq 0$), we obtain

$$\tan (u + v) = \frac{\left(\dfrac{\sin u}{\cos u} \right) \left(\dfrac{\cos v}{\cos v} \right) + \left(\dfrac{\cos u}{\cos u} \right) \left(\dfrac{\sin v}{\cos v} \right)}{\left(\dfrac{\cos u}{\cos u} \right) \left(\dfrac{\cos v}{\cos v} \right) - \left(\dfrac{\sin u}{\cos u} \right) \left(\dfrac{\sin v}{\cos v} \right)}$$

$$= \frac{\tan u + \tan v}{1 - \tan u \tan v}. \qquad \blacksquare$$

Example 3   Given $\sin \alpha = 4/5$, where α is an angle in quadrant I, and $\cos \beta = -12/13$, where β is in quadrant II, find $\sin (\alpha + \beta)$, $\tan (\alpha + \beta)$, and the quadrant containing $\alpha + \beta$.

Solution   It is convenient to represent α and β geometrically, as illustrated in Figure 3.2. There is no loss of generality in picturing α and β as positive angles between 0 and 2π, as we have done in the figure. Since $\sin \alpha = 4/5$, the point $(3, 4)$ is on the terminal side of α. (Why?) Similarly, since $\cos \beta = -12/13$, we may choose the point $(-12, 5)$ on the terminal side of β. Referring to Figure 3.2 and using the Theorem on Trigonometric Functions as Ratios (see Section 2.5), we obtain

$$\cos \alpha = \tfrac{3}{5}, \quad \tan \alpha = \tfrac{4}{3}, \quad \sin \beta = \tfrac{5}{13}, \quad \text{and} \quad \tan \beta = -\tfrac{5}{12}.$$

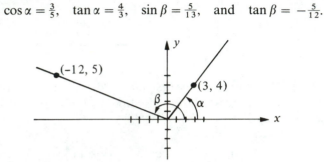

Figure 3.2

Using addition formulas gives us

$$\sin (\alpha + \beta) = \sin \alpha \cos \beta + \cos \alpha \sin \beta$$

$$= \left(\frac{4}{5}\right)\left(-\frac{12}{13}\right) + \left(\frac{3}{5}\right)\left(\frac{5}{13}\right)$$

$$= -\frac{33}{65}.$$

$$\tan (\alpha + \beta) = \frac{\tan \alpha + \tan \beta}{1 - \tan \alpha \tan \beta}$$

$$= \frac{\dfrac{4}{3} + \left(-\dfrac{5}{12}\right)}{1 - \left(\dfrac{4}{3}\right)\left(-\dfrac{5}{12}\right)}$$

$$= \frac{33}{56}.$$

Since $\sin (\alpha + \beta)$ is negative and $\tan (\alpha + \beta)$ is positive, it follows that $\alpha + \beta$ lies in quadrant III.   ∎

The addition formulas are very important in the study of calculus, where the type of simplification illustrated in the next example is required.

Example 4   If $f(x) = \sin x$ and $h \neq 0$, prove that

$$\frac{f(x + h) - f(x)}{h} = \sin x \left(\frac{\cos h - 1}{h}\right) + \cos x \left(\frac{\sin h}{h}\right).$$

Solution Using the definition of f and the addition formula for the sine function, we obtain

$$\frac{f(x+h)-f(x)}{h} = \frac{\sin(x+h)-\sin x}{h}$$

$$= \frac{\sin x \cos h + \cos x \sin h - \sin x}{h}$$

$$= \frac{\sin x(\cos h - 1) + \cos x \sin h}{h}$$

$$= \sin x \left(\frac{\cos h - 1}{h}\right) + \cos x \left(\frac{\sin h}{h}\right). \qquad\blacksquare$$

Example 5 Prove that for every x,

$$a \cos Bx + b \sin Bx = A \cos(Bx - C)$$

where $A = \sqrt{a^2 + b^2}$ and $\tan C = b/a$.

Solution Using the formula for $\cos(u - v)$ with $u = Bx$ and $v = C$ gives us

$$A \cos(Bx - C) = A(\cos Bx \cos C + \sin Bx \sin C).$$

We shall complete the proof by determining conditions on a and b such that

$$a \cos Bx + b \sin Bx = A \cos Bx \cos C + A \sin Bx \sin C.$$

The last formula is true for every x if and only if

$$a = A \cos C \quad \text{and} \quad b = A \sin C$$

(to verify this let $x = 0$ and $x = \pi/2$). Consequently,

$$a^2 + b^2 = A^2 \cos^2 C + A^2 \sin^2 C$$
$$= A^2 (\cos^2 C + \sin^2 C) = A^2$$

and we may choose $\qquad A = \sqrt{a^2 + b^2}.$

Finally, we note that

$$\frac{b}{a} = \frac{A \sin C}{A \cos C} = \frac{\sin C}{\cos C} = \tan C.$$

This establishes the identity. $\qquad\blacksquare$

Example 6 The graph of $f(x) = \cos x + \sin x$ was sketched in Section 2.9 by adding ordinates (see Figure 2.46). Use the formula derived in Example 5 to find the amplitude, period, and phase shift of f.

Solution   Letting $a = 1$, $b = 1$, and $B = 1$ in Example 5, we obtain

$$A = \sqrt{a^2 + b^2} = \sqrt{1 + 1} = \sqrt{2} \quad \text{and} \quad \tan C = b/a = 1/1 = 1.$$

Since $\tan C = 1$, we may choose $C = \pi/4$. Substitution in the formula gives us

$$\cos x + \sin x = \sqrt{2}\cos\left(x - \frac{\pi}{4}\right).$$

It follows from our work in Section 2.8 that the amplitude is $\sqrt{2}$, the period is 2π, and the phase shift is $\pi/4$. The reader may check these facts by referring to Figure 2.46. ∎

EXERCISES 3.4

Write the expressions in Exercises 1–4 in terms of cofunctions of complementary angles.

1 (a) $\sin 46°37'$ (b) $\cos 73°12'$ (c) $\tan \pi/6$

2 (a) $\tan 24°12'$ (b) $\sin 89°41'$ (c) $\cos \pi/3$

3 (a) $\cos 7\pi/20$ (b) $\sin (1/4)$ (c) $\tan 1$

4 (a) $\sin \pi/12$ (b) $\cos (0.64)$ (c) $\tan \sqrt{2}$

Find the exact functional values in Exercises 5–10.

5 (a) $\cos \pi/4 + \cos \pi/3$ (b) $\cos 7\pi/12$

6 (a) $\sin 2\pi/3 + \sin \pi/4$ (b) $\sin 11\pi/12$

7 (a) $\tan 60° + \tan 225°$ (b) $\tan 285°$

8 (a) $\cos 135° - \cos 60°$ (b) $\cos 75°$

9 (a) $\sin 3\pi/4 - \sin \pi/6$ (b) $\sin 7\pi/12$

10 (a) $\tan 3\pi/4 - \tan \pi/6$ (b) $\tan 7\pi/12$

Express each of Exercises 11–16 in terms of one function of one angle.

11 $\cos 48° \cos 23° + \sin 48° \sin 23°$

12 $\cos 13° \cos 50° - \sin 13° \sin 50°$

13 $\cos 10° \sin 5° - \sin 10° \cos 5°$

14 $\sin 57° \cos 4° + \cos 57° \sin 4°$

15 $\cos 3 \sin (-2) - \cos 2 \sin 3$

16 $\sin (-5)\cos 2 + \cos 5 \sin (-2)$

17 If α and β are acute angles such that $\cos \alpha = 4/5$ and $\tan \beta = 8/15$, find $\cos (\alpha + \beta)$, $\sin (\alpha + \beta)$, and the quadrant containing $\alpha + \beta$.

18 If $\sin \alpha = -4/5$ and $\sec \beta = 5/3$, where α is a third-quadrant angle and β is a first-quadrant angle, find $\sin (\alpha + \beta)$, $\tan (\alpha + \beta)$, and the quadrant containing $\alpha + \beta$.

19 If $\tan \alpha = -7/24$ and $\cot \beta = 3/4$, where α is in the second quadrant and β is in the third quadrant, find $\sin (\alpha + \beta)$, $\cos (\alpha + \beta)$, $\tan (\alpha + \beta)$, $\sin (\alpha - \beta)$, $\cos (\alpha - \beta)$, and $\tan (\alpha - \beta)$.

20 If $P(t_1)$ and $P(t_2)$ are in quadrant III, and if $\cos t_1 = -2/5$ and $\cos t_2 = -3/5$, find $\sin (t_1 - t_2)$, $\cos (t_1 - t_2)$, and the quadrant containing $P(t_1 - t_2)$.

Verify the identities in Exercises 21–40.

21 $\sin\left(x + \frac{\pi}{2}\right) = \cos x$

22 $\cos\left(x + \frac{\pi}{2}\right) = -\sin x$

23 $\cos\left(\theta + \frac{3\pi}{2}\right) = \sin \theta$

24 $\sin\left(\alpha - \frac{3\pi}{2}\right) = \cos \alpha$

25 $\sin\left(\theta + \frac{\pi}{4}\right) = \left(\frac{\sqrt{2}}{2}\right)(\sin \theta + \cos \theta)$

26 $\cos\left(\theta + \dfrac{\pi}{4}\right) = \left(\dfrac{\sqrt{2}}{2}\right)(\cos\theta - \sin\theta)$

27 $\tan\left(u + \dfrac{\pi}{4}\right) = \dfrac{1 + \tan u}{1 - \tan u}$

28 $\tan\left(x - \dfrac{\pi}{4}\right) = \dfrac{\tan x - 1}{\tan x + 1}$

29 $\tan\left(u + \dfrac{\pi}{2}\right) = -\cot u$

30 $\cot\left(t - \dfrac{\pi}{3}\right) = \dfrac{\sqrt{3}\tan t + 1}{\tan t - \sqrt{3}}$

31 $\sin(u + v)\cdot\sin(u - v) = \sin^2 u - \sin^2 v$

32 $\cos(u + v)\cdot\cos(u - v) = \cos^2 u - \sin^2 v$

33 $\cos(u + v) + \cos(u - v) = 2\cos u\cos v$

34 $\sin(u + v) + \sin(u - v) = 2\sin u\cos v$

35 $\sin 2u = 2\sin u\cos u$ (*Hint:* $2u = u + u$)

36 $\cos 2u = \cos^2 u - \sin^2 u$

37 $\dfrac{\sin(u + v)}{\cos(u - v)} = \dfrac{\tan u + \tan v}{1 + \tan u\tan v}$

38 $\dfrac{\cos(u + v)}{\cos(u - v)} = \dfrac{1 - \tan u\tan v}{1 + \tan u\tan v}$

39 $\dfrac{\sin(u + v)}{\sin(u - v)} = \dfrac{\tan u + \tan v}{\tan u - \tan v}$

40 $\tan u + \tan v = \dfrac{\sin(u + v)}{\cos u\cos v}$

41 Express $\sin(u + v + w)$ in terms of functions of u, v, and w. (*Hint:* Write $\sin(u + v + w) = \sin[(u + v) + w]$ and use an addition formula.)

42 Express $\tan(u + v + w)$ in terms of functions of u, v, and w.

43 Derive the formula

$$\cot(u + v) = \dfrac{\cot u\cot v - 1}{\cot u + \cot v}.$$

44 If α and β are complementary angles, prove that

$$\sin^2\alpha + \sin^2\beta = 1.$$

45 Derive the subtraction formulas for the sine and tangent functions.

46 Prove each of the following:
   (a) $\sec(\pi/2 - u) = \csc u$
   (b) $\csc(\pi/2 - u) = \sec u$
   (c) $\cot(\pi/2 - u) = \tan u$

47 If $f(x) = \cos x$, prove that

$$\dfrac{f(x + h) - f(x)}{h}$$

$$= \cos x\left(\dfrac{\cos h - 1}{h}\right) - \sin x\left(\dfrac{\sin h}{h}\right).$$

48 If $f(x) = \tan x$, prove that

$$\dfrac{f(x + h) - f(x)}{h}$$

$$= \sec^2 x\left(\dfrac{\sin h}{h}\right)\dfrac{1}{\cos h - \sin h\tan x}.$$

In Exercises 49 and 50, find the solutions of the given equation which are in the interval $[0, 2\pi)$ and also find the degree measure of each solution.

49 $\sin 4t\cos t = \sin t\cos 4t$

50 $\cos 5t\cos 3t = 2^{-1} + \sin(-5t)\sin 3t$

In each of Exercises 51–54, use the formula given in Example 5 to express f in terms of the cosine function and determine the amplitude, period, and phase shift.

51 $f(x) = \sqrt{3}\cos 2x + \sin 2x$

52 $f(x) = \cos 4x + \sqrt{3}\sin 4x$

53 $f(x) = 2\cos 3x - 2\sin 3x$

54 $f(x) = -5\cos 10x + 5\sin 10x$

CALCULATOR EXERCISES 3.4

1 Demonstrate, by direct calculations, that the addition formulas for the sine, cosine, and tangent functions are true for the following values of u and v: $u = 1.46$, $v = 8.27$.

2 If u and v are in the interval $[0, \pi]$ such that $\cos u = -0.4163$ and $\sin v = 0.7216$, find $\cos(u + v)$ and $\sin(u + v)$.

3.5 MULTIPLE-ANGLE FORMULAS

In the preceding section we were interested primarily in trigonometric identities that involve values of $u \pm v$. In this section we shall obtain formulas for values of nu, where n represents a certain integer or rational number. The formulas are referred to as **multiple-angle formulas**. In particular, the following identities are called **double-angle formulas**, because of the expression $2u$ which appears.

Double-Angle Formulas

$$
\begin{aligned}
\sin 2u &= 2 \sin u \cos u \\
\cos 2u &= \cos^2 u - \sin^2 u = 1 - 2 \sin^2 u = 2 \cos^2 u - 1 \\
\tan 2u &= \frac{2 \tan u}{1 - \tan^2 u}
\end{aligned}
$$

These identities may be proved by letting $u = v$ in the appropriate addition formulas. If we use the formula for $\sin (u + v)$, then

$$
\begin{aligned}
\sin 2u &= \sin (u + u) \\
&= \sin u \cos u + \cos u \sin u \\
&= 2 \sin u \cos u.
\end{aligned}
$$

Similarly, using the formula for $\cos (u + v)$ gives us

$$
\begin{aligned}
\cos 2u &= \cos (u + u) \\
&= \cos u \cos u - \sin u \sin u \\
&= \cos^2 u - \sin^2 u.
\end{aligned}
$$

The other two forms for $\cos 2u$ may be obtained by using the fundamental identity $\sin^2 u + \cos^2 u = 1$. Thus,

$$
\begin{aligned}
\cos 2u &= \cos^2 u - \sin^2 u \\
&= (1 - \sin^2 u) - \sin^2 u \\
&= 1 - 2 \sin^2 u.
\end{aligned}
$$

Similarly, if we substitute for $\sin^2 u$ instead of $\cos^2 u$, we obtain

$$
\begin{aligned}
\cos 2u &= \cos^2 u - (1 - \cos^2 u) \\
&= 2 \cos^2 u - 1.
\end{aligned}
$$

The formula for $\tan 2u$ may be obtained by taking $u = v$ in the formula for $\tan (u + v)$.

Example 1   Find $\sin 2\alpha$ and $\cos 2\alpha$ if $\sin \alpha = \frac{4}{5}$ and α is in quadrant I.

Solution   As in Example 3 of the preceding section, $\cos \alpha = 3/5$. Substitution in double-angle formulas gives us

$$\sin 2\alpha = 2 \sin \alpha \cos \alpha = 2 \left(\frac{4}{5}\right) \left(\frac{3}{5}\right) = \frac{24}{25}$$

$$\cos 2\alpha = \cos^2 \alpha - \sin^2 \alpha = \frac{9}{25} - \frac{16}{25} = -\frac{7}{25}. \qquad \blacksquare$$

Example 2   Express $\cos 3\theta$ in terms of $\cos \theta$.

Solution

$$
\begin{aligned}
\cos 3\theta &= \cos(2\theta + \theta) \\
&= \cos 2\theta \cos \theta - \sin 2\theta \sin \theta \\
&= (2\cos^2 \theta - 1)\cos \theta - (2\sin \theta \cos \theta)\sin \theta \\
&= 2\cos^3 \theta - \cos \theta - 2\cos \theta \sin^2 \theta \\
&= 2\cos^3 \theta - \cos \theta - 2\cos \theta(1 - \cos^2 \theta) \\
&= 2\cos^3 \theta - \cos \theta - 2\cos \theta + 2\cos^3 \theta \\
&= 4\cos^3 \theta - 3\cos \theta. \qquad \blacksquare
\end{aligned}
$$

The next three identities are useful for simplifying certain expressions involving powers of trigonometric functions.

$$\sin^2 u = \frac{1 - \cos 2u}{2}, \qquad \cos^2 u = \frac{1 + \cos 2u}{2}, \qquad \tan^2 u = \frac{1 - \cos 2u}{1 + \cos 2u}$$

The first and second of these identities may be verified by solving the equations

$$\cos 2u = 1 - 2\sin^2 u \quad \text{and} \quad \cos 2u = 2\cos^2 u - 1$$

for $\sin^2 u$ and $\cos^2 u$, respectively. The third identity may be obtained from the first two by using the fact that $\tan^2 u = \sin^2 u / \cos^2 u$.

Example 3   Verify the identity $\sin^2 x \cos^2 x = \frac{1}{8}(1 - \cos 4x)$.

Solution   Using the preceding identities for $\sin^2 u$ and $\cos^2 u$ with $u = x$, we obtain

$$
\begin{aligned}
\sin^2 x \cos^2 x &= \left(\frac{1 - \cos 2x}{2}\right)\left(\frac{1 + \cos 2x}{2}\right) \\
&= \frac{1}{4}(1 - \cos^2 2x) \\
&= \frac{1}{4}\sin^2 2x.
\end{aligned}
$$

Finally, using the formula $\sin^2 u = (1 - \cos 2u)/2$ with $u = 2x$ gives us

$$\sin^2 x \cos^2 x = \frac{1}{4}\left(\frac{1 - \cos 4x}{2}\right)$$

$$= \frac{1}{8}(1 - \cos 4x).$$

Another method of proof is to use the fact that $\sin 2x = 2\sin x \cos x$ and hence that

$$\sin x \cos x = \tfrac{1}{2}\sin 2x.$$

Squaring both sides, we have

$$\sin^2 x \cos^2 x = \tfrac{1}{4}\sin^2 2x.$$

The remainder of the solution is the same as that given above.   ■

Example 4   Express $\cos^4 t$ in terms of values of cos with exponent 1.

Solution   Supply reasons for the following steps:

$$\cos^4 t = (\cos^2 t)^2$$

$$= \left(\frac{1 + \cos 2t}{2}\right)^2$$

$$= \frac{1}{4}(1 + 2\cos 2t + \cos^2 2t)$$

$$= \frac{1}{4}\left(1 + 2\cos 2t + \frac{1 + \cos 4t}{2}\right)$$

$$= \frac{3}{8} + \frac{1}{2}\cos 2t + \frac{1}{8}\cos 4t.$$ ■

Substituting $v/2$ for u in the three formulas for $\sin^2 u$, $\cos^2 u$, and $\tan^2 u$ gives us

$$\sin^2\frac{v}{2} = \frac{1 - \cos v}{2}$$

$$\cos^2\frac{v}{2} = \frac{1 + \cos v}{2}$$

$$\tan^2\frac{v}{2} = \frac{1 - \cos v}{1 + \cos v}.$$

If we take the square root of both sides of the latter equations and use the fact that $\sqrt{a^2} = |a|$ for every real number a, the following identities result. They are called *half-angle formulas* because of the expression $v/2$ which appears.

**Half-Angle
Formulas**

$$\left|\sin\frac{v}{2}\right| = \sqrt{\frac{1-\cos v}{2}}$$

$$\left|\cos\frac{v}{2}\right| = \sqrt{\frac{1+\cos v}{2}}$$

$$\left|\tan\frac{v}{2}\right| = \sqrt{\frac{1-\cos v}{1+\cos v}}$$

The absolute value signs may be eliminated if more information is known about $v/2$. For example, if the point $P(v/2)$ on the unit circle U is in either quadrant I or quadrant II (or, equivalently, if the angle determined by $v/2$ lies in one of these quadrants), then $\sin v/2$ is positive and we may write

$$\sin\frac{v}{2} = \sqrt{\frac{1-\cos v}{2}}.$$

However, if $v/2$ leads to a point (or angle) in either quadrant III or quadrant IV, then

$$\sin\frac{v}{2} = -\sqrt{\frac{1-\cos v}{2}}.$$

Similar remarks are true for the other formulas.

An alternative form for $\tan v/2$ can be obtained. Multiplying numerator and denominator of the radicand in the third half-angle formula by $1-\cos v$ gives us

$$\left|\tan\frac{v}{2}\right| = \sqrt{\frac{1-\cos v}{1+\cos v}\cdot\frac{1-\cos v}{1-\cos v}}$$

$$= \sqrt{\frac{(1-\cos v)^2}{\sin^2 v}}$$

$$= \frac{1-\cos v}{|\sin v|}.$$

The absolute value sign is unnecessary in the numerator, since $1-\cos v$ is never negative. It can be shown that $\tan v/2$ and $\sin v$ always have the same sign. For example, if $0 < v < \pi$, then $0 < v/2 < \pi/2$, and hence, both $\sin v$ and $\tan v/2$ are positive. If $\pi < v < 2\pi$, then $\pi/2 < v/2 < \pi$, and hence, both $\sin v$ and $\tan v/2$ are negative. It is possible to generalize these remarks to all values of v for which the expressions $\tan v/2$ and $(1-\cos v)/|\sin v|$ have meaning. This gives us the first of the next two identities. The second identity for $\tan(v/2)$ may be obtained by multiplying numerator and denominator of the radicand in the third half-angle formula by $1+\cos v$.

**Half-Angle
Formulas for
Tangent**

$$\tan\frac{v}{2} = \frac{1-\cos v}{\sin v}, \qquad \tan\frac{v}{2} = \frac{\sin v}{1+\cos v}$$

Example 5   Find the exact values of $\sin 22.5°$ and $\cos 22.5°$.

Solution   Using the formula for $\sin (v/2)$ and the fact that $22.5°$ is in quadrant I, we have

$$\sin 22.5° = \sin \frac{45°}{2} = \sqrt{\frac{1 - \cos 45°}{2}}$$

$$= \sqrt{\frac{1 - \sqrt{2}/2}{2}}$$

$$= \frac{\sqrt{2 - \sqrt{2}}}{2}$$

$$\cos 22.5° = \sqrt{\frac{1 + \cos 45°}{2}}$$

$$= \sqrt{\frac{1 + \sqrt{2}/2}{2}}$$

$$= \frac{\sqrt{2 + \sqrt{2}}}{2}.$$

∎

Example 6   If $\tan \alpha = -4/3$, where α is in quadrant IV, find $\tan \alpha/2$.

Solution   If we choose the point $(3, -4)$ on the terminal side of α, as illustrated in Figure 3.3, then $\sin \alpha = -4/5$ and $\cos \alpha = 3/5$. (Why?) Applying a half-angle formula, we have

$$\tan \frac{\alpha}{2} = \frac{1 - \cos \alpha}{\sin \alpha} = \frac{1 - \frac{3}{5}}{-\frac{4}{5}} = -\frac{1}{2}.$$

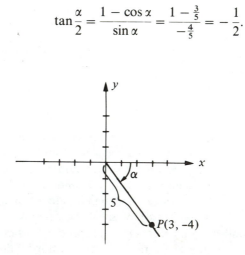

Figure 3.3

∎

Example 7   Find the solutions of the equation $\cos 2x + \cos x = 0$ which are in the interval $[0, 2\pi)$. Express the solutions in both radian measure and degree measure.

Solution   We first use a double-angle formula to write the equation in terms of $\cos x$ and then solve by factoring, as follows:

$$\cos 2x + \cos x = 0$$
$$(2\cos^2 x - 1) + \cos x = 0$$
$$2\cos^2 x + \cos x - 1 = 0$$
$$(2\cos x - 1)(\cos x + 1) = 0.$$

Setting each factor equal to zero, we obtain

$$\cos x = \frac{1}{2} \quad \text{and} \quad \cos x = -1.$$

The solutions of the last two equations (and hence of the given equation) in $[0, 2\pi)$ are

$$\pi/3, \quad 5\pi/3, \quad \text{and} \quad \pi.$$

The corresponding degree measures are

$$60°, \quad 300°, \quad \text{and} \quad 180°. \qquad ■$$

EXERCISES 3.5

In Exercises 1–4, find the exact values of $\sin 2\theta$, $\cos 2\theta$, and $\tan 2\theta$ subject to the given conditions.

1 $\cos \theta = \frac{3}{5}$ and θ acute

2 $\cot \theta = \frac{4}{3}$ and $180° < \theta < 270°$

3 $\sec \theta = -3$ and $90° < \theta < 180°$

4 $\sin \theta = -\frac{4}{5}$ and $270° < \theta < 360°$

In Exercises 5–8, find the exact values of $\sin \theta/2$, $\cos \theta/2$, and $\tan \theta/2$ subject to the given conditions.

5 $\sec \theta = \frac{5}{4}$ and θ acute

6 $\csc \theta = -\frac{5}{3}$ and $-90° < \theta < 0°$

7 $\tan \theta = 1$ and $-180° < \theta < -90°$

8 $\sec \theta = -4$ and $180° < \theta < 270°$

In Exercises 9 and 10, use half-angle formulas to find exact values for the given numbers.

9 (a) $\cos 67°30'$ (b) $\sin 15°$
   (c) $\tan 3\pi/8$

10 (a) $\cos 165°$ (b) $\sin 157°30'$
    (c) $\tan \pi/8$

Verify the identities stated in Exercises 11–28.

11 $\sin 10\theta = 2\sin 5\theta \cos 5\theta$

12 $\cos^2 3x - \sin^2 3x = \cos 6x$

13 $4\sin \dfrac{x}{2} \cos \dfrac{x}{2} = 2\sin x$

14 $\dfrac{\sin^2 2\alpha}{\sin^2 \alpha} = 4 - 4\sin^2 \alpha$

15 $(\sin t + \cos t)^2 = 1 + \sin 2t$

16 $\csc 2u = \frac{1}{2}\sec u \csc u$

17 $\sin 3u = \sin u(3 - 4\sin^2 u)$

18 $\sin 4t = 4\cos t \sin t(1 - 2\sin^2 t)$

19 $\cos 4\theta = 8\cos^4 \theta - 8\cos^2 \theta + 1$

20 $\cos 6t = 32\cos^6 t - 48\cos^4 t + 18\cos^2 t - 1$

21 $\sin^4 t = \frac{3}{8} - \frac{1}{2}\cos 2t + \frac{1}{8}\cos 4t$

22 $\cos^4 x - \sin^4 x = \cos 2x$

23 $\sec 2\theta = \dfrac{\sec^2 \theta}{2 - \sec^2 \theta}$

24 $\cot 2u = \dfrac{\cot^2 u - 1}{2 \cot u}$

25 $2 \sin^2 2t + \cos 4t = 1$

26 $\tan \theta + \cot \theta = 2 \csc 2\theta$

27 $\tan 3u = \dfrac{(3 - \tan^2 u) \tan u}{1 - 3 \tan^2 u}$

28 $\dfrac{1 + \sin 2v + \cos 2v}{1 + \sin 2v - \cos 2v} = \cot v$

Write the expressions in Exercises 29 and 30 in terms of values of cos with exponent 1.

29 $\cos^4 (\theta/2)$ **30** $\sin^4 2x$

In Exercises 31–38, find all solutions of the given equations in the interval $[0, 2\pi)$. Express the solutions in both radian measure and degree measure.

31 $\sin 2t + \sin t = 0$ **32** $\cos t - \sin 2t = 0$

33 $\cos u + \cos 2u = 0$ **34** $\cos 2\theta - \tan \theta = 1$

35 $\tan 2x = \tan x$ **36** $\tan 2t - 2 \cos t = 0$

37 $\sin \frac{1}{2}u + \cos u = 1$ **38** $2 - \cos^2 x$
$\qquad\qquad\qquad\qquad\qquad = 4 \sin^2 \frac{1}{2}x.$

39 If $a > 0$, $b > 0$, and $0 < u < \pi/2$, prove that

$$a \sin u + b \cos u = \sqrt{a^2 + b^2} \sin (u + v)$$

where $0 < v < \pi/2$, $\sin v = b/\sqrt{a^2 + b^2}$, and $\cos v = a/\sqrt{a^2 + b^2}$.

40 Use Exercise 39 to express $8 \sin u + 15 \cos u$ in the form $c \sin (u + v)$.

CALCULATOR EXERCISES 3.5

1 Approximate $\sin 2\theta$ if θ is a fourth-quadrant angle and $\sin \theta = -0.4637$.

2 Approximate $\cos (\theta/2)$ if θ is a third-quadrant angle and $\tan \theta = 3.8105$.

In each of Exercises 3–6, demonstrate, by direct calculations, that the indicated formula is true for the stated value of x.

3 $\sin 2x = 2 \sin x \cos x;\ \ x = 3.624$

4 $\cos 2x = \cos^2 x - \sin^2 x;\ \ x = \sqrt{2\pi + e^{\sqrt{7}}}$

5 $\tan 2x = 2 \tan x/(1 - \tan^2 x);\ \ x = \log (13.6)^5$

6 $|\sin (x/2)| = \sqrt{(1 - \cos x)/2}\,;\ \ x = \tan 0.1634$

3.6 PRODUCT AND FACTORING FORMULAS

The following identities may be used to change the form of certain trigonometric expressions.

Product Formulas

$$\sin (u + v) + \sin (u - v) = 2 \sin u \cos v$$
$$\sin (u + v) - \sin (u - v) = 2 \cos u \sin v$$
$$\cos (u + v) + \cos (u - v) = 2 \cos u \cos v$$
$$\cos (u - v) - \cos (u + v) = 2 \sin u \sin v$$

Each of these identities is a consequence of our work in Section 3.4. For example, to verify the first product formula, we merely add the left- and right-hand sides of the identities we obtained for $\sin(u + v)$ and $\sin(u - v)$. The remaining product formulas are obtained in similar fashion.

By starting with the expression on the *right* side of each product formula, we can express certain products as sums, as illustrated in the next example.

Example 1 Express each of the following as a sum.

(a) $\sin 4\theta \cos 3\theta$ (b) $\sin 3x \sin x$

Solution

(a) Using the first product formula with $u = 4\theta$ and $v = 3\theta$ gives us

$$2 \sin 4\theta \cos 3\theta = \sin(4\theta + 3\theta) + \sin(4\theta - 3\theta)$$

or
$$\sin 4\theta \cos 3\theta = \tfrac{1}{2} \sin 7\theta + \tfrac{1}{2} \sin \theta.$$

This relationship could also have been obtained by using the second product formula.

(b) Using the fourth product formula with $u = 3x$ and $v = x$ gives us

$$2 \sin 3x \sin x = \cos(3x - x) - \cos(3x + x)$$

or
$$\sin 3x \sin x = \tfrac{1}{2} \cos 2x - \tfrac{1}{2} \cos 4x. \qquad \blacksquare$$

The product formulas may also be employed to express a sum as a product. In order to obtain a form that can be applied more easily, we shall change the notation as follows. If we let

$$u + v = a \quad \text{and} \quad u - v = b$$

then $(u + v) + (u - v) = a + b$, which simplifies to

$$u = \frac{a + b}{2}.$$

Similarly, from $(u + v) - (u - v) = a - b$ we obtain

$$v = \frac{a - b}{2}.$$

If we now substitute for $u + v$ and $u - v$ on the left sides of the product formulas, and for u and v on the right sides, we obtain the following.

Factoring Formulas

$$\sin a + \sin b = 2 \sin \frac{a + b}{2} \cos \frac{a - b}{2}$$

$$\sin a - \sin b = 2 \cos \frac{a + b}{2} \sin \frac{a - b}{2}$$

$$\cos a + \cos b = 2 \cos \frac{a + b}{2} \cos \frac{a - b}{2}$$

$$\cos b - \cos a = 2 \sin \frac{a + b}{2} \sin \frac{a - b}{2}$$

Example 2   Express $\sin 5x - \sin 3x$ as a product.

Solution   Using the second factoring formula with $a = 5x$ and $b = 3x$,

$$\sin 5x - \sin 3x = 2 \cos \frac{5x + 3x}{2} \sin \frac{5x - 3x}{2}$$

$$= 2 \cos 4x \sin x.$$ ∎

Example 3   Verify the identity $\dfrac{\sin 3t + \sin 5t}{\cos 3t - \cos 5t} = \cot t.$

Solution   Using the first and fourth factoring formulas,

$$\frac{\sin 3t + \sin 5t}{\cos 3t - \cos 5t} = \frac{2 \sin \dfrac{3t + 5t}{2} \cos \dfrac{3t - 5t}{2}}{2 \sin \dfrac{5t + 3t}{2} \sin \dfrac{5t - 3t}{2}}$$

$$= \frac{2 \sin 4t \cos (-t)}{2 \sin 4t \sin t}$$

$$= \frac{\cos (-t)}{\sin t}$$

$$= \frac{\cos t}{\sin t}$$

$$= \cot t.$$ ∎

Example 4   Find the solutions of the equation $\cos t - \sin 2t - \cos 3t = 0$.

Solution   Using the fourth factoring formula,

$$\cos t - \cos 3t = 2 \sin \frac{3t + t}{2} \sin \frac{3t - t}{2}$$

$$= 2 \sin 2t \sin t.$$

Hence, the given equation is equivalent to

$$2 \sin 2t \sin t - \sin 2t = 0$$

or to $$\sin 2t(2 \sin t - 1) = 0.$$

Thus, the solutions of the given equation are the solutions of

$$\sin 2t = 0 \quad \text{and} \quad \sin 2t = \frac{1}{2}.$$

The first of these equations has the solution

$$2t = n\pi \quad \text{or} \quad t = \frac{\pi}{2}n$$

where n is any integer. The second equation has solutions

$$t = \frac{\pi}{6} + 2n\pi \quad \text{and} \quad t = \frac{5\pi}{6} + 2n\pi$$

where n is any integer. ∎

The addition formulas may also be employed to derive the so-called **reduction formulas**. The latter formulas can be used to write expressions such as

$$\sin\left(\theta + n\cdot\frac{\pi}{2}\right) \quad \text{and} \quad \cos\left(\theta + n\cdot\frac{\pi}{2}\right)$$

where n is any integer, in terms of only $\sin\theta$ or $\cos\theta$. Similar formulas are true for the other trigonometric functions. Instead of deriving general reduction formulas, we shall illustrate several special cases in the next example.

Example 5 Express $\sin(\theta - 3\pi/2)$ and $\cos(\theta + \pi)$ in terms of a function of θ.

Solution We may proceed as follows.

$$\sin\left(\theta - \frac{3\pi}{2}\right) = \sin\theta\cos\frac{3\pi}{2} - \cos\theta\sin\frac{3\pi}{2}$$
$$= \sin\theta\cdot(0) - \cos\theta\cdot(-1)$$
$$= \cos\theta$$
$$\cos(\theta + \pi) = \cos\theta\cos\pi - \sin\theta\sin\pi$$
$$= \cos\theta\cdot(-1) - \sin\theta\cdot(0)$$
$$= -\cos\theta.$$
∎

We have derived many important identities thus far in this chapter. In order to make them readily available for reference, they are listed on the inside of the covers of the text.

EXERCISES 3.6

In each of Exercises 1–8, express the product as a sum or difference.

1 $2\sin 9\theta\cos 3\theta$

2 $2\cos 5\theta\sin 5\theta$

3 $\sin 7t\sin 3t$

4 $\sin(-4x)\cos 8x$

5 $\cos 6u\cos(-4u)$

6 $\sin 4t\sin 6t$

7 $3\cos x\sin 2x$

8 $5\cos u\sin 5u$

In each of Exercises 9–16, write the expression as a product.

9 $\sin 6\theta + \sin 2\theta$

10 $\sin 4\theta - \sin 8\theta$

11 $\cos 5x - \cos 3x$

12 $\cos 5t + \cos 6t$

13 $\sin 3t - \sin 7t$

14 $\cos \theta - \cos 5\theta$

15 $\cos x + \cos 2x$

16 $\sin 8t + \sin 2t$

Verify the identities in Exercises 17–24.

17 $\dfrac{\sin 4t + \sin 6t}{\cos 4t - \cos 6t} = \cot t$

18 $\dfrac{\sin \theta + \sin 3\theta}{\cos \theta + \cos 3\theta} = \tan 2\theta$

19 $\dfrac{\sin u + \sin v}{\cos u + \cos v} = \tan \dfrac{u + v}{2}$

20 $\dfrac{\sin u - \sin v}{\cos u - \cos v} = -\cot \dfrac{u + v}{2}$

21 $\dfrac{\sin u - \sin v}{\sin u + \sin v} = \dfrac{\tan \frac{1}{2}(u - v)}{\tan \frac{1}{2}(u + v)}$

22 $\dfrac{\cos u - \cos v}{\cos u + \cos v} = \tan \frac{1}{2}(u + v)\tan \frac{1}{2}(u - v)$

23 $\sin 2x + \sin 4x + \sin 6x = 4\cos x \cos 2x \sin 3x$

24 $\dfrac{\cos t + \cos 4t + \cos 7t}{\sin t + \sin 4t + \sin 7t} = \cot 4t$

25 Express $(\sin ax)(\cos bx)$ as a sum.

26 Express $(\cos mu)(\cos nu)$ as a sum.

In Exercises 27–30, find the solutions of the given equations.

27 $\sin 5t + \sin 3t = 0$

28 $\sin t + \sin 3t = \sin 2t$

29 $\cos x = \cos 3x$

30 $\cos 4x - \cos 3x = 0$

In Exercises 31–36, verify the given reduction formulas by using addition formulas.

31 $\sin (\theta + \pi) = -\sin \theta$

32 $\sin \left(\theta + \dfrac{3\pi}{2}\right) = -\cos \theta$

33 $\cos \left(\theta - \dfrac{5\pi}{2}\right) = \sin \theta$

34 $\cos (\theta - 3\pi) = -\cos \theta$

35 $\tan (\pi - \theta) = -\tan \theta$

$\left(Hint: \tan (\pi - \theta) = \dfrac{\sin (\pi - \theta)}{\cos (\pi - \theta)}\right)$

36 $\tan (\theta + \pi/2) = -\cot \theta$

CALCULATOR EXERCISES 3.6

1 Demonstrate, by direct calculations, that the first product formula is true if $u = 4.631$ and $v = -8.059$.

2 Demonstrate that the first factoring formula is true if $a = 10^{\sqrt{148}}$ and $b = \log 735$.

3.7 THE INVERSE TRIGONOMETRIC FUNCTIONS

Suppose f is a *one-to-one function* with domain A and range B. As mentioned in Section 1.4, this implies that each element of B is the image of precisely one element of A. Another way of phrasing this is to state that for each element u in B there is one and only one element v in A such that $f(v) = u$. In this case we can define a function g *from B to A* by letting $g(u) = v$. This amounts to *reversing* the correspondence given by f. If f is represented by drawing arrows from A to B, as in (i) of Figure 3.4, then g can be represented by simply *reversing* these arrows, as in (ii) of the figure. The function g

obtained in this manner is called the **inverse function** of f and is often denoted by f^{-1}. Since f^{-1} *reverses* the correspondence from A to B given by f, we have

$$v = f^{-1}(u) \quad \text{if and only if} \quad f(v) = u$$

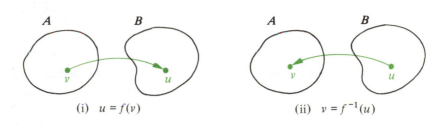

(i) $u = f(v)$ (ii) $v = f^{-1}(u)$

Figure 3.4

for every u in B and v in A. The -1 used in this notation should not be confused with the exponent -1 used for real numbers. It is employed here merely as a notation for denoting inverse functions.

Since the notation for the variables is immaterial, we shall use the traditional symbols x and y, and write

(I)
$$\boxed{y = f^{-1}(x) \quad \text{if and only if} \quad f(y) = x}$$

for every x in the domain of f^{-1} and every y in the domain of f. Note that if we begin with $f^{-1}(x) = y$, then $x = f(y)$, and substitution of $f(y)$ for x in the first equation gives us $f^{-1}(f(y)) = y$. In like manner, if we begin with $f(y) = x$, then $y = f^{-1}(x)$, and substitution of $f^{-1}(x)$ for y in the first of *these* equations gives us $f(f^{-1}(x)) = x$. This establishes the following identities.

(II)
$$\boxed{\begin{aligned} f^{-1}(f(y)) &= y \text{ for every } y \text{ in the domain of } f \\ f(f^{-1}(x)) &= x \text{ for every } x \text{ in the domain of } f^{-1} \end{aligned}}$$

Since the trigonometric functions are not one-to-one, they do not have inverse functions. However, by restricting the domains, it is possible to obtain functions that behave in the same way as the trigonometric functions (over the smaller domains) and that do possess inverse functions. Given a trigonometric function, we shall choose a subset S of the domain throughout which the function is either increasing or decreasing, since this will guarantee the existence of an inverse. Of course, we must also choose S in such a way that the function takes on all of its values.

Let us first consider the sine function, whose domain is $\mathbb{R}$ and range is the set of real numbers in the interval $[-1, 1]$. The sine function is not one-to-one, since, for example, numbers such as $\pi/6$, $5\pi/6$, and $-7\pi/6$ give rise to the same functional value, $1/2$. If we restrict y to the interval $[-\pi/2, \pi/2]$, then as y varies from $-\pi/2$ to $\pi/2$, $\sin y$ takes on each value between -1 and 1 once and only once. Hence, the new function obtained by restricting the domain to $[-\pi/2, \pi/2]$ has an inverse function. Applying the relationship in (I) leads to the following definition.

Definition

> The **inverse sine function**, denoted by $\sin^{-1}$, is defined by
>
> $$y = \sin^{-1}x \quad \text{if and only if} \quad \sin y = x$$
>
> where $-1 \leq x \leq 1$ and $-\pi/2 \leq y \leq \pi/2$.

It is also customary to refer to $\sin^{-1}$ as the **arcsine function** and to use the notation arcsin x in place of $\sin^{-1} x$. The expression arcsin x is used because if $y = $ arcsin x, then $\sin y = x$, that is, y is a number (or an *arc*length) whose sine is x. Since both notations $\sin^{-1}$ and arcsin are commonly used in mathematics and its applications, we shall employ both of them in our work. Note that by definition we have

$$-\frac{\pi}{2} \leq \sin^{-1}x \leq \frac{\pi}{2}$$

or, equivalently,
$$-\frac{\pi}{2} \leq \text{arcsin } x \leq \frac{\pi}{2}.$$

Example 1 Sketch the graph of $y = \sin^{-1}x$.

Solution By definition, the graph of $y = \sin^{-1} x$ is the same as the graph of $\sin y = x$, except that the variables are restricted as follows:

$$-\frac{\pi}{2} \leq y \leq \frac{\pi}{2} \quad \text{and} \quad -1 \leq x \leq 1.$$

Several coordinates of points on the graph are given in the following table.

y	$-\dfrac{\pi}{2}$	$-\dfrac{\pi}{3}$	$-\dfrac{\pi}{6}$	0	$\dfrac{\pi}{6}$	$\dfrac{\pi}{3}$	$\dfrac{\pi}{2}$
x	-1	$-\dfrac{\sqrt{3}}{2}$	$-\dfrac{1}{2}$	0	$\dfrac{1}{2}$	$\dfrac{\sqrt{3}}{2}$	1

The graph is sketched in Figure 3.5.

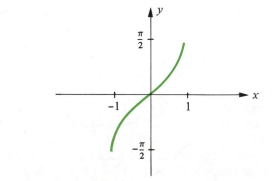

Figure 3.5 $y = $ arcsin $x = \sin^{-1} x$

Using the relationships stated in (II) gives us the following important identities:

$$\sin^{-1}(\sin y) = y \quad \text{if} \quad -\frac{\pi}{2} \le y \le \frac{\pi}{2}$$

$$\sin(\sin^{-1} x) = x \quad \text{if} \quad -1 \le x \le 1.$$

These may also be written in the form

$$\arcsin(\sin y) = y \quad \text{and} \quad \sin(\arcsin x) = x$$

provided that y and x are suitably restricted.

Example 2   Find $\sin^{-1}(\sqrt{2}/2)$ and $\arcsin(-1/2)$.

Solution   If $y = \sin^{-1}(\sqrt{2}/2)$, then $\sin y = \sqrt{2}/2$, and consequently, $y = \pi/4$. Note that it is essential to choose y in the interval $[-\pi/2, \pi/2]$. A number such as $3\pi/4$ is incorrect, even though $\sin(3\pi/4) = \sqrt{2}/2$.

In like manner, if $y = \arcsin(-1/2)$, then $\sin y = -1/2$. Since, by definition, we must choose y in the interval $[-\pi/2, \pi/2]$, it follows that $y = -\pi/6$.   ■

Example 3   Find $\sin^{-1}(\tan 3\pi/4)$.

Solution   If we let

$$y = \sin^{-1}\left(\tan\frac{3\pi}{4}\right) = \sin^{-1}(-1)$$

then, by definition, $\sin y = -1.$

Consequently, $y = -\pi/2$.   ■

The other trigonometric functions may also be used to introduce inverse functions. The procedure is first to determine a convenient subset of the domain so that a one-to-one function is obtained and then to apply the formulas in (I).

If the domain of the cosine function is restricted to the interval $[0, \pi]$ and if y increases from 0 to π, then $\cos y$ decreases and takes on each value between -1 and 1 once and only once. This leads to the following.

Definition

The **inverse cosine function**, denoted by $\cos^{-1}$, is defined by

$$y = \cos^{-1} x \quad \text{if and only if} \quad \cos y = x$$

where $-1 \le x \le 1$ and $0 \le y \le \pi$.

The inverse cosine function is also referred to as the **arccosine function**, and the notation $\arccos x$ is used interchangeably with $\cos^{-1} x$.

Applying the formulas in (II), we see that if $0 \leq y \leq \pi$ and $-1 \leq x \leq 1$, then

$$\cos{(\cos^{-1}x)} = \cos{(\arccos x)} = x$$
$$\cos^{-1}{(\cos y)} = \arccos{(\cos y)} = y.$$

By definition, the graph of $y = \cos^{-1}x$ is the same as the graph of $\cos y = x$, where $0 \leq y \leq \pi$. It is left as an exercise to verify that the graph has the appearance indicated in Figure 3.6.

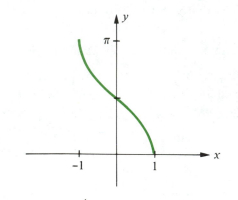

Figure 3.6 $y = \arccos x = \cos^{-1}x$

Example 4

(a) Find $\cos^{-1}(-\sqrt{3}/2)$.

(b) Approximate $\cos^{-1}(-0.7951)$.

Solution

(a) If we let $y = \cos^{-1}(-\sqrt{3}/2)$, then $\cos y = -\sqrt{3}/2$. The reference number for y is $\pi/6$. (Why?) By definition, y must be chosen in the interval $[0, \pi]$, and hence, $y = \pi - (\pi/6) = 5\pi/6$. Thus,

$$\cos^{-1}(-\sqrt{3}/2) = 5\pi/6.$$

(b) If $y = \cos^{-1}(-0.7951)$, then $\cos y = -0.7951$. If y' is the reference number for y, then $\cos y' = 0.7951$. From Table 2 we see that $y' \approx 0.6516$. According to the definition of the inverse cosine function, y must be chosen between 0 and π. Hence,

$$y = \pi - y' \approx 3.1416 - 0.6516.$$

That is, $\cos^{-1}(-0.7951) \approx 2.4900.$ ∎

If we restrict the domain of the tangent function to the open interval $(-\pi/2, \pi/2)$, then a one-to-one correspondence is obtained. We may, therefore, adopt the following definition.

Definition

> The **inverse tangent function** or **arctangent function**, denoted by $\tan^{-1}$ or arctan, is defined by
>
> $$y = \tan^{-1} x = \arctan x \quad \text{if and only if} \quad \tan y = x$$
>
> where x is any real number and $-\pi/2 < y < \pi/2$.

Note that the domain of the arctangent function is all of $\mathbb{R}$ and the range is the open interval $(-\pi/2, \pi/2)$. In Exercise 42 you are asked to verify the graph of the inverse tangent function sketched in Figure 3.7.

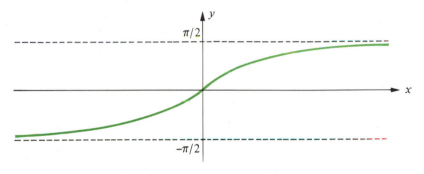

Figure 3.7 $y = \tan^{-1} x = \arctan x$

An analogous procedure may be used for the remaining trigonometric functions. The functions we have defined are generally referred to as the **inverse trigonometric functions**.

Example 5   Without using tables or calculators, find $\sec(\arctan \frac{2}{3})$.

Solution   If $y = \arctan \frac{2}{3}$, then $\tan y = \frac{2}{3}$. Since $\sec^2 y = 1 + \tan^2 y$ and $0 < y < \pi/2$, we may write

$$\sec y = \sqrt{1 + \tan^2 y} = \sqrt{1 + \left(\frac{2}{3}\right)^2}$$

$$= \sqrt{1 + \frac{4}{9}} = \sqrt{\frac{13}{9}} = \frac{\sqrt{13}}{3}.$$

Hence, $\sec(\arctan \frac{2}{3}) = \sec y = \sqrt{13}/3.$ ∎

The next three examples illustrate some of the manipulations that can be carried out with the inverse trigonometric functions.

Example 6   Evaluate $\sin(\arctan\frac{1}{2} - \arccos\frac{4}{5})$.

Solution   If we let $u = \arctan\frac{1}{2}$ and $v = \arccos\frac{4}{5}$, then $\tan u = \frac{1}{2}$ and $\cos v = \frac{4}{5}$. We wish to find $\sin(u - v)$. Since u and v are in the interval $(0, \pi/2)$, they may be considered as the radian measure of positive acute angles, and other functional values of u and v may be found by referring to the right triangles in Figure 3.8. This gives us $\sin u = 1/\sqrt{5}$, $\cos u = 2/\sqrt{5}$, and $\sin v = \frac{3}{5}$. Consequently,

$$\sin(u - v) = \sin u \cos v - \cos u \sin v$$

$$= \frac{1}{\sqrt{5}}\frac{4}{5} - \frac{2}{\sqrt{5}}\frac{3}{5}$$

$$= \frac{-2}{5\sqrt{5}} = \frac{-2\sqrt{5}}{25}.$$

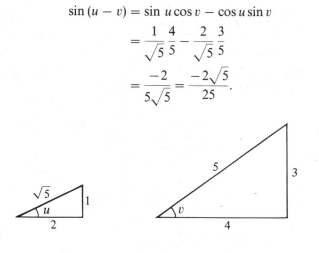

Figure 3.8

Example 7   Write $\cos(\sin^{-1}x)$ as an algebraic expression in x.

Solution   Let $y = \sin^{-1}x$, so that $\sin y = x$. We wish to find $\cos y$. Since $-\pi/2 \le y \le \pi/2$, it follows that $\cos y \ge 0$, and hence,

$$\cos y = \sqrt{1 - \sin^2 y} = \sqrt{1 - x^2}.$$

Consequently, $\cos(\sin^{-1}x) = \sqrt{1 - x^2}.$

Example 8   Verify the identity

$$\frac{1}{2}\cos^{-1}x = \tan^{-1}\sqrt{\frac{1 - x}{1 + x}}$$

where $|x| < 1$.

Solution   Let $y = \cos^{-1}x$. We wish to show that

$$\frac{y}{2} = \tan^{-1}\sqrt{\frac{1 - x}{1 + x}}.$$

By a half-angle formula (see Section 3.5),

$$\left|\tan\frac{y}{2}\right| = \sqrt{\frac{1 - \cos y}{1 + \cos y}}.$$

Since $y = \cos^{-1} x$ and $|x| < 1$, it follows that $0 < y < \pi$ and hence that $0 < (y/2) < \pi/2$. Consequently, $\tan(y/2) > 0$, and we may drop the absolute value sign, obtaining

$$\tan \frac{y}{2} = \sqrt{\frac{1 - \cos y}{1 + \cos y}}.$$

Using the fact that $\cos y = x$ gives us

$$\tan \frac{y}{2} = \sqrt{\frac{1 - x}{1 + x}}$$

or, equivalently,

$$\frac{y}{2} = \tan^{-1} \sqrt{\frac{1 - x}{1 + x}}$$

which is what we wished to show. ∎

Most of the trigonometric equations considered in Section 3.3 had solutions that were rational multiples of π, such as $\pi/3$, $3\pi/4$, π, and so on. If solutions are not of that type, we can sometimes use inverse functions to express them in exact form, as illustrated in the next example.

Example 9 Find the solutions of the equation

$$5 \sin^2 t + 3 \sin t - 1 = 0$$

which are in the interval $[-\pi/2, \pi/2]$.

Solution The given equation may be regarded as a quadratic equation in $\sin t$. Applying the Quadratic Formula gives us

$$\sin t = \frac{-3 \pm \sqrt{9 + 20}}{10} = \frac{-3 \pm \sqrt{29}}{10}.$$

Hence, by the definition of the inverse sine function, with $v = t$ and $u = (-3 \pm \sqrt{29})/10$, we obtain the solutions

$$t = \sin^{-1} \frac{1}{10}(-3 + \sqrt{29})$$

and

$$t = \sin^{-1} \frac{1}{10}(-3 - \sqrt{29}).$$ ∎

If approximations to the solutions in Example 9 are desired, one may refer to Table 2. If a calculator is available, the task is much simpler. To illustrate, using a typical calculator we first calculate

$$\frac{1}{10}(-3 + \sqrt{29}) \approx 0.2385.$$

If we next press the inverse sine key, the result is

$$t \approx \sin^{-1}(0.2385) \approx 0.2408.$$

In like manner,

$$t = \sin^{-1}\frac{1}{10}(-3 - \sqrt{29}) \approx \sin^{-1}(-0.8385) \approx -0.9946.$$

EXERCISES 3.7

Find the numbers in Exercises 1–10 without the use of tables or calculators.

1 (a) $\sin^{-1}(1/2)$ (b) $\cos^{-1}(1/2)$

2 (a) $\sin^{-1}\sqrt{3}/2$ (b) $\sin^{-1}(-\sqrt{3}/2)$

3 (a) $\arcsin 0$ (b) $\arccos 0$

4 (a) $\cos^{-1}\sqrt{2}/2$ (b) $\cos^{-1}(-\sqrt{2}/2)$

5 (a) $\arcsin 1$ (b) $\arccos 1$

6 (a) $\sin^{-1}(-1)$ (b) $\cos^{-1}(-1)$

7 (a) $\tan^{-1}\sqrt{3}$ (b) $\arctan(-\sqrt{3})$

8 (a) $\tan^{-1}(-1)$ (b) $\arccos(-1/2)$

9 (a) $\arcsin(-\sqrt{2}/2)$ (b) $\tan^{-1}(-\sqrt{3}/3)$

10 (a) $\tan^{-1}0$ (b) $\arctan 1$

In Exercises 11–14, use Table 2 to approximate the given numbers.

11 $\sin^{-1}(-0.6494)$ 12 $\cos^{-1}(-0.9112)$

13 $\arctan(2.1775)$ 14 $\arcsin(0.8004)$

Determine the numbers in Exercises 15–26 without the use of tables or calculators.

15 $\sin[\cos^{-1}\frac{1}{2}]$ 16 $\cos[\sin^{-1}0]$

17 $\sin[\arccos\frac{4}{5}]$ 18 $\tan[\tan^{-1}5]$

19 $\arcsin(\sin 5\pi/4)$

20 $\cos^{-1}(\cos 3\pi/4)$

21 $\cos[\sin^{-1}\frac{4}{5} + \tan^{-1}\frac{3}{4}]$

22 $\sin[\arcsin\frac{1}{2} + \arccos 0]$

23 $\tan[\arctan\frac{4}{3} + \arccos\frac{8}{17}]$

24 $\cos[2\sin^{-1}\frac{15}{17}]$

25 $\sin[2\arccos(-\frac{3}{5})]$

26 $\cos[\frac{1}{2}\tan^{-1}\frac{8}{15}]$

In each of Exercises 27–30, rewrite the given expression as an algebraic expression in u.

27 $\sin(\tan^{-1}x)$ 28 $\tan(\arccos x)$

29 $\cos(\frac{1}{2}\arccos x)$ 30 $\cos(2\tan^{-1}x)$

Verify the identities in Exercises 31–38.

31 $\sin^{-1}x + \cos^{-1}x = \pi/2$
(*Hint:* Let $\alpha = \sin^{-1}x$, $\beta = \cos^{-1}x$, and consider $\sin(\alpha + \beta)$.)

32 $\arctan x + \arctan(1/x) = \pi/2$, where $x > 0$

33 $\arcsin\dfrac{2x}{1 + x^2} = 2\arctan x$, where $|x| < 1$

34    $2\cos^{-1}x = \cos^{-1}(2x^2 - 1)$, where $0 \le x \le 1$

35    $\arcsin(-x) = -\arcsin x$

36    $\arccos(-x) = \pi - \arccos x$

37    $\sin^{-1}x = \tan^{-1}\dfrac{x}{\sqrt{1 - x^2}}$

38    $\tan^{-1}u + \tan^{-1}v = \tan^{-1}\dfrac{u + v}{1 - uv}$,   where $|u| < 1$ and $|v| < 1$

39   Define $\cot^{-1}$ by restricting the domain of cot to the interval $(0, \pi)$.

40   Define $\sec^{-1}$ by restricting the domain of sec to $[0, \pi/2) \cup [\pi, 3\pi/2)$.

41   Verify the sketch in Figure 3.6.

42   Verify the sketch in Figure 3.7.

Sketch the graphs of the equations in Exercises 43–52.

43    $y = \sin^{-1}2x$ 44 $y = \cos^{-1}(x/2)$

45    $y = \frac{1}{2}\sin^{-1}x$ 46 $y = 2\cos^{-1}x$

47    $y = 2\tan^{-1}x$ 48 $y = \tan^{-1}2x$

49    $y = 2 + \tan^{-1}x$ 50 $y = \sin^{-1}(x + 1)$

51    $y = \sin(\arccos x)$ 52 $y = \sin(\sin^{-1}x)$

Prove that the equations in Exercises 53 and 54 are not identities.

53    $\tan^{-1}x = \dfrac{1}{\tan x}$

54    $(\arcsin x)^2 + (\arccos x)^2 = 1$

In each of Exercises 55–60, use inverse trigonometric functions to state the solutions of the given equation in the given interval.

55    $2\tan^2 t + 9\tan t + 3 = 0$; $(-\pi/2, \pi/2)$

56    $3\sin^2 t + 7\sin t + 3 = 0$; $[-\pi/2, \pi/2]$

57    $15\cos^4 x - 14\cos^2 x + 3 = 0$; $[0, \pi]$

58    $3\tan^4 \theta - 19\tan^2 \theta + 2 = 0$; $(-\pi/2, \pi/2)$

59    $6\sin^3 \theta + 18\sin^2 \theta - 5\sin \theta - 15 = 0$; $(-\pi/2, \pi/2)$

60    $6\sin 2x - 8\cos x + 9\sin x - 6 = 0$; $(-\pi/2, \pi/2)$

CALCULATOR EXERCISES 3.7

1–6   Approximate the solutions of the equations in Exercises 55–60 to four decimal places.

7   Show, by actual calculations, that $\sin(\arcsin x) = x$ for the following values of x:
     (a)   0.4631   (b) $\log 3.64$ (c) $1/\sqrt{\pi}$

8   Show that $\tan^{-1}(\tan x) = x$ for the following values of x:
     (a)   74.85   (b) $\log(\pi^2 + 94.7)$
     (c) $10^{6.39}$

Exercises 9 and 10 employ the notation introduced in the Calculator Exercises of Section 2.7. Use a calculator to support the given statements by substituting the following values for t: 0.1, 0.01, 0.001, 0.0001.

9    $\dfrac{\arcsin 2x}{\arcsin x} \to 2$ as $x \to 0^+$

10    $\csc x \tan^{-1}x \to 1$ as $x \to 0^+$

3.8   REVIEW

Concepts

Define or discuss each of the following:

1   The Fundamental Identities

2   Verifying identities

3   Trigonometric equations

4 The addition formulas

5 The double-angle formulas

6 The half-angle formulas

7 The product formulas

8 The factoring formulas

9 Reduction formulas

10 The inverse trigonometric functions

Exercises

Verify the identities in Exercises 1–16.

1 $(\cot^2 x + 1)(1 - \cos^2 x) = 1$

2 $\cos\theta + \sin\theta\tan\theta = \sec\theta$

3 $\dfrac{(\sec^2\theta - 1)\cot\theta}{\tan\theta\sin\theta + \cos\theta} = \sin\theta$

4 $(\tan x + \cot x)^2 = \sec^2 x \csc^2 x$

5 $\dfrac{1}{1 + \sin t} = (\sec t - \tan t)\sec t$

6 $\dfrac{\sin(\alpha - \beta)}{\cos(\alpha + \beta)} = \dfrac{\tan\alpha - \tan\beta}{1 - \tan\alpha\tan\beta}$

7 $\dfrac{2\cot u}{\csc^2 u - 2} = \tan 2u$

8 $\cos^2\dfrac{v}{2} = \dfrac{1 + \sec v}{2\sec v}$

9 $\dfrac{\tan^3\phi - \cot^3\phi}{\tan^2\phi + \csc^2\phi} = \tan\phi - \cot\phi$

10 $\dfrac{\sin u + \sin v}{\csc u + \csc v} = \dfrac{1 - \sin u\sin v}{-1 + \csc u\csc v}$

11 $\cos\left(x - \dfrac{5\pi}{2}\right) = \sin x$

12 $\tan\left(x + \dfrac{3\pi}{4}\right) = \dfrac{\tan x - 1}{\tan x + 1}$

13 $\frac{1}{4}\sin 4\beta = \sin\beta\cos^3\beta - \cos\beta\sin^3\beta$

14 $\tan\frac{1}{2}\theta = \csc\theta - \cot\theta$

15 $\sin 8\theta =$
$8\sin\theta\cos\theta(1 - 2\sin^2\theta)\cdot(1 - 8\sin^2\theta\cos^2\theta)$

16 $\arctan x = \frac{1}{2}\arctan\dfrac{2x}{1 - x^2}$, where $|x| \le 1$

In each of Exercises 17–28, find the solutions of the given equation which are in the interval $[0, 2\pi)$, and also find the degree measure of each solution.

17 $2\cos^3\theta - \cos\theta = 0$

18 $2\cos\alpha + \tan\alpha = \sec\alpha$

19 $\sin\theta = \tan\theta$

20 $\csc^5\theta - 4\csc\theta = 0$

21 $2\cos^3 t + \cos^2 t - 2\cos t - 1 = 0$

22 $\cos x\cot^2 x = \cos x$

23 $\sin\beta + 2\cos^2\beta = 1$

24 $\cos 2x + 3\cos x + 2 = 0$

25 $2\sec u\sin u + 2 = 4\sin u + \sec u$

26 $\sin 2u = \sin u$

27 $2\cos^2\frac{1}{2}\theta - 3\cos\theta = 0$

28 $\sec 2x\csc 2x = 2\csc 2x$

In Exercises 29–32, find the exact values without the use of tables or calculators.

29 $\cos 75°$

30 $\tan 285°$

31 $\sin 195°$

32 $\csc \pi/8$

If θ and ϕ are acute angles such that $\csc\theta = 5/3$ and $\cos\phi = 8/17$, find the numbers in Exercises 33–41 without the use of tables or calculators.

33 $\sin(\theta + \phi)$

34 $\cos(\theta + \phi)$

35 $\tan(\theta - \phi)$

36 $\sin(\phi - \theta)$

37 $\sin 2\phi$

38 $\cos 2\phi$

39 $\tan 2\theta$

40 $\sin\theta/2$

41 $\tan\theta/2$

42 Express $\cos(\alpha + \beta + \gamma)$ in terms of functions of α, β, and γ.

43 Express each of the following products as a sum or difference.
   (a) $\sin 7t \sin 4t$
   (b) $\cos (u/4) \cos (-u/6)$
   (c) $6 \cos 5x \sin 3x$

44 Express each of the following as a product.
   (a) $\sin 8u + \sin 2u$
   (b) $\cos 3\theta - \cos 8\theta$
   (c) $\sin (t/4) - \sin (t/5)$

Find the numbers in Exercises 45–53 without the use of tables or calculators.

45 $\cos^{-1}\left(\dfrac{-\sqrt{3}}{2}\right)$

46 $\sin^{-1}\left(\dfrac{\sqrt{2}}{2}\right)$

47 $\arccos (-1)$

48 $\arctan\left(\dfrac{-\sqrt{3}}{3}\right)$

49 $\sin \arccos\left(\dfrac{-\sqrt{3}}{2}\right)$

50 $\cos\left[\sin^{-1}\dfrac{15}{17} - \sin^{-1}\dfrac{8}{17}\right]$

51 $\cos [2 \sin^{-1}\tfrac{4}{5}]$

52 $\sin [\sin^{-1}\tfrac{2}{3}]$

53 $\cos^{-1} (\sin 0)$

Sketch the graphs of the equations in Exercises 54–56.

54 $y = \cos^{-1} 3x$

55 $y = 4 \sin^{-1} x$

56 $y = 1 - \sin^{-1} x$

OBLIQUE TRIANGLES AND VECTORS

A triangle that does not contain a right angle is referred to as an oblique triangle. *Since it is always possible to divide such triangles into two right triangles, methods developed in Chapter Two may be used for solving them; however, sometimes it is cumbersome to proceed in this manner. In this chapter, formulas are obtained which aid in simplifying solutions of oblique triangles. The last two sections contain a discussion of* vectors.

4.1   THE LAW OF SINES

If two angles and a side of a triangle are known, or if two sides and an angle opposite one of them are known, then the remaining parts of the triangle may be found by means of the formula given in this section. We shall use the letters A, B, C, a, b, c, α, β, and γ for parts of triangles as they were used in Section 2.10. Given triangle ABC, let us place angle α in standard position on a rectangular coordinate system so that B is on the positive x-axis. The case where α is obtuse is illustrated in Figure 4.1. The type of argument we shall give may also be used if α is acute.

Consider the line through C parallel to the y-axis and intersecting the x-axis at point D. Suppose that $d(C, D) = h$, so that the ordinate of C is h. It follows that

$$\sin \alpha = \frac{h}{b} \quad \text{or} \quad h = b \sin \alpha.$$

Referring to triangle BDC, we see that

$$\sin \beta = \frac{h}{a} \quad \text{or} \quad h = a \sin \beta.$$

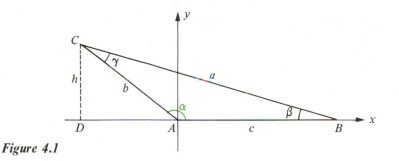

Figure 4.1

Consequently, $a \sin \beta = b \sin \alpha$

which may be written $\dfrac{a}{\sin \alpha} = \dfrac{b}{\sin \beta}.$

If α is taken in standard position, so that C is on the positive x-axis, then by the same reasoning,

$$\frac{a}{\sin \alpha} = \frac{c}{\sin \gamma}.$$

The last two equalities give us the following result.

The Law of Sines

> If ABC is any oblique triangle labeled in the usual manner, then
>
> $$\frac{a}{\sin \alpha} = \frac{b}{\sin \beta} = \frac{c}{\sin \gamma}.$$

The next example illustrates a method of applying the Law of Sines to the case in which two angles and a side of a triangle are known. We shall use the rules for rounding off answers discussed in Section 2.10.

Example 1   Given triangle ABC with $\alpha = 48°20'$, $\gamma = 57°30'$, and $b = 47.3$, approximate the remaining parts.

Solution   The triangle is represented in Figure 4.2. Since the sum of the angles is 180°,

$$\beta = 180° - (57°30' + 48°20') = 74°10'.$$

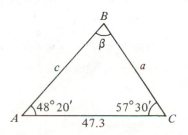

Figure 4.2

Applying the Law of Sines,

$$a = \frac{b \sin \alpha}{\sin \beta} = \frac{(47.3) \sin 48°20'}{\sin 74°10'}.$$

Consulting Table 2, $a \approx \dfrac{(47.3)(0.7470)}{(0.9621)} \approx 36.7.$

Similarly, $c \approx \dfrac{b \sin \gamma}{\sin \beta} = \dfrac{(47.3) \sin 57°30'}{\sin 74°10'}$

$$\approx \frac{(47.3)(0.8434)}{(0.9621)} \approx 41.5. \qquad \blacksquare$$

Data such as those given in Example 1 always give us a unique triangle ABC. However, if two sides and an angle opposite one of them are given, a unique triangle is not always determined. To illustrate, suppose that two numbers a and b are to be lengths of sides of a triangle ABC. In addition, suppose that there is given an angle α which is to be opposite the side of length a. Let us consider the case in which α is acute. Place α in standard position on a rectangular coordinate system and consider the line segment AC of length b on the terminal side of α, as shown in Figure 4.3. The third vertex B should be somewhere on the x-axis. Since the length a of the side opposite α is given, B may be found by striking off a circular arc of length a with center at C. There are four possible outcomes for the construction, as illustrated in Figure 4.4, where the coordinate axes have been deleted.

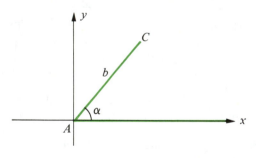

Figure 4.3

The four possibilities may be listed as follows:

(i)   The arc does not intersect the x-axis and no triangle is formed.

(ii)   The arc is tangent to the x-axis and a right triangle is formed.

(iii)   The arc intersects the positive x-axis in two distinct points and two triangles are formed.

(iv)   The arc intersects both the positive and nonpositive parts of the x-axis and one triangle is formed.

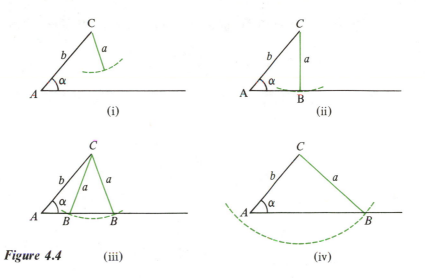

Figure 4.4   (iii)   (iv)

Since the distance from C to the x-axis is $b \sin \alpha$ (Why?), we see that (i) occurs if $a < b \sin \alpha$, (ii) occurs if $a = b \sin \alpha$, (iii) occurs if $b \sin \alpha < a < b$, and (iv) occurs if $a \geq b$. It is unnecessary to memorize these facts, since in any specific problem the case that occurs will become evident when the solution is attempted. For example, in solving the equation

$$\frac{a}{\sin \alpha} = \frac{b}{\sin \beta}$$

suppose that we obtain $|\sin \beta| > 1$. This will indicate that no triangle exists. If the equation $\sin \beta = 1$ is obtained, then $\beta = 90°$ and hence case (ii) occurs. However, if $|\sin \beta| < 1$, then there are two possible choices for the angle β. By checking both possibilities, it will become apparent whether (iii) or (iv) occurs.

If the measure of α is greater than $90°$, then, as in Figure 4.5, a triangle exists if and only if $a > b$. Needless to say, our discussion is independent of the symbols we have used; that is, we might be given b, c, β, or a, c, γ, and so on.

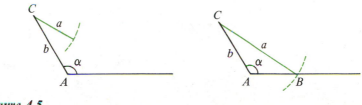

Figure 4.5

Since different possibilities may arise, the case in which two sides and an angle opposite one of them are given is sometimes called the **ambiguous case**.

Example 2 Solve triangle ABC if $\alpha = 67°$, $c = 125$, and $a = 100$.

Solution   Using $\sin \gamma = \dfrac{c \sin \alpha}{a}$, we obtain

$$\sin \gamma = \frac{(125) \sin 67°}{100}$$

$$\approx \frac{(125)(0.9205)}{100}$$

$$\approx 1.1506.$$

Since $\sin \gamma > 1$, there is no triangle with the given parts.   ■

Example 3 Approximate the remaining parts of triangle ABC if $a = 12.4$, $b = 8.7$, and $\beta = 36°40'$.

Solution   Using $\sin \alpha = \dfrac{a \sin \beta}{b}$, we have

$$\sin \alpha = \frac{(12.4) \sin 36°40'}{8.7}$$

$$\approx \frac{(12.4)(0.5972)}{8.7} \approx 0.8512.$$

There are two possible angles α between $0°$ and $180°$ such that $\sin \alpha \approx 0.8512$. If we let α' denote the reference angle for α, then from Table 2 we obtain

$$\alpha' \approx 58°20'.$$

Consequently, the two possibilities for α are

$$\alpha_1 \approx 58°20' \quad \text{and} \quad \alpha_2 \approx 121°40'.$$

If we let γ_1 and γ_2 denote the third angle of the triangle corresponding to the angles α_1 and α_2, respectively, then

$$\gamma_1 \approx 180° - (36°40' + 58°20') = 85°$$

and

$$\gamma_2 \approx 180° - (36°40' + 121°40') = 21°40'.$$

Thus, there are two possible triangles that have the given parts. They are the triangles A_1BC and A_2BC shown in Figure 4.6.

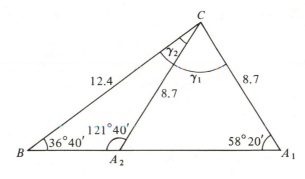

Figure 4.6

If c_1 is the side opposite γ_1 in triangle A_1BC, then

$$c_1 = \frac{a \sin \gamma_1}{\sin \alpha_1}$$

$$c_1 \approx \frac{(12.4) \sin 85°}{\sin 58°20'}$$

$$\approx \frac{(12.4)(0.9962)}{0.8511} \approx 14.5.$$

Hence, the solution for triangle A_1BC is $\alpha_1 \approx 58°20'$, $\gamma_1 \approx 85°$, and $c_1 \approx 14.5$. Similarly, if c_2 is the side opposite angle γ_2 in triangle A_2BC, we have

$$c_2 = \frac{a \sin \gamma_2}{\sin \alpha_2}$$

or

$$c_2 \approx \frac{(12.4) \sin 21°40'}{\sin 121°40'} \approx \frac{(12.4)(0.3692)}{0.8511} \approx 5.4.$$

Consequently, the solution for triangle A_2BC is $\alpha_2 \approx 121°40'$, $\gamma_2 \approx 21°40'$, and $c_2 \approx 5.4$. ∎

EXERCISES 4.1

In each of Exercises 1–12, approximate the remaining parts of triangle ABC.

1 $\alpha = 41°$, $\gamma = 77°$, $a = 10.5$

2 $\beta = 20°$, $\gamma = 31°$, $b = 210$

3 $\alpha = 27°40'$, $\beta = 52°10'$, $a = 32.4$

4 $\alpha = 42°10'$, $\gamma = 61°20'$, $b = 19.7$

5 $\beta = 50°50'$, $\gamma = 70°30'$, $c = 537$

6 $\alpha = 7°10'$, $\beta = 11°40'$, $a = 2.19$

7 $\alpha = 65°10'$, $a = 21.3$, $b = 18.9$

8 $\beta = 30°$, $b = 17.9$, $a = 35.8$

9 $\gamma = 53°20'$, $a = 140$, $c = 115$

10 $\alpha = 27°30'$, $c = 52.8$, $a = 28.1$

11 $\beta = 113°10'$, $b = 248$, $c = 195$

12 $\gamma = 81°$, $c = 11$, $b = 12$

13 It is desired to find the distance between two points A and B lying on opposite banks of a river. A line segment AC of length 240 yards is laid off, and the measure of angles BAC and ACB are found to be $63°20'$ and $54°10'$, respectively. Approximate the distance from A to B.

14 In order to determine the distance between two points A and B, a surveyor chooses a point C which is 375 yards from A and 530 yards from B. If angle BAC has measure $49°30'$, approximate the required distance.

15 When the angle of elevation of the sun is $64°$, a telegraph pole that is tilted at an angle of $12°$ directly away from the sun casts a shadow 34 feet long on level ground. Approximate the length of the pole.

16 A straight road makes an angle of $15°$ with the horizontal. When the angle of elevation of the sun is $57°$, a vertical pole at the side of the road casts a shadow 75 feet long directly down the road. Approximate the length of the pole.

17 The angles of elevation of a balloon from two points A and B on level ground are $24°10'$ and $47°40'$, respectively. If A and B are 8.4 miles apart and the balloon is between A and B in the same vertical plane, approximate the height of the balloon above the ground to the nearest tenth of a mile.

18 An airport A is 480 miles due east of airport B. A pilot flew in the direction $235°$ from A to C and then in the direction $320°$ from C to B. Approximate the total distance the pilot flew, to the nearest mile.

19 A forest ranger at an observation point A sights a fire in the direction N27°10'E. Another ranger at an observation point B, 6.0 miles due east of A, sights the same fire at N52°40'W. Approximate, to the nearest mile, the distance from each observation point to the fire.

20 A surveyor notes that the direction from point A to point B is S63°W and the direction from A to C is S38°W. If the distance from A to B is 239 yards and the distance from B to C is 374 yards, approximate the distance from A to C.

21 A straight road makes an angle of $22°$ with the horizontal. From a certain point P on the road, the angle of elevation of an airplane is $57°$. At the same instant, from another point 100 meters farther up the road, the angle of elevation is $63°$. Approximate, to the nearest meter, the distance from P to the airplane.

22 A point P on level ground is 3.0 km due north of a point Q. If a person jogged in the direction N25°E from Q to a point R, and then from R to P in the direction S40°W, approximate, to the nearest km, the total distance jogged.

CALCULATOR EXERCISES 4.1

In the following, approximate the remaining parts of triangle ABC.

1 $\beta = 25.6°$, $\gamma = 34.7°$, $b = 184.8$

2 $\alpha = 6.24°$, $\beta = 14.08°$, $a = 4.56$

3 $\alpha = 103.45°$, $\gamma = 27.19°$, $b = 38.84$

4 $\gamma = 47.74°$, $a = 131.08$, $c = 97.84$

5 $\beta = 121.624°$, $b = 0.283$, $c = 0.178$

6 $\alpha = 32.32°$, $c = 574.3$, $a = 263.6$

4.2 THE LAW OF COSINES

If two sides and the included angle or the three sides of a triangle are given, then the Law of Sines cannot be applied directly. We may, however, use the following result.

The Law of Cosines

> If ABC is any triangle labeled in the usual manner, then
>
> $$a^2 = b^2 + c^2 - 2bc\cos\alpha$$
> $$b^2 = a^2 + c^2 - 2ac\cos\beta$$
> $$c^2 = a^2 + b^2 - 2ab\cos\gamma.$$

Instead of memorizing each of the formulas given in this law, it is more convenient to remember the following statement, which takes all of them into account.

> The square of the length of any side of a triangle equals the sum of the squares of the lengths of the other two sides minus twice the product of the lengths of the other two sides and the cosine of the angle between them.

We shall use the Distance Formula to establish the Law of Cosines. We again place α in standard position on a rectangular coordinate system, as illustrated in Figure 4.7.

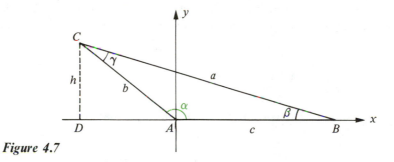

Figure 4.7

Although α is pictured as an obtuse angle, our development is also true if α is acute. Since the segment AB has length c, the coordinates of B are $(c, 0)$. It follows from the Theorem on Trigonometric Functions as Ratios (see Section 2.5) that the coordinates of C are $(b\cos\alpha, b\sin\alpha)$. We also have $a = d(B, C)$, and hence $a^2 = [d(B, C)]^2$. Using the Distance Formula in Section 1.2 leads to the following equations:

$$a^2 = (b\cos\alpha - c)^2 + (b\sin\alpha - 0)^2$$
$$= b^2\cos^2\alpha - 2bc\cos\alpha + c^2 + b^2\sin^2\alpha$$
$$= b^2(\cos^2\alpha + \sin^2\alpha) + c^2 - 2bc\cos\alpha$$
$$= b^2 + c^2 - 2bc\cos\alpha.$$

This gives us the first formula stated in the Law of Cosines. The second and third formulas may be obtained by placing β and γ, respectively, in standard position on a rectangular coordinate system and using a similar procedure.

Example 1 Approximate the remaining parts of triangle ABC if $a = 5.0$, $c = 8.0$, and $\beta = 77°10'$.

Solution Using the Law of Cosines,

$$b^2 = (5.0)^2 + (8.0)^2 - 2(5.0)(8.0)\cos 77°10'$$
$$\approx 25 + 64 - (80)(0.2221)$$
$$\approx 71.2.$$

Consequently, $b \approx \sqrt{71.2} \approx 8.44$.

We next use the Law of Sines to find α. Thus,

$$\sin \alpha = \frac{a \sin \beta}{b} \approx \frac{(5.0)\sin 77°10'}{8.44} \approx \frac{(5.0)(0.9750)}{8.44} \approx 0.5776.$$

Consulting Table 2, we see that $\alpha \approx 35°20'$. Hence,

$$\gamma \approx 180° - (77°10' + 35°20') = 67°30'. \qquad\blacksquare$$

After the length of the third side was found in Example 1, the Law of Sines was used to find a second angle of the triangle. Whenever this procedure is followed, it is best to find the angle opposite the shortest side (as we did), since that angle is always acute. Of course, the Law of Cosines can also be used to find the remaining angles.

Example 2 Given sides $a = 90$, $b = 70$, and $c = 40$ of triangle ABC, approximate angles α, β, and γ.

Solution According to the first formula stated in the Law of Cosines,

$$\cos \alpha = \frac{b^2 + c^2 - a^2}{2bc}$$
$$= \frac{4900 + 1600 - 8100}{5600}$$
$$\approx -0.2857.$$

From Table 2 we see that the reference angle for α is approximately $73°20'$. Hence, $\alpha \approx 180° - 73°20' = 106°40'$.

Similarly, from the second formula stated in the Law of Cosines,

$$\cos \beta = \frac{a^2 + c^2 - b^2}{2ac}$$
$$= \frac{8100 + 1600 - 4900}{7200}$$
$$\approx 0.6667$$

and hence, $\beta \approx 48°10'$. Finally,

$$\gamma \approx 180° - (106°40' + 48°10') = 25°10'. \qquad \blacksquare$$

After finding the first angle in the preceding solution, we could have used the Law of Sines to find a second angle. Whenever this procedure is followed, it is best to use the Law of Cosines to find the angle opposite the longer side, that is, the largest angle of the triangle. This will guarantee that the remaining two angles are acute.

EXERCISES 4.2

In Exercises 1–10, approximate the remaining parts of triangle ABC.

1 $\alpha = 60°$, $b = 20$, $c = 30$

2 $\gamma = 45°$, $b = 10.0$, $a = 15.0$

3 $\beta = 150°$, $a = 150$, $c = 30.0$

4 $\beta = 73°50'$, $c = 14.0$, $a = 87.0$

5 $\gamma = 115°10'$, $a = 1.10$, $b = 2.10$

6 $\alpha = 23°40'$, $c = 4.30$, $b = 70.0$

7 $a = 2.0$, $b = 3.0$, $c = 4.0$

8 $a = 10$, $b = 15$, $c = 12$

9 $a = 25.0$, $b = 80.0$, $c = 60.0$

10 $a = 20.0$, $b = 20.0$, $c = 10.0$

11 A parallelogram has sides of length 30 inches and 70 inches. If one of the angles has measure 65°, approximate the length of each diagonal.

12 The angle at one corner of a triangular plot of ground has measure 73°40'. If the sides that meet at this corner are 175 feet and 150 feet long, approximate the length of the third side.

13 A vertical pole 40 feet tall stands on a hillside that makes an angle of 17° with the horizontal. Approximate the minimal length of rope that will reach from the top of the pole to a point directly down the hill 72 feet from the base of the pole.

14 To find the distance between two points A and B, a surveyor chooses a point C which is 420 yards from A and 540 yards from B. If angle ACB has measure 63°10', approximate the distance.

15 Two automobiles leave from the same point and travel along straight highways which differ in direction by 84°. If their speeds are 60 miles per hour and 45 miles per hour, respectively, approximately how far apart will they be at the end of 20 minutes?

16 A triangular plot of land has sides of length 420 feet, 350 feet, and 180 feet. Find the smallest angle between the sides.

17 A ship leaves P at 1:00 P.M. and travels S35°E at the rate of 24 miles per hour. Another ship leaves P at 1:30 P.M. and travels S20°W at 18 miles per hour. Approximately how far apart are the ships at 3:00 P.M.?

18 An airplane flies 165 miles from point A in the direction 130° and then travels in the direction 245° for 80 miles. Approximately how far is the airplane from A?

19 A jogger, running at a constant speed of one mile every eight minutes, runs in the direction S40°E for 20 minutes and then in the direction N20°E for the next 16 minutes. Approximate, to the nearest tenth of a mile, the distance from the jogger to the starting point.

20 Two points P and Q on level ground are on opposite sides of a building. In order to find the distance d between the points, a surveyor chooses a point R which is 300 feet from P and 438 feet from Q, and then determines that angle PRQ has measure 37°40'. Approximate d.

21 A motor boat traveled along a triangular course of sides 2 km, 4 km, and 3 km, respectively. If the first side was traversed in the direction N20°W

and the second in the southwest direction, approximate, to the nearest minute, the direction that the third side was traversed.

22 If a rhombus has sides of length 100 cm and if the angle at one of the vertices is 70°, approximate the lengths of the diagonals to the nearest tenth of a cm.

23 Show that for every triangle ABC,
   (a) $a^2 + b^2 + c^2 =$
      $2(bc \cos \alpha + ac \cos \beta + ab \cos \gamma)$.

(b) $\dfrac{\cos \alpha}{a} + \dfrac{\cos \beta}{b} + \dfrac{\cos \gamma}{c} = \dfrac{a^2 + b^2 + c^2}{2abc}$.

24 Show that if ABC is a right triangle, then one part of the Law of Cosines reduces to the Pythagorean Theorem.

CALCULATOR EXERCISES 4.2

Approximate the remaining parts of triangle ABC in Exercises 1–6.

1 $\alpha = 48.3°$, $b = 24.7$, $c = 52.8$

2 $\beta = 137.8°$, $a = 178.2$, $c = 431.4$

3 $\gamma = 6.85°$, $a = 0.846$, $b = 0.364$

4 $a = 435$, $b = 482$, $c = 78$

5 $a = 5,150$, $b = 1814$, $c = 3,429$

6 $a = 0.64$, $b = 0.27$, $c = 0.49$

4.3 THE LAW OF TANGENTS

Another useful formula for solving oblique triangles can be derived from the Law of Sines. Let us begin with

$$\frac{a}{b} = \frac{\sin \alpha}{\sin \beta}.$$

Adding 1 to both sides gives us equation (i) below, whereas adding -1 to both sides gives us equation (ii).

(i) $\dfrac{a}{b} + 1 = \dfrac{\sin \alpha}{\sin \beta} + 1$ (ii) $\dfrac{a}{b} - 1 = \dfrac{\sin \alpha}{\sin \beta} - 1$

These may be rewritten as

(i) $\dfrac{a + b}{b} = \dfrac{\sin \alpha + \sin \beta}{\sin \beta}$ (ii) $\dfrac{a - b}{b} = \dfrac{\sin \alpha - \sin \beta}{\sin \beta}.$

If we divide the left- and right-hand sides of (ii) by the corresponding sides of (i) and simplify, we obtain

$$\frac{a - b}{a + b} = \frac{\sin \alpha - \sin \beta}{\sin \alpha + \sin \beta}.$$

Applying factoring formulas (see Section 3.6) gives us

$$\frac{a-b}{a+b} = \frac{2\cos\frac{1}{2}(\alpha+\beta)\sin\frac{1}{2}(\alpha-\beta)}{2\sin\frac{1}{2}(\alpha+\beta)\cos\frac{1}{2}(\alpha-\beta)}$$

which may be expressed as

$$\frac{a-b}{a+b} = \cot\tfrac{1}{2}(\alpha+\beta)\tan\tfrac{1}{2}(\alpha-\beta).$$

Finally, since $\cot\theta = 1/\tan\theta$, we have the following.

The Law of Tangents

$$\boxed{\frac{a-b}{a+b} = \frac{\tan\frac{1}{2}(\alpha-\beta)}{\tan\frac{1}{2}(\alpha+\beta)}}$$

By beginning with the other equations given by the Law of Sines we could obtain similar formulas that involve *any* two angles of a triangle and the sides opposite them. The following statement takes all possibilities into account.

The Law of Tangents (General Form)

The ratio of the difference of any two sides of a triangle to their sum is equal to the ratio of the tangent of half the difference of the angles opposite the two sides to the tangent of half their sum, where the differences are taken in the same order.

Since the sum of the angles of a triangle is 180°, if we know one angle θ, then half the sum of the remaining two angles is $\frac{1}{2}(180° - \theta)$. Consequently, the Law of Tangents may be used to solve triangles in which two sides and the angle between them are known.

Example 1 Approximate the remaining parts of triangle ABC if $\alpha = 70°20'$, $b = 58.3$, and $c = 21.6$.

Solution By the Law of Tangents, we may write

$$\frac{b-c}{b+c} = \frac{\tan\frac{1}{2}(\beta-\gamma)}{\tan\frac{1}{2}(\beta+\gamma)}.$$

Since $\alpha + \beta + \gamma = 180°$, we have

$$\beta + \gamma = 180° - \alpha = 180° - 72°20' = 107°40'.$$

Hence, $\frac{1}{2}(\beta + \gamma) = 53°50'$. Since $b + c = 79.9$ and $b - c = 36.7$, we obtain

$$\frac{36.7}{79.9} = \frac{\tan\frac{1}{2}(\beta-\gamma)}{\tan 53°50'}$$

$$\tan\tfrac{1}{2}(\beta-\gamma) = \frac{(36.7)\tan 53°50'}{79.9}$$

$$\approx \frac{(36.7)(1.3680)}{79.9}$$

$$\approx 0.6284.$$

It follows from Table 2 that

$$\tfrac{1}{2}(\beta - \gamma) \approx 32°10'.$$

However,

$$\tfrac{1}{2}(\beta + \gamma) = 53°50'.$$

Adding corresponding sides of the last two expressions we obtain $\beta \approx 86°$, whereas subtracting corresponding sides gives us $\gamma \approx 21°40'$.

Finally, we use the Law of Sines to find a. Thus,

$$a = \frac{b \sin \alpha}{\sin \beta} \approx \frac{(58.3)\sin 72°20'}{\sin 86°}$$
$$\approx \frac{(58.3)(0.9528)}{0.9976}$$
$$\approx 55.7.$$

EXERCISES 4.3

1–6 Use the Law of Tangents to solve Exercises 1–6 of Section 4.2.

CALCULATOR EXERCISES 4.3

1–3 Use the Law of Tangents to solve Calculator Exercises 1–3 of Section 4.2.

4.4 AREAS OF TRIANGLES

Given triangle ABC, let us place angle α in standard position, as in Figure 4.1. As usual, our discussion is valid whether α is obtuse or acute. The altitude h from vertex C is given by $h = b \sin \alpha$. Since the length of the base AB is c, we obtain the following formula for the area K of triangle ABC:

$$K = \tfrac{1}{2}bc \sin \alpha.$$

Our argument is independent of the specific angle that is placed in standard position. By taking β and γ in standard position, the formulas $K = \tfrac{1}{2}ac \sin \beta$ and $K = \tfrac{1}{2}ab \sin \gamma$, respectively, are obtained. This gives us the next theorem.

Theorem

> The area of a triangle equals one-half the product of the lengths of any two sides and the sine of the included angle.

Example 1 Find the area K of triangle ABC if $a = 2.2$ cm, $b = 1.3$ cm, and $\gamma = 43°10'$.

Solution By the preceding theorem, $K = \frac{1}{2}ab \sin \gamma$. Hence,

$$K = \frac{1}{2}(2.2)(1.3) \sin 43°10'$$
$$\approx (1.43)(0.6841)$$
$$\approx 0.98 \text{ cm}^2. \qquad \blacksquare$$

Using the Law of Sines, we may write $c = (b \sin \gamma)/\sin \beta$. Substituting for c in $K = \frac{1}{2}bc \sin \alpha$ gives us the first formula of the next theorem. The remaining formulas are obtained by using other forms for K.

Theorem

> If ABC is any triangle labeled in the usual manner, then its area K is given by
>
> $$K = \frac{b^2 \sin \alpha \sin \gamma}{2 \sin \beta} = \frac{a^2 \sin \beta \sin \gamma}{2 \sin \alpha} = \frac{c^2 \sin \alpha \sin \beta}{2 \sin \gamma}.$$

Note that the length of the side that appears in each formula of the theorem is opposite the angle given in the denominator. These formulas are useful if the angles and one side of a triangle are known.

Example 2 Approximate the area K of triangle ABC if $\alpha = 77°40'$, $\beta = 43°10'$, and $c = 4.19$.

Solution First we calculate

$$\gamma = 180° - (77°40' + 43°10') = 59°10'.$$

Next we obtain

$$K = \frac{c^2 \sin \alpha \sin \beta}{2 \sin \gamma}$$
$$= \frac{(4.19)^2 (\sin 77°40')(\sin 43°10')}{2 \sin 59°10'}$$
$$\approx \frac{(17.56)(0.9769)(0.6841)}{2(0.8587)} \approx 6.83. \qquad \blacksquare$$

We shall conclude this section with an interesting formula that expresses the area K of a triangle in terms of the lengths of its sides.

Theorem

> The area K of a triangle with sides a, b, and c is given by
>
> $$K = \sqrt{s(s-a)(s-b)(s-c)}$$
>
> whereas $s = \frac{1}{2}(a + b + c)$.

Proof   Using $K = \frac{1}{2}bc \sin \alpha$ leads to the following equations:

$$K = \sqrt{\tfrac{1}{4}b^2c^2 \sin^2 \alpha}$$

$$= \sqrt{\tfrac{1}{4}b^2c^2(1 - \cos^2 \alpha)}.$$

$$= \sqrt{\tfrac{1}{2}bc(1 + \cos \alpha) \cdot \tfrac{1}{2}bc(1 - \cos \alpha)}.$$

We shall obtain the desired formula by replacing the expressions under the radical sign by equivalent expressions involving a, b, and c.

Using the Law of Cosines,

$$\tfrac{1}{2}bc(1 + \cos \alpha) = \tfrac{1}{2}bc\left(1 + \frac{b^2 + c^2 - a^2}{2bc}\right)$$

$$= \frac{2bc + b^2 + c^2 - a^2}{4}$$

$$= \frac{(b + c)^2 - a^2}{4}.$$

Hence,

$$\tfrac{1}{2}bc(1 + \cos \alpha) = \frac{(b + c) + a}{2} \cdot \frac{(b + c) - a}{2}.$$

By the same type of manipulation,

$$\tfrac{1}{2}bc(1 - \cos \alpha) = \frac{a - b + c}{2} \cdot \frac{a + b - c}{2}.$$

If we now substitute for the expressions under the radical sign, we obtain

$$K = \sqrt{\frac{b + c + a}{2} \cdot \frac{b + c - a}{2} \cdot \frac{a - b + c}{2} \cdot \frac{a + b - c}{2}}.$$

Letting $s = \frac{1}{2}(a + b + c)$, we see that

$$s - a = \frac{b + c - a}{2}, \quad s - b = \frac{a - b + c}{2}, \quad s - c = \frac{a + b - c}{2}.$$

Substitution in the last formula for K gives us the formula in the statement of the theorem.

◼

EXERCISES 4.4

1–4 Approximate the areas of the triangles described in Exercises 1–4 of Section 4.2.

5–8 Approximate the areas of the triangles described in Exercises 1–4 of Section 4.1.

9–12 Approximate the areas of the triangles described in Exercises 7–10 of Section 4.2.

13 Approximately how many acres are in a triangular field with sides of lengths 115 yards, 140 yards, and 200 yards if one acre is equivalent to 4840 square yards?

14 Find the area of a parallelogram which has sides of lengths 12 and 16 feet if one of the angles at a vertex has measure 40°.

15 Given the length a and the measures β and γ of triangle ABC, prove that the area K of the triangle is given by

$$K = \frac{a^2 \sin \beta \sin \gamma}{2 \sin (\beta + \gamma)}.$$

16 Prove that the area of any quadrilateral equals one-half the product of the diagonals and the sine of either of the angles between the diagonals.

CALCULATOR EXERCISES 4.4

1–8 Approximate the areas of the triangles described in Calculator Exercises 1–3 of Section 4.1 and 1–5 of Section 4.2.

4.5 VECTORS

In previous work we assigned directions to certain lines, such as the x- and y-axes. In similar fashion, a **directed line segment** is a line segment to which a direction has been assigned. Another name for a directed line segment is a **vector**. If a vector extends from a point A (called the **initial point**) to a point B (called the **terminal point**), it is customary to place an arrowhead at B and use $\overrightarrow{AB}$ to represent the vector (see Figure 4.8). The length of the directed line segment is called the **magnitude** of the vector $\overrightarrow{AB}$ and is denoted by $|\overrightarrow{AB}|$. The vectors $\overrightarrow{AB}$ and $\overrightarrow{CD}$ are considered **equal**, and we write $\overrightarrow{AB} = \overrightarrow{CD}$ if

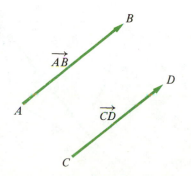

Figure 4.8

and only if they have the same magnitude and direction, as illustrated in Figure 4.8. Consequently, vectors may be translated from one position to another, provided neither the magnitude nor the direction is changed. Vectors of this type are often referred to as **free vectors**.

Many physical concepts may be represented by vectors. To illustrate, suppose an airplane is descending at a constant rate of 100 mph and the line of flight makes an angle of 20° with the horizontal. Both of these facts are represented by the vector in (i) of Figure 4.9, where it is assumed that units have been chosen so that the magnitude is 100. As shown in the figure, we will use a boldface letter such as **v** to denote a vector whose endpoints are not specified. The vector **v** in this illustration is called a **velocity vector**. The magnitude |**v**| of **v** is the speed of the airplane.

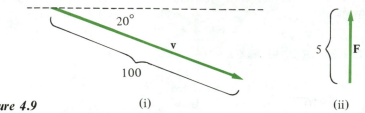

Figure 4.9 (i) (ii)

As a second illustration, suppose a person pulls directly upward on an object with a force of 5 kg, as would be the case in lifting a 5 kg weight. We may indicate this fact by the vector **F** in (ii) of Figure 4.9. A vector that represents a pull or push of some type is called a **force vector**.

Another use for vectors is to let $\overrightarrow{AB}$ represent the path of a point (or some physical particle) as it moves along the line segment from A to B. We then refer to $\overrightarrow{AB}$ as a **displacement** of the point (or particle). As illustrated in Figure 4.10, a displacement $\overrightarrow{AB}$ followed by a displacement $\overrightarrow{BC}$ will lead to the same point as the single displacement $\overrightarrow{AC}$. The latter vector is called the **sum** of the first two, and we write

$$\overrightarrow{AC} = \overrightarrow{AB} + \overrightarrow{BC}.$$

Since we are working with free vectors, any two vectors can be added by placing the initial point of one on the terminal point of the other and then proceeding as shown in Figure 4.10.

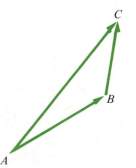

Figure 4.10

Another way to find the sum of two vectors is to consider vectors that are equal to the given ones and have the same initial point, as illustrated by $\overrightarrow{PQ}$ and $\overrightarrow{PR}$ in Figure 4.11. If we construct the parallelogram $RPQS$ with adjacent sides $\overrightarrow{PR}$ and $\overrightarrow{PQ}$, then since $\overrightarrow{PR} = \overrightarrow{QS}$, it follows that

$$\overrightarrow{PS} = \overrightarrow{PQ} + \overrightarrow{PR}.$$

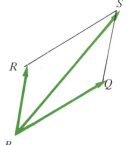

Figure 4.11

If $\overrightarrow{PQ}$ and $\overrightarrow{PR}$ are two forces acting at P, then it can be shown experimentally that $\overrightarrow{PS}$ is the **resultant** force, that is, the single force that produces the same effect as the two combined forces.

If c is a real number and $\overrightarrow{AB}$ is a vector, then the product $c\overrightarrow{AB}$ is defined as a vector whose magnitude is $|c|$ times the magnitude of $\overrightarrow{AB}$ and whose direction is the same as that of $\overrightarrow{AB}$ if $c > 0$, and opposite that of $\overrightarrow{AB}$ if $c < 0$. Geometric illustrations are given in Figure 4.12. We refer to c as a **scalar** and to $c\overrightarrow{AB}$ as a **scalar multiple** of $\overrightarrow{AB}$.

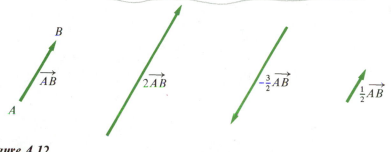

Figure 4.12

Let us next introduce a coordinate plane and assume that all vectors under discussion are in that plane. Since the position of a vector may be changed, provided the magnitude and direction are not altered, we may place the initial point of each vector at the origin. The terminal point of a typical vector $\overrightarrow{OP}$ may then be assigned coordinates (a, b) as shown in Figure 4.13. Conversely, every ordered pair (a, b) determines the vector $\overrightarrow{OP}$, where P has coordinates (a, b). We thus obtain a one-to-one correspondence between vectors and ordered pairs. This allows us to regard a vector in a plane as an ordered pair of real numbers instead of a directed line segment. To avoid confusion with the notation for open intervals or points, we shall use the symbol $\langle a, b \rangle$ for an ordered pair that represents a vector. Moreover, we shall refer to $\langle a, b \rangle$ as a vector and denote it by a boldface letter. The numbers a and b are called the **components** of the vector $\langle a, b \rangle$. The magnitude of $\langle a, b \rangle$ is, by definition, the distance from the origin to the point $P(a, b)$. This may also be stated as follows.

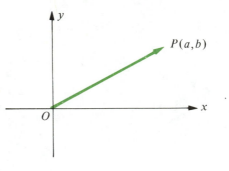

Figure 4.13

Definition

> The **magnitude** $|\mathbf{v}|$ of the vector $\mathbf{v} = \langle a, b \rangle$ is given by $|\mathbf{v}| = \sqrt{a^2 + b^2}$.

Example 1   Sketch the vectors corresponding to each of the following, and find the magnitude and the smallest positive angle θ from the positive x-axis to each vector.

(a) $\mathbf{a} = \langle -3, -3 \rangle$ (b) $\mathbf{b} = \langle 0, -2 \rangle$ (c) $\mathbf{c} = \langle 4/5, 3/5 \rangle$

Solution   The vectors are sketched in Figure 4.14. Applying the definition of magnitude and our knowledge of trigonometry, we obtain:

(a) $|\mathbf{a}| = \sqrt{9 + 9} = 3\sqrt{2}; \theta = 5\pi/4$

(b) $|\mathbf{b}| = \sqrt{0 + 4} = 2; \theta = 3\pi/2$

(c) $|\mathbf{c}| = \sqrt{(16/25) + (9/25)} = 1; \theta = \arctan 3/4.$

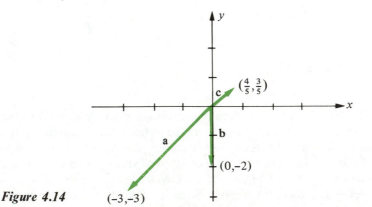

Figure 4.14 $(-3,-3)$

If, as in Figure 4.15, we consider vectors $\overrightarrow{OQ}$ and $\overrightarrow{OR}$ corresponding to $\langle a, b \rangle$ and $\langle c, d \rangle$, respectively, and if we let $\overrightarrow{OS}$ be the vector corresponding to $\langle a + c, b + d \rangle$, then it can be shown that O, Q, S, and R are vertices of a parallelogram. It follows that

$$\overrightarrow{OQ} + \overrightarrow{OR} = \overrightarrow{OS}.$$

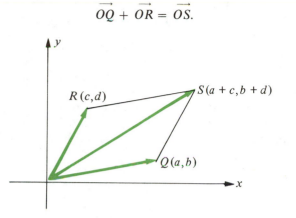

Figure 4.15

Expressing this fact in terms of ordered pairs gives us the following rule for addition of vectors.

Addition of Vectors

$$\langle a, b \rangle + \langle c, d \rangle = \langle a + c, b + d \rangle$$

Although we shall not prove it, the rule corresponding to a scalar multiple $k\overrightarrow{OP}$ of a vector is as follows.

Scalar Multiples of Vectors

$$k \langle a, b \rangle = \langle ka, kb \rangle$$

Example 2 If $\mathbf{a} = \langle 2, 1 \rangle$, find $3\mathbf{a}$ and $-2\mathbf{a}$, and represent all three vectors geometrically.

Solution If $\mathbf{a} = \langle 2, 1 \rangle$, then, by the preceding rule for scalar multiples, $3\mathbf{a} = \langle 6, 3 \rangle$ and $-2\mathbf{a} = \langle -4, -2 \rangle$. The geometric representations are shown in Figure 4.16.

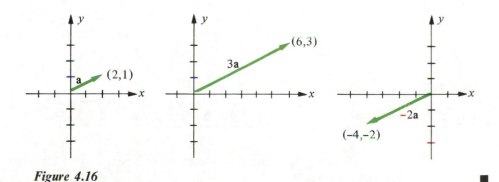

Figure 4.16

Example 3   If $\mathbf{a} = \langle 3, -2 \rangle$ and $\mathbf{b} = \langle -6, 7 \rangle$, find $\mathbf{a} + \mathbf{b}$, $4\mathbf{a}$, and $2\mathbf{a} + 3\mathbf{b}$.

Solution   Using the rules for addition and scalar multiples of vectors,

$$\mathbf{a} + \mathbf{b} = \langle 3, -2 \rangle + \langle -6, 7 \rangle = \langle -3, 5 \rangle$$
$$4\mathbf{a} = 4\langle 3, -2 \rangle = \langle 12, -8 \rangle$$
$$2\mathbf{a} + 3\mathbf{b} = \langle 6, -4 \rangle + \langle -18, 21 \rangle = \langle -12, 17 \rangle. \qquad \blacksquare$$

By definition, the **zero vector 0** corresponds to $\langle 0, 0 \rangle$. Also, if $\mathbf{a} = \langle a, b \rangle$, then we define $-\mathbf{a} = \langle -a, -b \rangle$. Using these definitions, we may establish the following properties, where $\mathbf{a}$, $\mathbf{b}$, and $\mathbf{c}$ denote arbitrary vectors.

Properties of Addition of Vectors

$$\mathbf{a} + \mathbf{b} = \mathbf{b} + \mathbf{a}$$
$$\mathbf{a} + (\mathbf{b} + \mathbf{c}) = (\mathbf{a} + \mathbf{b}) + \mathbf{c}$$
$$\mathbf{a} + \mathbf{0} = \mathbf{a}$$
$$\mathbf{a} + (-\mathbf{a}) = \mathbf{0}$$

The proof of each property follows readily from the rule for addition of vectors and properties of real numbers. For example, if $\mathbf{a} = \langle a_1, a_2 \rangle$ and $\mathbf{b} = \langle b_1, b_2 \rangle$, then, since $a_1 + b_1 = b_1 + a_1$ and $a_2 + b_2 = b_2 + a_2$,

$$\mathbf{a} + \mathbf{b} = \langle a_1 + b_1, a_2 + b_2 \rangle$$
$$= \langle b_1 + a_1, b_2 + a_2 \rangle$$
$$= \mathbf{b} + \mathbf{a}.$$

The remainder of the proof is left as an exercise (see Exercise 15). The reader should also give geometric interpretations for each property.

The operation of **subtraction** of vectors, denoted by "$-$", is defined as follows.

Subtraction of Vectors

$$\mathbf{a} - \mathbf{b} = \mathbf{a} + (-\mathbf{b})$$

If we use the ordered pair notation for $\mathbf{a}$ and $\mathbf{b}$, then since $-\mathbf{b} = \langle -b_1, -b_2 \rangle$,

$$\mathbf{a} - \mathbf{b} = \langle a_1, a_2 \rangle + \langle -b_1, -b_2 \rangle$$

and hence,

$$\mathbf{a} - \mathbf{b} = \langle a_1 - b_1, a_2 - b_2 \rangle.$$

Thus, to find $\mathbf{a} - \mathbf{b}$, we merely subtract the components of $\mathbf{b}$ from the corresponding components of $\mathbf{a}$.

Example 4 If $\mathbf{a} = \langle 2, -4 \rangle$ and $\mathbf{b} = \langle 6, 7 \rangle$, find $3\mathbf{a} - 5\mathbf{b}$.

Solution We proceed as follows:

$$3\mathbf{a} - 5\mathbf{b} = \langle 6, -12 \rangle - \langle 30, 35 \rangle = \langle -24, -47 \rangle. \qquad \blacksquare$$

The following properties can be proved for any vectors $\mathbf{a}$, $\mathbf{b}$ and real numbers c, d.

Properties of Scalar Multiples of Vectors

$$c(\mathbf{a} + \mathbf{b}) = c\mathbf{a} + c\mathbf{b}$$
$$(c + d)\mathbf{a} = c\mathbf{a} + d\mathbf{a}$$
$$(cd)\mathbf{a} = c(d\mathbf{a}) = d(c\mathbf{a})$$
$$1\mathbf{a} = \mathbf{a}$$
$$0\mathbf{a} = \mathbf{0} = c\mathbf{0}$$

We shall prove the first property and leave the remaining proofs as an exercise (see Exercise 16). Letting $\mathbf{a} = \langle a_1, a_2 \rangle$ and $\mathbf{b} = \langle b_1, b_2 \rangle$, we have

$$\begin{aligned} c(\mathbf{a} + \mathbf{b}) &= c\langle a_1 + b_1, a_2 + b_2 \rangle \\ &= \langle ca_1 + cb_1, ca_2 + cb_2 \rangle \\ &= \langle ca_1, ca_2 \rangle + \langle cb_1, cb_2 \rangle \\ &= c\mathbf{a} + c\mathbf{b}. \end{aligned}$$

The special vectors $\mathbf{i}$ and $\mathbf{j}$ are defined as follows:

Definition of i and j

$$\mathbf{i} = \langle 1, 0 \rangle, \quad \mathbf{j} = \langle 0, 1 \rangle.$$

The vectors $\mathbf{i}$ and $\mathbf{j}$ can be used to obtain an alternative way of denoting vectors. Specifically, if $\mathbf{a} = \langle a_1, a_2 \rangle$, then we may write

$$\begin{aligned} \mathbf{a} &= \langle a_1, 0 \rangle + \langle 0, a_2 \rangle \\ &= a_1 \langle 1, 0 \rangle + a_2 \langle 0, 1 \rangle \end{aligned}$$

that is,

$$\mathbf{a} = \langle a_1, a_2 \rangle = a_1\mathbf{i} + a_2\mathbf{j}.$$

The vector sum on the right in the last formula is called a **linear combination** of $\mathbf{i}$ and $\mathbf{j}$. If this notation is employed, then previous rules for addition, subtraction, and multiplication by a scalar may be written as follows, where $\mathbf{b} = \langle b_1, b_2 \rangle = b_1\mathbf{i} + b_2\mathbf{j}$:

$$(a_1\mathbf{i} + a_2\mathbf{j}) + (b_1\mathbf{i} + b_2\mathbf{j}) = (a_1 + b_1)\mathbf{i} + (a_2 + b_2)\mathbf{j}$$
$$(a_1\mathbf{i} + a_2\mathbf{j}) - (b_1\mathbf{i} + b_2\mathbf{j}) = (a_1 - b_1)\mathbf{i} + (a_2 - b_2)\mathbf{j}$$
$$c(a_1\mathbf{i} + a_2\mathbf{j}) = (ca_1)\mathbf{i} + (ca_2)\mathbf{j}.$$

These formulas show that linear combinations of $\mathbf{i}$ and $\mathbf{j}$ may be regarded as ordinary algebraic sums.

Example 5   If $\mathbf{a} = 5\mathbf{i} + \mathbf{j}$ and $\mathbf{b} = 4\mathbf{i} - 7\mathbf{j}$, express $3\mathbf{a} - 2\mathbf{b}$ as a linear combination of $\mathbf{i}$ and $\mathbf{j}$.

Solution
$$3\mathbf{a} - 2\mathbf{b} = 3(5\mathbf{i} + \mathbf{j}) - 2(4\mathbf{i} - 7\mathbf{j})$$
$$= (15\mathbf{i} + 3\mathbf{j}) - (8\mathbf{i} - 14\mathbf{j})$$
$$= 7\mathbf{i} + 17\mathbf{j}. \qquad \blacksquare$$

A **unit vector** is a vector of magnitude 1. The vectors $\mathbf{i}$ and $\mathbf{j}$ are unit vectors, as is the vector $\mathbf{c}$ in Example 1 of this section.

The formula $\mathbf{a} = a_1\mathbf{i} + a_2\mathbf{j}$ for the vector $\mathbf{a} = \langle a_1, a_2 \rangle$ has a useful geometric interpretation. Vectors corresponding to $\mathbf{i}$, $\mathbf{j}$, and $\mathbf{a}$ are illustrated in (i) of Figure 4.17. Since $\mathbf{i}$ and $\mathbf{j}$ are unit vectors, $a_1\mathbf{i}$ and $a_2\mathbf{j}$ may be represented by horizontal and vertical vectors of magnitudes $|a_1|$ and $|a_2|$, respectively, as illustrated in (ii) of Figure 4.17. The vector $\mathbf{a}$ may be regarded as the sum of these vectors. For this reason, a_1 is called the **horizontal component** and a_2 the **vertical component** of the vector $\mathbf{a}$.

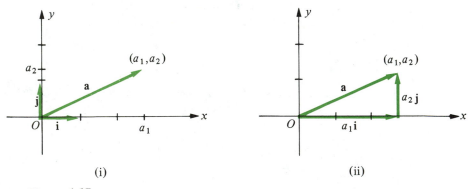

(i)   (ii)

Figure 4.17

Let θ be an angle in standard position, measured from the positive x-axis to the terminal side of the vector corresponding to $\mathbf{a} = \langle a_1, a_2 \rangle$, as illustrated in Figure 4.18.

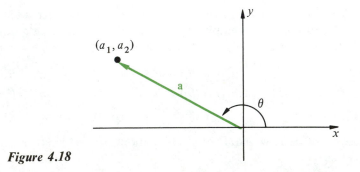

Figure 4.18

Since $\cos\theta = a_1/|\mathbf{a}|$ and $\sin\theta = a_2/|\mathbf{a}|$, we obtain the following useful formulas.

Horizontal and Vertical Components of a = $\langle a_1, a_2 \rangle$

$$a_1 = |\mathbf{a}|\cos\theta, \quad a_2 = |\mathbf{a}|\sin\theta$$

Note, in addition, that $\tan\theta = a_2/a_1$. An application of these formulas is given in the next example.

Example 6   Two forces $\overrightarrow{PQ}$ and $\overrightarrow{PR}$ of magnitudes 5.0 kg and 8.0 kg, respectively, act at a point P. If the direction of $\overrightarrow{PQ}$ is N20°E, and the direction of $\overrightarrow{PR}$ is N65°E, approximate the direction of the resultant vector $\overrightarrow{PS}$ to the nearest degree, and find $|\overrightarrow{PS}|$ to the nearest tenth.

Solution   In order to use components, let us introduce a coordinate system with origin at the point P, as in Figure 4.19.

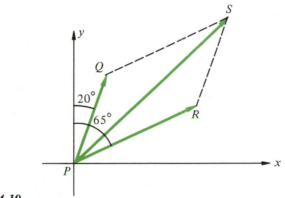

Figure 4.19

Note that the angles from the x-axis to $\overrightarrow{PQ}$ and $\overrightarrow{PR}$ have measures 70° and 25°, respectively. Using the formulas for horizontal and vertical components gives us

$$\overrightarrow{PQ} = \langle 5\cos 70°, \ 5\sin 70° \rangle, \quad \overrightarrow{PR} = \langle 8\cos 25°, \ 8\sin 25° \rangle.$$

Since $\overrightarrow{PS} = \overrightarrow{PQ} + \overrightarrow{PR}$, it follows that

$$\overrightarrow{PS} = \langle 5\cos 70° + 8\cos 25°, \ 5\sin 70° + 8\sin 25° \rangle.$$

Referring to Table 2 gives us the approximation

$$\overrightarrow{PS} \approx \langle 8.9604, \ 8.0793 \rangle.$$

Consequently,

$$|\overrightarrow{PS}| \approx \sqrt{(8.9604)^2 + (8.0793)^2} \approx 12.1 \text{ kg}.$$

If θ is the angle from the positive x-axis to the resultant $\overrightarrow{PS} = \langle c_1, c_2 \rangle$, then

$$\tan \theta = \frac{c_2}{c_1} \approx \frac{8.0793}{8.9604} \approx 0.9017.$$

Referring to Table 2, $\theta \approx 42°$, and hence, the direction of $\overrightarrow{PS}$ is approximately N48°E.

∎

The technique used in Example 6 has many practical applications (see, for example, Exercises 39–44).

EXERCISES 4.5

In each of Exercises 1–10, find $\mathbf{a} + \mathbf{b}$, $\mathbf{a} - \mathbf{b}$, $4\mathbf{a} + 5\mathbf{b}$, and $4\mathbf{a} - 5\mathbf{b}$.

1   $\mathbf{a} = \langle 2, -3 \rangle$, $\mathbf{b} = \langle 1, 4 \rangle$

2   $\mathbf{a} = \langle -2, 6 \rangle$, $\mathbf{b} = \langle 2, 3 \rangle$

3   $\mathbf{a} = -\langle 7, -2 \rangle$, $\mathbf{b} = 4\langle -2, 1 \rangle$

4   $\mathbf{a} = 2\langle 5, -4 \rangle$, $\mathbf{b} = -\langle 6, 0 \rangle$

5   $\mathbf{a} = \mathbf{i} + 2\mathbf{j}$, $\mathbf{b} = 3\mathbf{i} - 5\mathbf{j}$

6   $\mathbf{a} = -3\mathbf{i} + \mathbf{j}$, $\mathbf{b} = -3\mathbf{i} + \mathbf{j}$

7   $\mathbf{a} = -(4\mathbf{i} - \mathbf{j})$, $\mathbf{b} = 2(\mathbf{i} - 3\mathbf{j})$

8   $\mathbf{a} = 8\mathbf{j}$, $\mathbf{b} = (-3)(-2\mathbf{i} + \mathbf{j})$

9   $\mathbf{a} = 2\mathbf{j}$, $\mathbf{b} = -3\mathbf{i}$

10   $\mathbf{a} = 0$, $\mathbf{b} = \mathbf{i} + \mathbf{j}$

In Exercises 11–14, sketch vectors corresponding to $\mathbf{a}$, $\mathbf{b}$, $\mathbf{a} + \mathbf{b}$, $2\mathbf{a}$, and $-3\mathbf{b}$.

11   $\mathbf{a} = 3\mathbf{i} + 2\mathbf{j}$, $\mathbf{b} = -\mathbf{i} + 5\mathbf{j}$

12   $\mathbf{a} = -5\mathbf{i} + 2\mathbf{j}$, $\mathbf{b} = \mathbf{i} - 3\mathbf{j}$

13   $\mathbf{a} = \langle -4, 6 \rangle$, $\mathbf{b} = \langle -2, 3 \rangle$

14   $\mathbf{a} = \langle 2, 0 \rangle$, $\mathbf{b} = \langle -2, 0 \rangle$

15   Prove the second, third, and fourth properties of addition of vectors.

16   Prove the second through the fifth properties of scalar multiples of vectors.

Prove each of the properties in Exercises 17–24, where $\mathbf{a} = \langle a_1, a_2 \rangle$, $\mathbf{b} = \langle b_1, b_2 \rangle$, and c is any real number.

17   $(-1)\mathbf{a} = -\mathbf{a}$

18   $(-c)\mathbf{a} = -c\mathbf{a}$

19   $-(\mathbf{a} + \mathbf{b}) = -\mathbf{a} - \mathbf{b}$

20   $c(\mathbf{a} - \mathbf{b}) = c\mathbf{a} - c\mathbf{b}$

21   If $\mathbf{a} + \mathbf{b} = \mathbf{0}$, then $\mathbf{b} = -\mathbf{a}$.

22   If $\mathbf{a} + \mathbf{b} = \mathbf{a}$, then $\mathbf{b} = \mathbf{0}$.

23   If $c\mathbf{a} = \mathbf{0}$ and $c \neq 0$, then $\mathbf{a} = \mathbf{0}$.

24   If $c\mathbf{a} = \mathbf{0}$ and $\mathbf{a} \neq \mathbf{0}$, then $c = 0$.

25   If $\mathbf{v} = \langle a, b \rangle$, prove each of the following.
    (a) The magnitude of $2\mathbf{v}$ is twice the magnitude of $\mathbf{v}$.
    (b) The magnitude of $\frac{1}{2}\mathbf{v}$ is one-half the magnitude of $\mathbf{v}$.
    (c) The magnitude of $-2\mathbf{v}$ is twice the magnitude of $\mathbf{v}$.
    (d) If k is any real number, then the magnitude of $k\mathbf{v}$ is $|k|$ times the magnitude of $\mathbf{v}$.

26   If $\mathbf{v} = \langle a, b \rangle$ and $\mathbf{w} = \langle c, d \rangle$, give a geometric interpretation for $\mathbf{v} - \mathbf{w}$.

In Exercises 27–34, find the magnitude of $\mathbf{a}$ and the smallest positive angle θ from the positive x-axis to the vector $\overrightarrow{OP}$ corresponding to $\mathbf{a}$.

27   $\mathbf{a} = \langle 3, -3 \rangle$ 28 $\mathbf{a} = \langle -2, -2\sqrt{3} \rangle$

29   $\mathbf{a} = \langle -5, 0 \rangle$ 30 $\mathbf{a} = \langle 0, 10 \rangle$

31   $\mathbf{a} = -4\mathbf{i} + 5\mathbf{j}$ 32 $\mathbf{a} = 10\mathbf{i} - 10\mathbf{j}$

33   $\mathbf{a} = -18\mathbf{j}$ 34 $\mathbf{a} = 2\mathbf{i} - 3\mathbf{j}$

In each of Exercises 35–38, (a) and (b) represent the magnitudes and directions of two forces acting at a point *P*. Approximate the magnitude of the resultant (to two significant figures) and its direction (to the nearest degree).

35 (a) 90 kg, N75°W (b) 60 kg, S5°E

36 (a) 20 kg, S17°W (b) 50 kg, N82°W

37 (a) 6.0 lb, 110° (b) 2.0 lb, 215°

38 (a) 70 lb, 320° (b) 40 lb, 30°

39 An airplane with an airspeed of 200 mph is flying in the direction 50°, and a 40 mph wind is blowing directly from the west. As in Figure 4.20, these may be represented by vectors **p** and **w** of magnitudes 200 and 40, respectively. The direction of the resultant **p** + **w** gives the **true course** of the airplane relative to the ground, and the magnitude |**p** + **w**| is called the **ground speed** of the airplane. Approximate the true course to the nearest degree and the ground speed to the nearest mph.

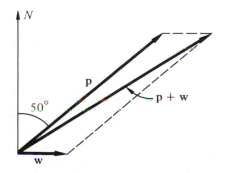

Figure 4.20

40 An airplane is flying in the direction 140° with an airspeed of 500 mph, and a 30 mph wind is blowing from the southwest, in the direction 65°. Approximate the true course (to the nearest degree) and the ground speed (to the nearest mph).

41 An airplane pilot wishes to maintain a true course in the direction 250°, with a ground speed of 400 mph. If the wind is blowing directly north at 50 mph, approximate the required airspeed (to the nearest mph) and compass heading (to the nearest degree).

42 An airplane is flying in the direction 20° with an airspeed of 300 mph. Its ground speed and true course are 350 mph and 30°, respectively. Approximate the direction and speed of the wind.

43 The current in a river flows directly from the west at a rate of 1.5 ft/sec. A person who rows a boat at a rate of 4 ft/sec in still water wishes to row directly across the river. Approximate, to the nearest 10′, the direction in which the person should row.

44 In order for a motor boat moving at a speed of 30 mph to travel directly north across a river, it must aim at a point that has a bearing of N15°E. If the current is flowing directly west, approximate the rate at which it flows, to the nearest mph.

4.6 THE DOT PRODUCT

The *dot product* of two vectors has many important applications. We shall begin with an algebraic definition and then, later in the section, consider several geometric and physical interpretations.

Definition

> Given the vectors
>
> $$\mathbf{a} = \langle a_1, a_2 \rangle = a_1\mathbf{i} + a_2\mathbf{j} \text{ and } \mathbf{b} = \langle b_1, b_2 \rangle = b_1\mathbf{i} + b_2\mathbf{j}$$
>
> the **dot product** $\mathbf{a} \cdot \mathbf{b}$ is given by
>
> $$\mathbf{a} \cdot \mathbf{b} = a_1 b_1 + a_2 b_2.$$

The dot product is also referred to as the **scalar product**, or **inner product**. It is important to note that $\mathbf{a} \cdot \mathbf{b}$ is a real number, and not a vector, as illustrated in the following example.

Example 1   Find $\mathbf{a} \cdot \mathbf{b}$ if

(a) $\mathbf{a} = \langle -5, 3 \rangle$, $\mathbf{b} = \langle 2, 6 \rangle$.

(b) $\mathbf{a} = 4\mathbf{i} + 6\mathbf{j}$, $\mathbf{b} = 3\mathbf{i} - 7\mathbf{j}$.

Solution   By definition,

(a) $\langle -5, 3 \rangle \cdot \langle 2, 6 \rangle = (-5)(2) + (3)(6) = -10 + 18 = 8$

(b) $(4\mathbf{i} + 6\mathbf{j}) \cdot (3\mathbf{i} - 7\mathbf{j}) = (4)(3) + (6)(-7) = 12 - 42 = -30.$ ∎

Properties of the Dot Product

> If $\mathbf{a}$, $\mathbf{b}$, $\mathbf{c}$ are vectors and c is a real number, then
>
> (i) $\mathbf{a} \cdot \mathbf{a} = |\mathbf{a}|^2$
>
> (ii) $\mathbf{a} \cdot \mathbf{b} = \mathbf{b} \cdot \mathbf{a}$
>
> (iii) $\mathbf{a} \cdot (\mathbf{b} + \mathbf{c}) = \mathbf{a} \cdot \mathbf{b} + \mathbf{a} \cdot \mathbf{c}$
>
> (iv) $(c\mathbf{a}) \cdot \mathbf{b} = c(\mathbf{a} \cdot \mathbf{b}) = \mathbf{a} \cdot (c\mathbf{b})$
>
> (v) $\mathbf{0} \cdot \mathbf{a} = 0.$

The proof of each property follows directly from the definition of dot product and properties of real numbers. Thus, if $\mathbf{a} = \langle a_1, a_2 \rangle$, $\mathbf{b} = \langle b_1, b_2 \rangle$, and $\mathbf{c} = \langle c_1, c_2 \rangle$, then

$$\begin{aligned}
\mathbf{a} \cdot (\mathbf{b} + \mathbf{c}) &= \langle a_1, a_2 \rangle \cdot \langle b_1 + c_1, b_2 + c_2 \rangle \\
&= a_1(b_1 + c_1) + a_2(b_2 + c_2) \\
&= (a_1 b_1 + a_2 b_2) + (a_1 c_1 + a_2 c_2) \\
&= \mathbf{a} \cdot \mathbf{b} + \mathbf{a} \cdot \mathbf{c}
\end{aligned}$$

which proves property (iii). The proofs of the remaining properties are left as an exercise.

Any two nonzero vectors $\mathbf{a} = \langle a_1, a_2 \rangle$ and $\mathbf{b} = \langle b_1, b_2 \rangle$ may be represented in a rectangular coordinate system by means of directed line segments from the origin O to the points $A(a_1, a_2)$ and $B(b_1, b_2)$, respectively. The **angle θ between a and b** is, by definition, angle AOB (see Figure 4.21). Note that $0 \leq \theta \leq \pi$, where $\theta = 0$ if **a** and **b** have the same direction, and $\theta = \pi$ if **a** and **b** have opposite directions.

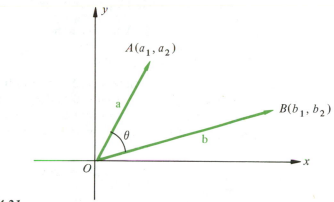

Figure 4.21

Definition

> Let θ be the angle between two nonzero vectors **a** and **b**.
>
> (a)   **a** and **b** are **parallel** if $\theta = 0$ or $\theta = \pi$.
>
> (b)   **a** and **b** are **orthogonal** if $\theta = \pi/2$.

Evidently, the vectors **a** and **b** in Figure 4.21 are parallel if and only if they lie on the same line that passes through the origin. In this case, $\mathbf{b} = c\mathbf{a}$ for some real number c. The vectors are orthogonal if and only if they lie on mutually perpendicular lines that pass through the origin. It is customary to assume that the zero vector **0** is parallel and orthogonal to *every* vector **a**.

The next theorem shows that there is a close relationship between the angle between two vectors and their dot product.

Theorem

> If θ is the angle between two nonzero vectors **a** and **b**, then
>
> $$\mathbf{a} \cdot \mathbf{b} = |\mathbf{a}||\mathbf{b}| \cos \theta.$$

Proof

If **a** and **b** are not parallel, we have a situation similar to that illustrated in Figure 4.21. We may then apply the Law of Cosines to triangle AOB. Since the lengths of the three sides of the triangle are $|\mathbf{a}|$, $|\mathbf{b}|$, and $d(A, B)$,

$$[d(A, B)]^2 = |\mathbf{a}|^2 + |\mathbf{b}|^2 - 2|\mathbf{a}||\mathbf{b}|\cos \theta.$$

Using the Distance Formula and the definition of magnitude of a vector, we obtain

$$(b_1 - a_1)^2 + (b_2 - a_2)^2 = a_1^2 + a_2^2 + b_1^2 + b_2^2 - 2|\mathbf{a}||\mathbf{b}| \cos \theta$$

which reduces to

$$-2a_1b_1 - 2a_2b_2 = -2|\mathbf{a}||\mathbf{b}|\cos\theta.$$

Dividing both sides of the last equation by -2 gives us

$$a_1b_1 + a_2b_2 = |\mathbf{a}||\mathbf{b}|\cos\theta$$

which is what we wished to prove.

If $\mathbf{a}$ and $\mathbf{b}$ are parallel, then either $\theta = 0$ or $\theta = \pi$. In this case, $\mathbf{b} = c\mathbf{a}$ for some real number c, where $c > 0$ if $\theta = 0$, and $c < 0$ if $\theta = \pi$. It can then be shown, using properties of the dot product, that $\mathbf{a} \cdot (c\mathbf{a}) = |\mathbf{a}||c\mathbf{a}|\cos\theta$, and hence, the theorem is true for all nonzero vectors $\mathbf{a}$ and $\mathbf{b}$.   ■

Corollary

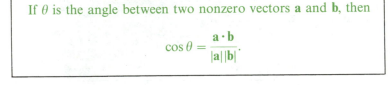

If θ is the angle between two nonzero vectors $\mathbf{a}$ and $\mathbf{b}$, then

$$\cos\theta = \frac{\mathbf{a}\cdot\mathbf{b}}{|\mathbf{a}||\mathbf{b}|}.$$

Example 2   Find the angle between $\mathbf{a} = \langle 4, -3\rangle$ and $\mathbf{b} = \langle 1, 2\rangle$.

Solution   The vectors are sketched in Figure 4.22.

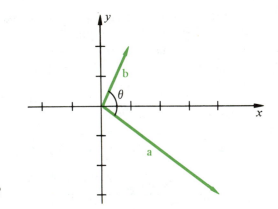

Figure 4.22

Applying the corollary,

$$\cos\theta = \frac{\mathbf{a}\cdot\mathbf{b}}{|\mathbf{a}||\mathbf{b}|} = \frac{(4)(1) + (-3)(2)}{\sqrt{16+9}\sqrt{1+4}} = \frac{-2}{5\sqrt{5}} = \frac{-2\sqrt{5}}{25}.$$

Hence,

$$\theta = \arccos\left(-2\sqrt{5}/25\right) \approx 100°18'.$$

■

Using the formula $\mathbf{a} \cdot \mathbf{b} = |\mathbf{a}||\mathbf{b}| \cos \theta$, together with the fact that two vectors are orthogonal if and only if the angle between them is $\pi/2$ (or one of the vectors is $\mathbf{0}$), gives us the following result.

Theorem

> Two vectors $\mathbf{a}$ and $\mathbf{b}$ are orthogonal if and only if $\mathbf{a} \cdot \mathbf{b} = 0$.

Example 3   Prove that the following pairs of vectors are orthogonal.

(a) $\mathbf{i}, \mathbf{j}$ (b) $2\mathbf{i} + 3\mathbf{j}, 6\mathbf{i} - 4\mathbf{j}$

Solution   We shall use the preceding theorem to prove orthogonality, Thus,

(a) $\mathbf{i} \cdot \mathbf{j} = \langle 1, 0 \rangle \cdot \langle 0, 1 \rangle = (1)(0) + (0)(1) = 0 + 0 = 0$

(b) $(2\mathbf{i} + 3\mathbf{j})(6\mathbf{i} - 4\mathbf{j}) = (2)(6) + (3)(-4) = 12 - 12 = 0.$ ∎

Definition

> Let θ be the angle between two nonzero vectors $\mathbf{a}$ and $\mathbf{b}$. The **component of a along b**, denoted by $\text{comp}_{\mathbf{b}}\, \mathbf{a}$, is given by
> $$\text{comp}_{\mathbf{b}}\, \mathbf{a} = |\mathbf{a}| \cos \theta.$$

The geometric significance of the preceding definition when θ is acute or obtuse is illustrated in Figure 4.23, where the x- and y-axes are not shown.

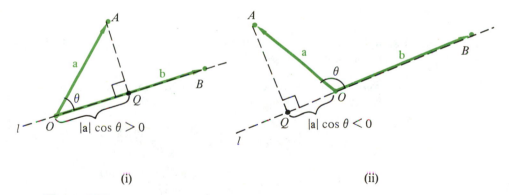

(i)   (ii)

Figure 4.23

If the angle θ is acute, then, as in (i) of Figure 4.23, we may form a right triangle by constructing a line segment AQ perpendicular to the line l through O and B. Note that the vector $\overrightarrow{OQ}$ has the same direction as $\overrightarrow{OB}$. Referring to (i) of the figure, we see that

$$\cos \theta = \frac{d(O, Q)}{|\mathbf{a}|}, \quad \text{or} \quad |\mathbf{a}| \cos \theta = d(O, Q).$$

If θ is obtuse, then, as in (ii) of Figure 4.23, we again construct AQ perpendicular to l. In this case, the direction of the vector $\overrightarrow{OQ}$ is opposite that of $\overrightarrow{OB}$, and since $\cos\theta$ is negative,

$$\cos\theta = \frac{-d(O,Q)}{|\mathbf{a}|}, \quad \text{or} \quad |\mathbf{a}|\cos\theta = -d(O,Q).$$

If $\theta = \pi/2$, then $\mathbf{a}$ is orthogonal to $\mathbf{b}$ and $\text{comp}_\mathbf{b}\,\mathbf{a} = 0$.
If $\theta = 0$, then $\mathbf{a}$ has the same direction as $\mathbf{b}$ and $\text{comp}_\mathbf{b}\,\mathbf{a} = |\mathbf{a}|$.
If $\theta = \pi$, then $\mathbf{a}$ and $\mathbf{b}$ have opposite directions and $\text{comp}_\mathbf{b}\,\mathbf{a} = -|\mathbf{a}|$.

The preceding discussion shows that the component of $\mathbf{a}$ along $\mathbf{b}$ may be found by *projecting* the endpoint of $\mathbf{a}$ onto the line l containing $\mathbf{b}$. For this reason, $|\mathbf{a}|\cos\theta$ is sometimes called the **projection of a on b**, and is denoted by $\text{proj}_\mathbf{b}\,\mathbf{a}$.

Theorem

> If $\mathbf{a}$ and $\mathbf{b}$ are nonzero vectors, then
>
> $$\text{comp}_\mathbf{b}\,\mathbf{a} = \frac{\mathbf{a}\cdot\mathbf{b}}{|\mathbf{b}|}.$$

Proof   If θ is the angle between $\mathbf{a}$ and $\mathbf{b}$, then, from the first theorem of this section,

$$\mathbf{a}\cdot\mathbf{b} = |\mathbf{a}||\mathbf{b}|\cos\theta.$$

Dividing both sides of this equation by $|\mathbf{b}|$ gives us

$$\frac{\mathbf{a}\cdot\mathbf{b}}{|\mathbf{b}|} = |\mathbf{a}|\cos\theta = \text{comp}_\mathbf{b}\,\mathbf{a}. \qquad \blacksquare$$

Example 4   If $\mathbf{c} = 10\mathbf{i} + 4\mathbf{j}$ and $\mathbf{d} = 3\mathbf{i} - 2\mathbf{j}$, find $\text{comp}_\mathbf{d}\,\mathbf{c}$ and $\text{comp}_\mathbf{c}\,\mathbf{d}$, and illustrate these numbers graphically.

Solution   The vectors $\mathbf{c}, \mathbf{d}$ and the desired components are illustrated in Figure 4.24. Using the preceding theorem,

$$\text{comp}_\mathbf{d}\,\mathbf{c} = \frac{\mathbf{c}\cdot\mathbf{d}}{|\mathbf{d}|} = \frac{(10)(3) + (4)(-2)}{\sqrt{9+4}} = \frac{22}{\sqrt{13}} \approx 6.10$$

$$\text{comp}_\mathbf{c}\,\mathbf{d} = \frac{\mathbf{d}\cdot\mathbf{c}}{|\mathbf{c}|} = \frac{(3)(10) + (-2)(4)}{\sqrt{100+16}} = \frac{22}{\sqrt{116}} \approx 2.04. \qquad \blacksquare$$

We shall conclude this section with an important physical application of the dot product. First let us briefly discuss the scientific concept of *work*.

A **force** may be thought of intuitively as the physical entity that is used to describe a push or pull on an object. For example, a force is needed to push or pull an object along a horizontal plane, to lift an object off the ground, or to move a charged particle through an electromagnetic field.

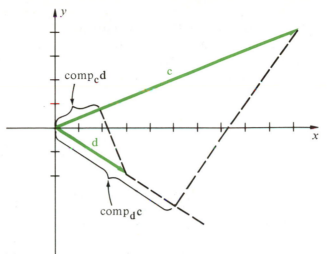

Figure 4.24

Forces are often measured in pounds. If an object weighs ten pounds, then by definition the force required to lift it (or hold it off the ground) is ten pounds. A force of this type is a **constant force**, since its magnitude does not change while it is applied to the given object.

If a constant force F is applied to an object, moving it a distance d in the direction of the force, then by definition the **work** W done on the object is given by

$$W = Fd.$$

If F is measured in pounds and d in feet, then the units for W are foot-pounds (ft-lb). In the metric system, a **dyne** is used as the unit of force. If F is expressed in dynes and d in centimeters, then the units for W are dyne-centimeters, or **ergs**.

Example 5   Find the work done in pushing an automobile along a level road from a point A to another point B, 20 feet from A, while exerting a constant force of 300 pounds.

Solution   The problem is illustrated in Figure 4.25, where we have pictured the road as part of a line l. Since the constant force is $F = 300$ lb and the distance the automobile moves is $d = 20$ ft, the work done is

$$W = (300)(20) = 6,000 \text{ ft-lb}.$$

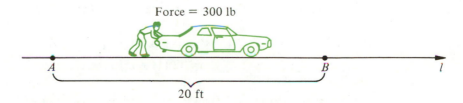

Force = 300 lb

A B l

20 ft

Figure 4.25

The formula $W = Fd$ is very restrictive, since it can only be used if the force is applied along the line of motion. More generally, suppose a vector **a** represents a force, and that its point of application moves along a vector **b**. This is illustrated in Figure 4.26, where the force **a** is used to pull an object along a level path from O to B.

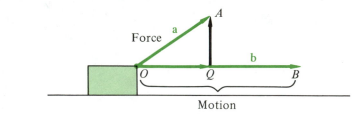

Motion

Figure 4.26

The vector **a** is the sum of the vectors $\overrightarrow{OQ}$ and $\overrightarrow{QA}$, where $\overrightarrow{QA}$ is orthogonal to **b**. Since $\overrightarrow{QA}$ does not contribute to the horizontal movement, we may assume that the motion from O to B is caused by $\overrightarrow{OQ}$ alone. Applying $W = Fd$, the work is the product of $|\overrightarrow{OQ}|$ and $|\mathbf{b}|$. Since $|\overrightarrow{OQ}| = \text{comp}_\mathbf{b}\, \mathbf{a}$, we obtain

$$W = (\text{comp}_\mathbf{b}\, \mathbf{a})|\mathbf{b}| = (|\mathbf{a}|\cos\theta)|\mathbf{b}| = \mathbf{a}\cdot\mathbf{b},$$

where θ represents angle AOQ. This leads to the following definition.

Definition

> The work W done by a constant force **a** as its point of application moves along a vector **b** is given by $W = \mathbf{a}\cdot\mathbf{b}$.

Example 6   The magnitude and direction of a constant force are given by $\mathbf{a} = 2\mathbf{i} + 5\mathbf{j}$. Find the work done if the point of application of the force moves a particle along a line from the origin to the point $P(4, 1)$.

Solution   The force **a** and the path $\mathbf{b} = \overrightarrow{OP}$ of the particle are sketched in Figure 4.27. Since $\mathbf{b} = \langle 4, 1\rangle = 4\mathbf{i} + \mathbf{j}$, we have, from the preceding definition,

$$W = \mathbf{a}\cdot\mathbf{b} = (2\mathbf{i} + 5\mathbf{j})\cdot(4\mathbf{i} + \mathbf{j})$$
$$= (2)(4) + (5)(1) = 13.$$

If, for example, the unit of length is feet and the magnitude of the force is measured in pounds, then the work done is 13 ft-lb.

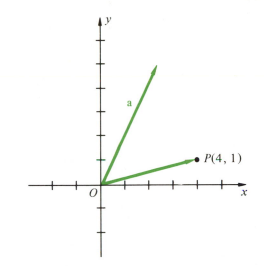

Figure 4.27

EXERCISES 4.6

In each of Exercises 1–6, find (a) the dot product of the two vectors; (b) the angle between the two vectors.

1 $\langle -2, 5 \rangle$, $\langle 3, 6 \rangle$ **2** $\langle 4, -7 \rangle$, $\langle -2, 3 \rangle$

3 $4\mathbf{i} - \mathbf{j}$, $-3\mathbf{i} + 2\mathbf{j}$ **4** $8\mathbf{i} - 3\mathbf{j}$, $2\mathbf{i} - 7\mathbf{j}$

5 $9\mathbf{i}$, $5\mathbf{i} + 4\mathbf{j}$ **6** $6\mathbf{j}$, $-4\mathbf{i}$

In each of Exercises 7–10, prove that the vectors are orthogonal.

7 $\langle 4, -1 \rangle$, $\langle 2, 8 \rangle$ **8** $\langle 3, 6 \rangle$, $\langle 4, -2 \rangle$

9 $-4\mathbf{j}$, $-7\mathbf{i}$ **10** $8\mathbf{i} - 4\mathbf{j}$, $-6\mathbf{i} - 12\mathbf{j}$

In each of Exercises 11 and 12, determine c such that the two vectors are orthogonal.

11 $3\mathbf{i} - 2\mathbf{j}$, $4\mathbf{i} + 5c\mathbf{j}$ **12** $4c\mathbf{i} + \mathbf{j}$, $9c\mathbf{i} - 25\mathbf{j}$

If $\mathbf{a} = \langle 2, -3 \rangle$, $\mathbf{b} = \langle 3, 4 \rangle$, and $\mathbf{c} = \langle -1, 5 \rangle$, find the numbers in Exercises 13–20.

13 (a) $\mathbf{a} \cdot (\mathbf{b} + \mathbf{c})$ (b) $\mathbf{a} \cdot \mathbf{b} + \mathbf{a} \cdot \mathbf{c}$

14 (a) $\mathbf{b} \cdot (\mathbf{a} - \mathbf{c})$ (b) $\mathbf{b} \cdot \mathbf{a} - \mathbf{b} \cdot \mathbf{c}$

15 $(2\mathbf{a} + \mathbf{b}) \cdot (3\mathbf{c})$ **16** $(\mathbf{a} - \mathbf{b}) \cdot (\mathbf{b} + \mathbf{c})$

17 $\text{comp}_\mathbf{c} \mathbf{b}$ **18** $\text{comp}_\mathbf{b} \mathbf{c}$

19 $\text{comp}_\mathbf{b} (\mathbf{a} + \mathbf{c})$ **20** $\text{comp}_\mathbf{c} \mathbf{c}$

In each of Exercises 21–24, $\mathbf{a}$ represents a constant force. Find the work done if $\mathbf{a}$ moves a particle along the line segment from P to Q.

21 $\mathbf{a} = 3\mathbf{i} + 4\mathbf{j}$; $P(0, 0)$, $Q(5, -2)$

22 $\mathbf{a} = -10\mathbf{i} + 12\mathbf{j}$; $P(0, 0)$, $Q(4, 7)$

23 $\mathbf{a} = 6\mathbf{i} + 4\mathbf{j}$; $P(2, -1)$, $Q(4, 3)$ (*Hint:* Find a vector $\mathbf{b} = \langle b_1, b_2 \rangle$ such that $\mathbf{b} = \vec{PQ}$.)

24 $\mathbf{a} = -\mathbf{i} + 7\mathbf{j}$; $P(-2, 5)$, $Q(6, 1)$

25 A constant force of magnitude 4 has the same direction as $\mathbf{j}$. Find the work done if its point of application moves from $P(0, 0)$ to $Q(8, 3)$.

26 A constant force of magnitude 10 has the same direction as $-\mathbf{i}$. Find the work done if its point of application moves from $P(0, 1)$ to $Q(1, 0)$.

27 Prove properties (i), (ii), (iv), and (v) of the dot product listed on page 180.

4.7 REVIEW

Concepts

Define or discuss each of the following

1   The Law of Sines

2   The Law of Cosines

3   The Law of Tangents

4   Formulas for areas of triangles

5   Vector

6   Magnitude of a vector

7   Addition of vectors

8   Scalar multiple of a vector

9   Vectors as ordered pairs

10   Components of a vector

11   Subtraction of vectors

12   Unit vector

13   Dot product

14   Parallel vectors

15   Orthogonal vectors

16   Component of **a** along **b**

17   Work

Exercises

In each of Exercises 1–12, approximate the remaining parts of triangle ABC. Solve Exercises 1–6 without the use of tables or calculators.

1   $\alpha = 60°$, $\beta = 45°$, $b = 100$

2   $\gamma = 30°$, $a = 2\sqrt{3}$, $c = 2$

3   $\alpha = 60°$, $b = 6$, $c = 7$

4   $a = 2$, $b = 3$, $c = 4$

5   $a = 10$, $b = 10$, $\gamma = 60°$

6   $a = 10$, $b = 10$, $\gamma = 120°$

7   $a = 78.5$, $\alpha = 72°50'$, $\beta = 47°20'$

8   $c = 127$, $\alpha = 16°30'$, $\beta = 135°20'$

9   $a = 25$, $b = 50$, $c = 70$

10   $a = 10.0$, $b = 11.0$, $\gamma = 50°10'$

11   $a = 320$, $b = 370$, $\alpha = 24°10'$

12   $a = 150$, $b = 80$, $c = 170$

13–14 Approximate the areas of the triangles in Exercises 7 and 9.

15   If $\mathbf{a} = \langle -4, 5 \rangle$ and $\mathbf{b} = \langle 2, -8 \rangle$, find $\mathbf{a} + \mathbf{b}$, $\mathbf{a} - \mathbf{b}$, $2\mathbf{a}$, and $-\frac{1}{2}\mathbf{b}$.

16   If $\mathbf{a} = 2\mathbf{i} + 5\mathbf{j}$ and $\mathbf{b} = 4\mathbf{i} - \mathbf{j}$, find the vectors or numbers corresponding to:
(a) $4\mathbf{a} + \mathbf{b}$ (b) $2\mathbf{a} - 3\mathbf{b}$ (c) $|\mathbf{a} - \mathbf{b}|$
(d) $|\mathbf{a}| - |\mathbf{b}|$.

17   If $\mathbf{a} = 6\mathbf{i} - 2\mathbf{j}$ and $\mathbf{b} = \mathbf{i} + 3\mathbf{j}$, find each of the following.
(a) $(2\mathbf{a} - 3\mathbf{b}) \cdot \mathbf{a}$
(b)   the angle between $\mathbf{a}$ and $\mathbf{a} + \mathbf{b}$
(c) $\text{comp}_{\mathbf{a}}\,(\mathbf{a} + \mathbf{b})$

18   A constant force has the magnitude and direction of $\mathbf{a} = 7\mathbf{i} + 4\mathbf{j}$. Find the work done if $\mathbf{a}$ moves a particle along the x-axis from $P(-5, 0)$ to $Q(3, 0)$.

COMPLEX NUMBERS

Complex numbers were invented to help solve equations of the form $f(x) = 0$, where $f(x)$ is any polynomial. In this chapter we shall define complex numbers and consider some of their basic properties.

5.1 DEFINITION OF COMPLEX NUMBERS

Although real numbers are adequate for many mathematical and scientific problems, there is a serious defect in the system when it comes to solving some equations. Indeed, since the square of a real number cannot be negative, an equation such as $x^2 = -5$ has no solutions if x is restricted to $\mathbb{R}$. For many applications we need a mathematical system in which such equations have solutions. Fortunately, it is possible to construct such a system: the system of *complex numbers* defined in this section.

Let us consider the problem of inventing a new mathematical system $\mathbb{C}$ that contains the real number system $\mathbb{R}$ and that can be used to solve equations such as $x^2 = -5$. Since $\mathbb{C}$ is to be used to find solutions of equations, it must possess *operations*, that is, rules which may be applied to every pair of its elements to obtain another element. As a matter of fact, we would like to define operations called *addition* and *multiplication* in such a way that if we restrict the elements to the subset $\mathbb{R}$, then the operations behave in the same way as addition and multiplication of real numbers. Since we are extending the notions of addition and multiplication to the set $\mathbb{C}$, we shall continue to use the symbols $+$ and $\cdot$ for those operations.

In order to gain some insight into the construction of $\mathbb{C}$, let us begin by taking an intuitive approach. If we want equations of the form $x^2 = -k$ to have solutions when k is a positive real number, then in particular when $k = 1$ it is necessary for $\mathbb{C}$ to contain some element i such that $i^2 = -1$. If b is in $\mathbb{R}$, then b is also in $\mathbb{C}$, and since $\mathbb{C}$ is to be closed relative to multiplication, bi must be in $\mathbb{C}$. Moreover, if a is in $\mathbb{R}$ and if $\mathbb{C}$ is to be closed relative to addition, then $a + bi$ is in $\mathbb{C}$. Thus, $\mathbb{C}$ contains elements of the form $a + bi$, $c + di$, etc., where a, b, c, and d are real numbers and $i^2 = -1$. If we want properties similar to those for real numbers to be valid, then these elements must add as follows:

$$(a + bi) + (c + di) = (a + c) + (bi + di)$$

or

(A)
$$(a + bi) + (c + di) = (a + c) + (b + d)i.$$

Similarly, if $i^2 = -1$, the following manipulations should be valid:

$$
\begin{aligned}
(a + bi)(c + di) &= (a + bi)c + (a + bi)(di) \\
&= ac + (bi)c + a(di) + (bi)(di) \\
&= ac + (bc)i + (ad)i + (bd)(i^2) \\
&= ac + (bd)(-1) + (ad)i + (bc)i \\
&= (ac - bd) + (ad + bc)i.
\end{aligned}
$$

To summarize, the following rule for multiplication must hold in $\mathbb{C}$:

(M)
$$(a + bi)(c + di) = (ac - bd) + (ad + bc)i.$$

The preceding discussion indicates the manner in which elements must behave if a system of the required type is to exist. Moreover, our discussion provides a key to the actual construction of $\mathbb{C}$. Thus, we begin by *defining* a **complex number** as any symbol of the form $a + bi$, where a and b are real numbers. The real number a is called the **real part** of the complex number and bi is called the **imaginary part**. At the outset the letter i is given no specific meaning and the $+$ sign that appears in $a + bi$ is not to be interpreted as the symbol for addition, but only as part of the notation for a complex number. As above, $\mathbb{C}$ will denote the set of all complex numbers. Two complex numbers $a + bi$ and $c + di$ are said to be **equal**, and we write

$$a + bi = c + di \quad \text{if and only if} \quad a = c \text{ and } b = d.$$

Next we *define* addition and multiplication of complex numbers by means of formulas (A) and (M). It should be observed that the $+$ sign is used in three different ways in (A). First, by our previous remarks, it is part of the symbol for a complex number. Second, it is used to denote addition of the complex numbers $a + bi$ and $c + di$. Third, it is the addition sign for real numbers, as in the expressions $a + c$ and $b + d$. The need for remembering this threefold use of $+$ will disappear after we agree on the notational conventions that follow.

Let us consider the subset $\mathbb{R}'$ of $\mathbb{C}$ consisting of all complex numbers of the form $a + 0i$, where a is a real number. By associating a with $a + 0i$, we obtain a one-to-one correspondence between the sets $\mathbb{R}$ and $\mathbb{R}'$. Applying (A) and (M) to the elements of $\mathbb{R}'$ (by letting $b = d = 0$), we obtain

$$(a + 0i) + (c + 0i) = (a + c) + 0i$$
$$(a + 0i)(c + 0i) = ac + 0i.$$

This shows that in order to add (or multiply) two elements of $\mathbb{R}'$, we merely add (or multiply) the real parts, *disregarding* the imaginary parts. Hence, as far as properties of addition and multiplication are concerned, the only difference between $\mathbb{R}$ and $\mathbb{R}'$ is the notation for the elements. Accordingly, we shall use the symbol a in place of $a + 0i$. For example, an element such as 3 of $\mathbb{R}$ (or $\mathbb{C}$) is considered the same as the element $3 + 0i$ of $\mathbb{C}$. It is also convenient to abbreviate the complex number $0 + bi$ by the symbol bi. Applying (A) gives us

$$(a + 0i) + (0 + bi) = (a + 0) + (0 + b)i = a + bi.$$

This indicates that $a + bi$ may be thought of as the sum of two complex numbers a and bi, that is, $a + 0i$ and $0 + bi$. With these agreements on notation, all the $+$ signs in (A) may be regarded as addition of complex numbers.

Example 1   Express each of the following in the form $a + bi$, where a and b are real numbers.

(a) $(3 + 4i) + (2 + 5i)$ (b) $(3 + 4i)(2 + 5i)$ (c) $(3 + 4i)^2$

Solution

(a)   Applying (A),

$$(3 + 4i) + (2 + 5i) = (3 + 2) + (4 + 5)i = 5 + 9i.$$

(b)   Using (M),

$$(3 + 4i)(2 + 5i) = (3 \cdot 2 - 4 \cdot 5) + (3 \cdot 5 + 4 \cdot 2)i = -14 + 23i.$$

(c)   Exponents are defined in $\mathbb{C}$ exactly as they are in $\mathbb{R}$. Thus,

$$
\begin{aligned}
(3 + 4i)^2 &= (3 + 4i)(3 + 4i) \\
&= (3 \cdot 3 - 4 \cdot 4) + (3 \cdot 4 + 4 \cdot 3)i \\
&= -7 + 24i.
\end{aligned}
$$
■

It is not difficult to show that addition and multiplication of complex numbers are both commutative and associative. The distributive property is also true. The identity element relative to addition is 0 (or, equivalently, $0 + 0i$), since

$$
\begin{aligned}
(a + bi) + 0 &= (a + bi) + (0 + 0i) \\
&= (a + 0) + (b + 0)i \\
&= a + bi.
\end{aligned}
$$

As usual, we refer to 0 as **zero** or the **zero element.** It follows from (M) that the *product* of zero and any complex number is zero. We may also use (M) to prove that 1 (that is, $1 + 0i$) is the identity element relative to multiplication.

If $(-a) + (-b)i$ is added to $a + bi$, we obtain 0. This implies that $(-a) + (-b)i$ is the additive inverse of $a + bi$, that is,

$$-(a + bi) = (-a) + (-b)i.$$

We shall postpone the discussion of multiplicative inverses until the next section.

Subtraction of complex numbers is defined using additive inverses as follows:

$$(a + bi) - (c + di) = (a + bi) + [-(c + di)].$$

Since $-(c + di) = (-c) + (-d)i$, it follows that

$$(a + bi) - (c + di) = (a - c) + (b - d)i.$$

The special case with $b = c = 0$ gives us

$$(a + 0i) - (0 + di) = (a - 0) + (0 - d)i$$

which may be written in the form

$$a - di = a + (-d)i.$$

The preceding formula is useful when the real number associated with the imaginary part of a complex number is negative.

If c, d, and k are real numbers, then by (M) and our agreement on notation,

$$k(c + di) = (k + 0i)(c + di) = (kc - 0d) + (kd + 0c)i$$

that is,

$$k(c + di) = kc + (kd)i.$$

One illustration of this formula is

$$3(5 + 2i) = 15 + 6i.$$

The special case with $k = -1$ gives us

$$(-1)(c + di) = (-c) + (-d)i = -(c + di).$$

Hence, as in $\mathbb{R}$, the additive inverse of a complex number may be found by multiplying it by -1.

The complex number $0 + 1i$ (or, equivalently, $1i$) will be denoted by i. Observe that

$$b(0 + 1i) = (b \cdot 0) + (b \cdot 1)i = 0 + bi = bi.$$

Thus, the symbol bi which has been used throughout this section may be regarded as the *product* of b and i.

Finally, using (M) with $a = c = 0$ and $b = d = 1$, we obtain

$$i^2 = (0 + 1i)(0 + 1i)$$
$$= (0 \cdot 0 - 1 \cdot 1) + (0 \cdot 1 + 1 \cdot 0)i$$
$$= -1 + 0i.$$

This gives us the following important rule:

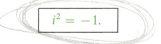

$$i^2 = -1.$$

If we collect all of the formulas and remarks made in this section, it becomes evident that, when working with complex numbers, *we may treat all symbols just as though they represented real numbers with exactly one exception: wherever the symbol i^2 appears it may be replaced by* -1. Consequently, manipulations can be carried out without referring to (A) or (M), which is what we had in mind from the very beginning of our discussion! We shall use this technique in the solution of the next example. If, as in Example 2, we are asked to write an expression in the form $a + bi$, we shall also accept the form $a - di$ since we have seen that it equals $a + (-d)i$.

Example 2   Write each of the following in the form $a + bi$.

(a) $4(2 + 5i) - (3 - 4i)$ (b) $(4 - 3i)(2 + i)$

(c) $i(3 - 2i)^2$ (d) i^{51}

Solution

(a) $4(2 + 5i) - (3 - 4i) = 8 + 20i - 3 + 4i = 5 + 24i$

(b) $(4 - 3i)(2 + i) = 8 - 6i + 4i - 3i^2 = 11 - 2i$

(c) $i(3 - 2i)^2 = i(9 - 12i + 4i^2) = i(5 - 12i) = 5i - 12i^2 = 12 + 5i$

(d)   Taking successive powers of i, we obtain $i^1 = i, i^2 = -1, i^3 = -i, i^4 = 1$, and then the cycle starts over: $i^5 = i,\ i^6 = i^2 = -1$, etc. In particular, $i^{51} = i^{48}i^3 = (i^4)^{12}i^3 = (1)^{12}i^3 = i^3 = -i.$ ■

Finally, it should be pointed out that there is another way to define complex numbers. Observe that each symbol $a + bi$ determines a unique ordered pair (a, b) of real numbers. Conversely, every ordered pair (a, b) can be used to obtain a symbol $a + bi$. In this way we obtain a one-to-one correspondence between the symbols $a + bi$ and ordered pairs (a, b). The correspondence suggests using ordered pairs of real numbers to define the system $\mathbb{C}$. Formulas (A) and (M) can then be used to motivate definitions for addition and multiplication. Specifically, we define $\mathbb{C}$ as the set of all ordered pairs of real numbers subject to the following two laws:

$$(a, b) + (c, d) = (a + c, b + d)$$
$$(a, b)(c, d) = (ac - bd, ad + bc).$$

Notice the manner in which (A) and (M) were used to help formulate the definition. We merely replaced symbols such as $a + bi$ by (a, b) and translated the rules accordingly. By a suitable change in notation we can obtain the $a + bi$ form for complex numbers introduced in this section.

EXERCISES 5.1

In each of Exercises 1–36, write the expression in the form $a + bi$.

1 $(3 + 2i) + (-5 + 4i)$

2 $(8 - 5i) + (2 - 3i)$

3 $(-4 + 5i) + (2 - i)$

4 $(5 + 7i) + (-8 - 4i)$

5 $(16 + 10i) - (9 + 15i)$

6 $(2 - 6i) - (7 + 2i)$

7 $-(-2 + 7i) + (-6 + 6i)$

8 $-(5 - 3i) - (-3 - 4i)$

9 $7 - (3 - 7i)$

10 $-9 + (5 + 9i)$

11 $5i - (6 + 2i)$

12 $(10 + 7i) - 12i$

13 $(4 + 3i)(-1 + 2i)$

14 $(3 - 6i)(2 + i)$

15 $(-7 + i)(-3 + i)$

16 $(5 + 2i)(5 - 2i)$

17 $(3 + 4i)(3 - 4i)$

18 $7i(13 + 8i)$

19 $-9i(4 - 8i)$

20 $(6i)(-2i)$

21 $4(8 - 11i)$

22 $-3(-6 + 12i)$

23 $(-3i)(5i)$

24 $(1 - i)(1 + i)$

25 $(\sqrt{7} + \sqrt{3}i)(\sqrt{7} - \sqrt{3}i)$

26 $(-7 + 3i)^2$

27 $(3 + 2i)^2$

28 $4i(2 + 5i)^2$

29 $i(3 - 2i)(5 + i)$

30 $(1 + i)^4$

31 $\left(-\dfrac{1}{2} - \dfrac{\sqrt{3}}{2}i\right)^3$

32 $\left(-\dfrac{1}{2} + \dfrac{\sqrt{3}}{2}i\right)^3$

33 i^{42}

34 i^{23}

35 i^{157}

36 $(-i)^{50}$

In Exercises 37–40, solve for x and y, if x and y are real.

37 $5x + 6i = -8 + 2yi$

38 $7 - 4yi = 9x + 3i$

39 $i(2x - 4y) = 4x + 2 + 3yi$

40 $(2x + y) + (3x - 4y)i = (x - 2) + (2y - 5)i$

5.2 CONJUGATES AND INVERSES

The complex number $a - bi$ is called the **conjugate** of the complex number $a + bi$. Since

$$\boxed{(a + bi)(a - bi) = a^2 + b^2}$$

we see that the product of a complex number and its conjugate is a real number. If $a^2 + b^2 \neq 0$, then multiplying both sides of the last equation by $1/(a^2 + b^2)$ and rearranging terms on the left-hand side gives us

$$\left(\frac{1}{a^2 + b^2}\right)(a - bi)(a + bi) = 1.$$

Hence, if $a + bi \neq 0$, then the complex number $a + bi$ has a multiplicative inverse denoted by $(a + bi)^{-1}$, or $1/(a + bi)$, where

$$\boxed{\frac{1}{a + bi} = \left(\frac{1}{a^2 + b^2}\right)(a - bi).}$$

If $c + di \neq 0$, we define the **quotient**

$$\frac{a + bi}{c + di}$$

to be the product of $a + bi$ and $1/(c + di)$. We can write this quotient in the form $u + vi$, where u and v are real numbers, by multiplying numerator and denominator by the conjugate $c - di$ of the denominator as follows:

$$\frac{a + bi}{c + di} = \frac{a + bi}{c + di} \cdot \frac{c - di}{c - di}$$

$$= \frac{(ac + bd) + (bc - ad)i}{c^2 + d^2}$$

$$= \left(\frac{ac + bd}{c^2 + d^2}\right) + \left(\frac{bc - ad}{c^2 + d^2}\right)i.$$

The above technique may also be used to find the multiplicative inverse of $(a + bi)$. Specifically, we multiply numerator and denominator of $1/(a + bi)$ by $a - bi$ as follows:

$$\frac{1}{a + bi} = \frac{1}{a + bi} \cdot \frac{a - bi}{a - bi}$$

$$= \frac{a - bi}{a^2 + b^2} = \frac{1}{a^2 + b^2}(a - bi).$$

Example 1   Express each of the following in the form $a + bi$.

(a) $\dfrac{1}{9 + 2i}$ (b) $\dfrac{7 - i}{3 - 5i}$

Solution

(a) $\dfrac{1}{9 + 2i} = \dfrac{1}{9 + 2i} \cdot \dfrac{9 - 2i}{9 - 2i} = \dfrac{9 - 2i}{81 + 4} = \dfrac{9}{85} - \dfrac{2}{85}i$

(b) $\dfrac{7 - i}{3 - 5i} = \dfrac{7 - i}{3 - 5i} \cdot \dfrac{3 + 5i}{3 + 5i}$

$\qquad = \dfrac{21 - 3i + 35i - 5i^2}{9 - 25i^2}$

$\qquad = \dfrac{26 + 32i}{34} = \dfrac{13}{17} + \dfrac{16}{17}i.$ ∎

Real numbers can be represented geometrically by means of points on a coordinate line. We can also obtain geometric representations for complex numbers by using points in a coordinate plane. Specifically, each complex number $a + bi$ determines a unique ordered pair (a, b). The corresponding point $P(a, b)$ in a coordinate plane is called the **geometric representation of** $a + bi$. To emphasize that we are assigning complex numbers to points in a plane, the point $P(a, b)$ will be labeled $a + bi$. A coordinate plane with a complex number assigned to each point is referred to as the **complex plane** instead of the xy-plane. Also, according to this scheme, the x-axis is called the **real axis** and the y-axis the **imaginary axis**. In Figure 5.1, we have indicated the geometric representations of several complex numbers. Note that to obtain the point corresponding to the conjugate $a - bi$ of any complex number $a + bi$ we simply reflect through the real axis.

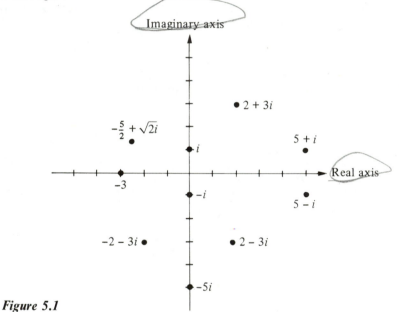

Figure 5.1

In Chapter One we defined the concept of the absolute value $|a|$ of a real number a and noted that geometrically a is the distance between the origin and the point on a coordinate line which corresponds to a. It is natural, therefore, to interpret the absolute value $a + bi$ of a complex number as the distance $\sqrt{a^2 + b^2}$ between the origin of a complex plane and the point (a, b) corresponding to $a + bi$, as in the following definition.

Definition

> The **absolute value** of a complex number $a + bi$ is denoted by $|a + bi|$ and is defined to be the nonnegative real number $\sqrt{a^2 + b^2}$.

Example 2   Find (a) $|2 - 6i|$;   (b) $|3i|$.

Solution   Using the definition of absolute value, we obtain

(a) $|2 - 6i| = \sqrt{4 + 36} = \sqrt{40} = 2\sqrt{10}$

(b) $|3i| = \sqrt{0 + 9} = 3.$ ∎

It is worth noting that the points which correspond to all of the complex numbers having a fixed absolute value lie on a circle with center at the origin in the complex plane. For example, the points corresponding to the complex numbers z with $|z| = 1$ lie on a unit circle.

EXERCISES 5.2

In each of Exercises 1–28, express the given number in the form $a + bi$.

1 $\dfrac{1}{3 + 2i}$

2 $\dfrac{1}{5 + 8i}$

3 $\dfrac{7}{5 - 6i}$

4 $\dfrac{-3}{2 - 5i}$

5 $\dfrac{4 - 3i}{2 + 4i}$

6 $\dfrac{4 + 3i}{-1 + 2i}$

7 $\dfrac{6 + 4i}{1 - 5i}$

8 $\dfrac{7 - 6i}{-5 - i}$

9 $\dfrac{21 - 7i}{i}$

10 $\dfrac{10 + 9i}{-3i}$

11 $\dfrac{2 - 3i}{1 + i} + \dfrac{7 + 4i}{3 + 5i}$

12 $\dfrac{6 - 2i}{3 + i} - \dfrac{3 - 7i}{i}$

13 $8 + \dfrac{4 - i}{1 + 2i}$

14 $\dfrac{1}{10 - i} + 5i$

15 $\dfrac{1}{(1 + i)^3}$

16 $\dfrac{(1 - i)^3}{1 + i}$

17 $\dfrac{4 - i^2}{i - 2}$

18 $\dfrac{4i^2 - 25}{5 + 2i}$

19 $\left(\dfrac{1}{5i}\right)^3$

20 $\dfrac{1}{(3 + 2i)^2}$

21 $|3 - 4i|$

22 $|5 + 8i|$

23 $|-6 - 7i|$

24 $|1 - i|$

25 $|8i|$

26 $|i^7|$

27 $|i^{500}|$

28 $|-15i|$

Represent the complex numbers in Exercises 29–38 geometrically.

29 $4 + 2i$

30 $-5 + 3i$

31 $3 - 5i$

32 $-2 - 6i$

33 $-(3 - 6i)$

34 $(1 + 2i)^2$

35 $2i(2 + 3i)$

36 $(-3i)(2 - i)$

37 $(1 + i)^2$

38 $4(-1 + 2i)$

In each of Exercises 39–42, find all complex numbers z that satisfy the given equation, and express z in the form $a + bi$.

39 $5z + 3i = 2iz + 4$

40 $2iz - 6 = 9i + z$

41 $(z - 2i)^2 = (z + 3i)^2$

42 $z(z + 4i) = (z + i)(z - 3i)$

5.3 COMPLEX ROOTS OF EQUATIONS

It is easy to see that if p is any positive real number, then the equation $x^2 = -p$ has solutions in $\mathbb{C}$. As a matter of fact, one solution is $\sqrt{p}i$, since

$$(\sqrt{p}i)^2 = (\sqrt{p})^2 i^2 = p(-1) = -p.$$

Similarly, $-\sqrt{p}i$ is also a solution. Moreover, they are the only solutions, for if a complex number z is a solution, then $z^2 + p = 0$, and hence,

$$(z + \sqrt{p}i)(z - \sqrt{p}i) = 0.$$

This implies that either $z = -\sqrt{p}i$ or $z = \sqrt{p}i$.

The next definition is motivated by the fact that $(\sqrt{p}i)^2 = -p$.

Definition

> If p is a positive real number, then the **principal square root** of $-p$ is denoted by $\sqrt{-p}$ and is defined to be the complex number $\sqrt{p}i$.

As illustrations, we have

$$\sqrt{-9} = \sqrt{9}i = 3i, \quad \sqrt{-5} = \sqrt{5}i, \quad \sqrt{-1} = \sqrt{1}i = i.$$

Care must be taken in using the radical sign if the radicand is negative. For example, the formula $\sqrt{a}\sqrt{b} = \sqrt{ab}$, which holds for positive real numbers, is not true when both a and b are negative. To illustrate,

$$\sqrt{-3}\sqrt{-3} = (\sqrt{3}i)(\sqrt{3}i) = (\sqrt{3})^2 i^2 = 3(-1) = -3$$

whereas

$$\sqrt{(-3)(-3)} = \sqrt{9} = 3.$$

Hence,

$$\sqrt{-3}\sqrt{-3} \neq \sqrt{(-3)(-3)}.$$

However, if only *one* of a or b is negative, then it can be shown that $\sqrt{a}\sqrt{b} = \sqrt{ab}$. In general, we shall not apply laws of radicals if radicands are negative. Instead, we shall change the form of radicals before performing any operations, as illustrated in the next example.

Example 1   Express $(5 - \sqrt{-3})(-1 + \sqrt{-4})$ in the form $a + bi$.

Solution
$$(5 - \sqrt{-3})(-1 + \sqrt{-4}) = (5 - \sqrt{3}i)(-1 + 2i)$$
$$= -5 - 2\sqrt{3}i^2 + 10i + \sqrt{3}i$$
$$= (-5 + 2\sqrt{3}) + (10 + \sqrt{3})i.$$ ∎

In Section 1.1 we pointed out that if a, b, and c are real numbers such that $b^2 - 4ac \geq 0$ and $a \neq 0$, then the solutions of the quadratic equation $ax^2 + bx + c = 0$ are given by the *Quadratic Formula*:

$$x = \frac{-b \pm \sqrt{b^2 - 4ac}}{2a}.$$

We may now extend this fact to the case where $b^2 - 4ac < 0$. Indeed, if $b^2 - 4ac < 0$, then the solutions of $ax^2 + bx + c = 0$ are the two *complex* numbers given by the formula. Notice that the solutions are conjugates of each other.

Example 2 Find the solutions of the equation $5x^2 + 2x + 1 = 0$.

Solution By the Quadratic Formula, we have

$$x = \frac{-2 \pm \sqrt{4 - 20}}{10} = \frac{-2 \pm \sqrt{-16}}{10} = \frac{-2 \pm 4i}{10}.$$

Dividing numerator and denominator by 2, we see that the solutions of the equation are $-\frac{1}{5} + (\frac{2}{5})i$ and $-\frac{1}{5} - (\frac{2}{5})i$. ∎

Example 3 Find the roots of the equation $x^3 - 1 = 0$.

Solution The given equation may be written as

$$(x - 1)(x^2 + x + 1) = 0.$$

Setting each factor equal to zero and solving the resulting equations, we obtain the solutions

$$1, \quad \frac{-1 \pm \sqrt{1 - 4}}{2}$$

which may be written as

$$1, \quad -\frac{1}{2} + \frac{\sqrt{3}}{2}i, \quad -\frac{1}{2} - \frac{\sqrt{3}}{2}i.$$ ∎

The three roots of $x^3 - 1 = 0$ are called the **cube roots of unity**. It can be shown that if n is any positive integer, then the equation $x^n - 1 = 0$ has n distinct complex roots. They are called the **nth roots of unity**.

It is easy to form a quadratic equation having complex roots z and w. We merely write

$$(x - z)(x - w) = 0.$$

The most important situation occurs if $w = \bar{z}$, the conjugate of z. In this case the equation has the form

$$(x - z)(x - \bar{z}) = 0$$

or, equivalently,

$$x^2 - (z + \bar{z})x + z\bar{z} = 0.$$

If $z = a + bi$, then $\bar{z} = a - bi$, and hence,

$$z + \bar{z} = 2a \quad \text{and} \quad z\bar{z} = a^2 + b^2;$$

that is, the quadratic equation has real coefficients.

Example 4   Find a quadratic equation that has roots $3 + 2i$ and $3 - 2i$.

Solution   By the preceding remarks, the equation is given by $(x - 3 - 2i)(x - 3 + 2i) = 0$. This simplifies to $x^2 - 6x + 13 = 0$. ∎

Quadratic equations with complex coefficients may also be considered. It can be shown that the solutions are again given by the Quadratic Formula. Since in this case $b^2 - 4ac$ may be complex, the solution of such an equation may involve finding the square root of a complex number. We shall not discuss the general theory of roots of complex numbers here.

EXERCISES 5.3

In each of Exercises 1–12, express the given number in the form $a + bi$.

1 $\sqrt{-5}\sqrt{-5}$

2 $(-\sqrt{5})(\sqrt{-5})$

3 $(3 + \sqrt{-16}) - (6 - \sqrt{-9})$

4 $(4 - \sqrt{-4}) + (3 - \sqrt{-25})$

5 $(7 + \sqrt{-5})(7 - \sqrt{-5})$

6 $(\sqrt{-9} + 3)(\sqrt{-16} - 5)$

7 $\sqrt{-2}(\sqrt{2} + \sqrt{-2})$

8 $\sqrt{-3}(3 - \sqrt{-12})$

9 $(\sqrt{-10})^3$

10 $\sqrt{(-10)^3}$

11 $\dfrac{5 + \sqrt{-4}}{1 + \sqrt{-9}}$

12 $\dfrac{1}{6 + \sqrt{-3}}$

Find the solutions of the equations in Exercises 13–26.

13 $x^2 - 3x + 10 = 0$

14 $x^2 - 5x + 20 = 0$

15 $x^2 + 2x + 5 = 0$

16 $x^2 + 3x + 6 = 0$

17 $4x^2 + x + 3 = 0$

18 $-3x^2 + x - 5 = 0$

19 $x^3 - 125 = 0$

20 $x^3 + 27 = 0$

21 $x^6 - 64 = 0$ **22** $x^4 = 81$

23 $4x^4 + 25x^2 + 36 = 0$

24 $27x^4 + 21x^2 + 4 = 0$

25 $x^3 + 3x^2 + 4x = 0$

26 $8x^3 - 12x^2 + 2x - 3 = 0$

In each of Exercises 27–38, find a quadratic equation with the given roots.

27 $4 + i, \quad 4 - i$

28 $1 + 3i, \quad 1 - 3i$

29 $-3 + 2i, \quad -3 - 2i$

30 $\frac{1}{2} + \frac{1}{3}i, \quad \frac{1}{2} - \frac{1}{3}i$

31 $-5i, \quad 5i$

32 $\sqrt{2}i, \quad -\sqrt{2}i$

33 $10, \quad i$ **34** $6, \quad -6i$

35 $i, \quad 1/i$ **36** $i, \quad i^3$

37 $2i, \quad 3i$ **38** $1 + i, \quad 2 + 2i$

39 Prove that if z is any complex number, then $z + \bar{z}$ is a real number. Is $z - \bar{z}$ necessarily a real number?

40 Prove that the sum and product of the roots of the equation $ax^2 + bx + c = 0$ are $-b/a$ and c/a, respectively.

5.4 TRIGONOMETRIC FORM FOR COMPLEX NUMBERS

The geometric representation of a complex number as a point in a coordinate plane leads to a method of representation that involves trigonometric functions. Let us consider a nonzero complex number $z = a + bi$ and its geometric representation $P(a, b)$. Let θ be any angle in standard position whose terminal side lies on the segment OP, and let $r = |z|$, that is, $r = d(O, P) = \sqrt{a^2 + b^2}$. An illustration of this situation is shown in Figure 5.2.

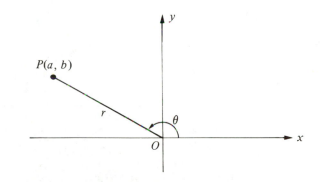

Figure 5.2 $z = a + bi = r(\cos\theta + i\sin\theta)$

Since $a = r\cos\theta$, $b = r\sin\theta$, and $z = a + bi$, we obtain

$$z = (r\cos\theta) + (r\sin\theta)i$$

which may be written in the form

$$z = r(\cos \theta + i \sin \theta).$$

It is important to remember that the number r is the absolute value of z. If $z = 0$, then $r = 0$, and hence, the preceding form may be used to represent the complex number 0 where θ is *any* angle. We call $r(\cos \theta + i \sin \theta)$ the **trigonometric form** or **polar form** for the complex number $z = a + bi$. The trigonometric form for z is not unique, since there is an unlimited number of different choices for the angle θ. When the trigonometric form is used, the absolute value r of z is often referred to as the **modulus** of z and the angle θ associated with z is called the **argument** (or **amplitude**) of z.

Example 1   Express each of the following complex numbers in trigonometric form.

(a) $-4 + 4i$ (b) $2\sqrt{3} - 2i$ (c) $2 + 7i$

Solution   The three complex numbers are represented geometrically in Figure 5.3. Using the trigonometric form gives us the following.

(a) $-4 + 4i = 4\sqrt{2}\left[\cos\dfrac{3\pi}{4} + i\sin\dfrac{3\pi}{4}\right]$

(b) $2\sqrt{3} - 2i = 4\left[\cos\left(-\dfrac{\pi}{6}\right) + i\sin\left(-\dfrac{\pi}{6}\right)\right]$

(c) $2 + 7i = \sqrt{53}\left[\cos\left(\arctan\dfrac{7}{2}\right) + i\sin\left(\arctan\dfrac{7}{2}\right)\right].$

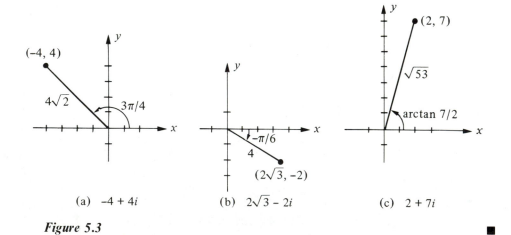

(a) $-4 + 4i$ (b) $2\sqrt{3} - 2i$ (c) $2 + 7i$

Figure 5.3   ■

If complex numbers are expressed in trigonometric form, then multiplications and divisions may be carried out in the simple manner indicated by the next theorem.

Theorem

If the trigonometric forms for two complex numbers z_1 and z_2 are given by

$$z_1 = r_1 (\cos\theta_1 + i\sin\theta_1) \quad \text{and} \quad z_2 = r_2 (\cos\theta_2 + i\sin\theta_2)$$

then

(i) $\quad z_1 z_2 = r_1 r_2 [\cos(\theta_1 + \theta_2) + i\sin(\theta_1 + \theta_2)]$

(ii) $\quad \dfrac{z_1}{z_2} = \dfrac{r_1}{r_2}\left[\cos(\theta_1 - \theta_2) + i\sin(\theta_1 - \theta_2)\right], \quad z_2 \neq 0.$

Proof

We shall prove (i) and leave (ii) as an exercise. Thus,

$$z_1 z_2 = r_1 (\cos\theta_1 + i\sin\theta_1) \cdot r_2 (\cos\theta_2 + i\sin\theta_2)$$
$$= r_1 r_2 \{[\cos\theta_1 \cos\theta_2 - \sin\theta_1 \sin\theta_2] + i[\sin\theta_1 \cos\theta_2 + \cos\theta_1 \sin\theta_2]\}.$$

Applying the addition formulas of Section 3.4 for $\cos(\theta_1 + \theta_2)$ and $\sin(\theta_1 + \theta_2)$ gives us (i). ∎

Part (i) of the preceding theorem states that the modulus of a product of two complex numbers is the product of their moduli, and the argument is the sum of their arguments. An analogous statement can be made for (ii).

Example 2 Use trigonometric forms to find $z_1 z_2$ and z_1/z_2 if $z_1 = 2\sqrt{3} - 2i$ and $z_2 = -1 + \sqrt{3}i$. Check by using the methods of Sections 5.1 and 5.2.

Solution From Example 1, we have

$$z_1 = 2\sqrt{3} - 2i = 4\left[\cos\left(-\frac{\pi}{6}\right) + i\sin\left(-\frac{\pi}{6}\right)\right].$$

Similarly, the reader may verify that

$$z_2 = -1 + \sqrt{3}i = 2\left[\cos\frac{2\pi}{3} + i\sin\frac{2\pi}{3}\right].$$

Applying (i) of the preceding theorem, we have

$$z_1 z_2 = 8\left[\cos\left(-\frac{\pi}{6} + \frac{2\pi}{3}\right) + i\sin\left(-\frac{\pi}{6} + \frac{2\pi}{3}\right)\right]$$
$$= 8\left[\cos\frac{\pi}{2} + i\sin\frac{\pi}{2}\right]$$
$$= 8i.$$

As a check, using the methods of Section 5.1, we have

$$
\begin{aligned}
z_1 z_2 &= (2\sqrt{3} - 2i)(-1 + \sqrt{3}i) \\
&= (-2\sqrt{3} + 2\sqrt{3}) + (2 + 6)i \\
&= 8i
\end{aligned}
$$

which is in agreement with our previous answer.

Applying (ii) of the preceding theorem, we obtain

$$
\begin{aligned}
\frac{z_1}{z_2} &= 2\left[\cos\left(-\frac{\pi}{6} - \frac{2\pi}{3} \right) + i\sin\left(-\frac{\pi}{6} - \frac{2\pi}{3} \right) \right] \\
&= 2\left[\cos\left(-\frac{5\pi}{6} \right) + i\sin\left(-\frac{5\pi}{6} \right) \right] \\
&= 2\left[-\frac{\sqrt{3}}{2} + i\left(-\frac{1}{2} \right) \right] \\
&= -\sqrt{3} - i.
\end{aligned}
$$

Using the methods of Section 5.2 gives us

$$
\begin{aligned}
\frac{z_1}{z_2} &= \frac{2\sqrt{3} - 2i}{-1 + \sqrt{3}i} \cdot \frac{-1 - \sqrt{3}i}{-1 - \sqrt{3}i} \\
&= \frac{(-2\sqrt{3} - 2\sqrt{3}) + (2 - 6)i}{4} \\
&= -\sqrt{3} - i.
\end{aligned}
$$
■

EXERCISES 5.4

Change the complex numbers in Exercises 1–20 to trigonometric form.

1 $1 - i$

2 $\sqrt{3} + i$

3 $-4\sqrt{3} + 4i$

4 $-2 - 2i$

5 $-20i$

6 15

7 $-5(1 + \sqrt{3}i)$

8 $-6i$

9 -7

10 $2i(1 - \sqrt{3}i)$

11 $2 + i$

12 $4 - 3i$

13 $-4 - 4i$

14 $-10 + 10i$

15 $6i$

16 -5

17 $-4\sqrt{3} + 4i$

18 $-5 - 5\sqrt{3}i$

19 12

20 0

In Exercises 21–28, find $z_1 z_2$ and z_1/z_2 by changing to trigonometric form and then using the last theorem of this section. Check by using the methods of Section 5.2.

21 $z_1 = -1 + i, z_2 = 1 + i$

22 $z_1 = \sqrt{3} - i, z_2 = -\sqrt{3} - i$

23 $z_1 = -2 - 2\sqrt{3}i, z_2 = 5i$

24 $z_1 = -5 + 5i, z_2 = -3i$

25 $z_1 = -10, z_2 = -4$

26 $z_1 = 2i,\ z_2 = -3i$

27 $z_1 = 4,\ z_2 = 2 - i$

28 $z_1 = -3,\ z_2 = 5 + 2i$

29   Extend (i) of the last theorem in this section to the case of three complex numbers. Generalize to n complex numbers.

30   Prove (ii) of the last theorem in this section.

5.5   DE MOIVRE'S THEOREM AND nTH ROOTS OF COMPLEX NUMBERS

If z is a complex number and n is a positive integer, then a complex number w is called an **nth root** of z if $w^n = z$. In this section we shall show that every nonzero complex number has n distinct nth roots. Since $\mathbb{R}$ is in $\mathbb{C}$, it will also follow that every nonzero real number has n distinct nth roots. If a is a positive real number and $n = 2$, then we already know that the roots are $\sqrt{a}$ and $-\sqrt{a}$.

If, in the last theorem of Section 5.4, we let both z_1 and z_2 equal $z = r(\cos\theta + i\sin\theta)$, we obtain

$$z^2 = r^2(\cos 2\theta + i\sin 2\theta).$$

If we now apply the same theorem to z and z^2, then

$$z^2 \cdot z = (r^2 \cdot r)[\cos(2\theta + \theta) + i\sin(2\theta + \theta)]$$

or

$$z^3 = r^3(\cos 3\theta + i\sin 3\theta).$$

Next, applying the theorem to z^3 and z produces

$$z^4 = r^4(\cos 4\theta + i\sin 4\theta).$$

In general we have the following result, which is named after the French mathematician Abraham De Moivre (1667–1754).

De Moivre's Theorem

> For every integer n,
>
> $$[r(\cos\theta + i\sin\theta)]^n = r^n[\cos n\theta + i\sin n\theta].$$

Example 1   Find $(1 + i)^{20}$.

Solution   Introducing the trigonometric form,

$$1 + i = \sqrt{2}\left(\cos\frac{\pi}{4} + i\sin\frac{\pi}{4}\right).$$

Next, by De Moivre's Theorem,

$$(1 + i)^{20} = (2^{1/2})^{20}\left[\cos 20\left(\frac{\pi}{4}\right) + i\sin 20\left(\frac{\pi}{4}\right)\right]$$
$$= 2^{10}(\cos 5\pi + i\sin 5\pi)$$
$$= -1024.$$
∎

If a nonzero complex number z has an nth root w, then $w^n = z$. If the trigonometric forms for w and z are

$$w = s(\cos\alpha + i\sin\alpha) \quad \text{and} \quad z = r(\cos\theta + i\sin\theta)$$

then, applying De Moivre's Theorem to $w^n = z$, we get

$$s^n[\cos n\alpha + i\sin n\alpha] = r(\cos\theta + i\sin\theta).$$

If two complex numbers are equal, then so are their absolute values. Consequently, $s^n = r$, and since s and r are nonnegative, $s = \sqrt[n]{r}$. Substituting s^n for r in the last displayed equation and dividing both sides by s^n, we obtain

$$\cos n\alpha + i\sin n\alpha = \cos\theta + i\sin\theta.$$

It follows that

$$\cos n\alpha = \cos\theta \quad \text{and} \quad \sin n\alpha = \sin\theta.$$

Since both the sine and cosine functions have period 2π, the last two equations are true if and only if $n\alpha$ and θ differ by a multiple of 2π. Thus, for some integer k,

$$n\alpha = \theta + 2\pi k$$

and hence,
$$\alpha = \frac{\theta + 2\pi k}{n}.$$

Substituting in the trigonometric form for w, we obtain the formula

$$w = \sqrt[n]{r}\left[\cos\left(\frac{\theta + 2\pi k}{n}\right) + i\sin\left(\frac{\theta + 2\pi k}{n}\right)\right].$$

If we substitute $k = 0, 1, \ldots, n - 1$ successively, there result n distinct values for w and hence n distinct nth roots of z. No other value of k will produce a new nth root. For example, if $k = n$, we obtain the angle $(\theta + 2\pi n)/n$, or $\theta/n + 2\pi$, which gives us the same nth root as $k = 0$. Similarly, $k = n + 1$ yields the same nth root as $k = 1$, etc. The same is true for negative values of k. Our discussion also shows that the numbers given by the formula are the only possible nth roots of z. We have proved the following theorem.

Theorem on nth Roots

> If $z = r(\cos\theta + i\sin\theta)$ is any nonzero complex number and if n is any positive integer, then z has precisely n distinct nth roots. Moreover, the roots are given by
>
> $$\sqrt[n]{r}\left[\cos\left(\frac{\theta + 2\pi k}{n}\right) + i\sin\left(\frac{\theta + 2\pi k}{n}\right)\right]$$
>
> where $k = 0, 1, \ldots, n - 1$.

Note that the nth roots of z all have modulus $\sqrt[n]{r}$, and hence, they lie on a circle of radius $\sqrt[n]{r}$ with center at O. Moreover, they are equispaced on this circle, since the difference in the arguments of successive nth roots is $2\pi/n$.

It is sometimes convenient to use degree measure for θ. In this event, the formula in the preceding theorem becomes

$$\sqrt[n]{r}\left[\cos\left(\frac{\theta + k \cdot 360°}{n}\right) + i\sin\left(\frac{\theta + k \cdot 360°}{n}\right)\right]$$

where $k = 0, 1, \ldots, n - 1$.

Example 2   Find the four fourth roots of $-8(1 + i\sqrt{3})$.

Solution   The geometric representation of the given number is shown in Figure 5.4.

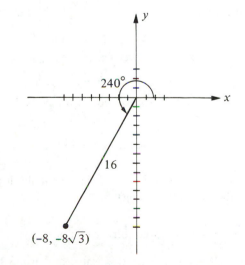

Figure 5.4

Introducing the trigonometric form, we have

$$-8(1 + i\sqrt{3}) = 16\left[\cos 240° + i\sin 240°\right].$$

By the preceding theorem with $n = 4$, the fourth roots are given by

$$2\left[\cos\left(\frac{240° + k \cdot 360°}{4}\right) + i\sin\left(\frac{240° + k \cdot 360°}{4}\right)\right]$$

where $k = 0, 1, 2,$ and 3. The formula may be rewritten as

$$2[\cos(60° + k \cdot 90°) + i\sin(60° + k \cdot 90°)].$$

Substituting 0, 1, 2, and 3 for k yields the following fourth roots:

$$2(\cos 60° \ + i\sin 60°) \ = 1 + \sqrt{3}i$$
$$2(\cos 150° + i\sin 150°) = -\sqrt{3} + i$$
$$2(\cos 240° + i\sin 240°) = -1 - \sqrt{3}i$$
$$2(\cos 330° + i\sin 330°) = \sqrt{3} - i.$$

$\blacksquare$

Example 3   Find the six sixth roots of -1.

Solution   Writing $-1 = 1(\cos\pi + i\sin\pi)$ and using the Theorem on nth Roots with $n = 6$, we find that the sixth roots of -1 are given by

$$\cos\left(\frac{\pi + 2\pi k}{6}\right) + i\sin\left(\frac{\pi + 2\pi k}{6}\right)$$

or

$$\cos\left(\frac{\pi}{6} + \frac{\pi}{3}k\right) + i\sin\left(\frac{\pi}{6} + \frac{\pi}{3}k\right).$$

Substituting 0, 1, 2, 3, 4, and 5 for k gives us the sixth roots of -1, namely,

$$\cos \pi/6 + i\sin \pi/6 = \sqrt{3}/2 + (1/2)i$$
$$\cos \pi/2 + i\sin \pi/2 = i$$
$$\cos 5\pi/6 + i\sin 5\pi/6 = -\sqrt{3}/2 + (1/2)i$$
$$\cos 7\pi/6 + i\sin 7\pi/6 = -\sqrt{3}/2 - (1/2)i$$
$$\cos 3\pi/2 + i\sin 3\pi/2 = -i$$
$$\cos 11\pi/6 + i\sin 11\pi/6 = \sqrt{3}/2 - (1/2)i.$$

$\blacksquare$

The special case in which $z = 1$ is of particular interest. The n distinct nth roots of 1 are called the **nth roots of unity**.

Example 4   Find the three third roots of unity.

Solution   Writing $1 = \cos 0 + i\sin 0$ and using the Theorem on nth Roots with $n = 3$, we obtain the three roots

$$\cos\frac{2\pi k}{3} + i\sin\frac{2\pi k}{3}$$

where $k = 0$, 1, and 2. Substituting for k gives us

$$\cos 0 + i \sin 0 = 1$$

$$\cos \frac{2\pi}{3} + i \sin \frac{2\pi}{3} = -\frac{1}{2} + \left(\frac{\sqrt{3}}{2}\right) i$$

$$\cos \frac{4\pi}{3} + i \sin \frac{4\pi}{3} = -\frac{1}{2} - \left(\frac{\sqrt{3}}{2}\right) i.$$

Compare this solution with Example 3 of Section 5.3. ∎

EXERCISES 5.5

In Exercises 1—12, use De Moivre's Theorem to express the given numbers in the form $a + bi$, where a and b are real numbers.

1 $(3 + 3i)^5$

2 $(1 + i)^{12}$

3 $(1 - i)^{10}$

4 $(-1 + i)^8$

5 $(1 - \sqrt{3}i)^3$

6 $(1 - \sqrt{3}i)^5$

7 $\left(-\frac{\sqrt{2}}{2} + \frac{\sqrt{2}}{2}i\right)^{15}$

8 $\left(\frac{\sqrt{2}}{2} + \frac{\sqrt{2}}{2}i\right)^{25}$

9 $\left(-\frac{\sqrt{3}}{2} - \frac{1}{2}i\right)^{20}$

10 $\left(-\frac{\sqrt{3}}{2} - \frac{1}{2}i\right)^{50}$

11 $(\sqrt{3} + i)^7$

12 $(-2 - 2i)^{10}$

13 Find the two square roots of $1 + \sqrt{3}i$.

14 Find the two square roots of $-9i$.

15 Find the four fourth roots of $-1 - \sqrt{3}i$.

16 Find the four fourth roots of $-8 + 8\sqrt{3}i$.

17 Find the three cube roots of $-27i$.

18 Find the three cube roots of $64i$.

19 Find the six sixth roots of unity.

20 Find the eight eighth roots of unity.

21 Find the five fifth roots of $1 + i$.

22 Find the five fifth roots of $-\sqrt{3} - i$.

Find the solutions of the equations in Exercises 23–30.

23 $x^4 - 16 = 0$

24 $x^6 - 64 = 0$

25 $x^6 + 64 = 0$

26 $x^5 + 1 = 0$

27 $x^3 + 8i = 0$

28 $x^3 - 64i = 0$

29 $x^5 - 243 = 0$

30 $x^4 + 81 = 0$

5.6 REVIEW

Concepts

Define or discuss the following.

1 System of complex numbers

2 Conjugate of a complex number

3 Absolute value of a complex number

4 nth roots of unity

5 Geometric representation of a complex number

6 The complex plane

7 Trigonometric form for complex numbers

8 De Moivre's Theorem

Exercises

Express each number in Exercises 1–20 in the form $a + bi$, where a and b are real numbers.

1 $(7 + 5i) + (-8 + 3i)$

2 $(-4 + 7i) - (3 - 3i)$

3 $(4 + 2i)(-5 + 4i)$

4 $(-8 + 2i)(-7 + 5i)$

5 $8i(7 - 5i)$

6 $(-5 + 6i)(-5 - 6i)$

7 $(9 + 4i)(9 - 4i)$ 8 $(3 + 8i)^2$

9 $i(6 + i)(2 - 3i)$ 10 $(6 - 3i)/(2 + 7i)$

11 $(4 + 6i)/(5 - i)$ 12 $(20 - 8i)/4i$

13 $1/(10 - 8i)$ 14 $3/(-2i)$

15 $|6 - 10i|$ 16 $|-11 + 10i|$

17 $-5(3 + i) - (4 + 2i)$

18 $(2 + i)^4$

19 $(1 + i)^{-1} - (1 - i)^{-1}$

20 i^{99}

Find the solutions of the equations in Exercises 21–24.

21 $5x^2 - 2x + 3 = 0$

22 $3x^2 + x + 6 = 0$

23 $6x^4 + 29x^2 + 28 = 0$

24 $x^4 + x^2 + 1 = 0$

In each of Exercises 25–28, find a quadratic equation with the given roots.

25 $7 + i, 7 - i$

26 $12i, -12i$

27 $-1 - 4i, -1 + 4i$

28 $1 + i, 3i$

Change the complex numbers in Exercises 29–34 to trigonometric form.

29 $-10 + 10i$ 30 $2 - 2\sqrt{3}i$

31 -17 32 $-12i$

33 $-5\sqrt{3} - 5i$ 34 $4 + 5i$

In each of Exercises 35–38, use De Moivre's Theorem to write the given number in the form $a + bi$, where a and b are real numbers.

35 $(-\sqrt{3} + i)^9$ 36 $\left(\dfrac{\sqrt{2}}{2} - \dfrac{\sqrt{2}}{2}i\right)^{30}$

37 $(3 - 3i)^5$ 28 $(2 + 2\sqrt{3}i)^{10}$

39 Find the three cube roots of -27.

40 Find the solutions of the equation $x^5 - 32 = 0$.

EXPONENTIAL AND LOGARITHMIC FUNCTIONS

Exponential and logarithmic functions are very important in mathematics and the sciences. In this chapter we shall define these functions and study some of their properties.

6.1 EXPONENTIAL FUNCTIONS

Throughout this section the letter a will denote a positive real number. Exponents are used to denote products of a with itself. We write

$$a^2 = a \cdot a, \ a^3 = a \cdot a \cdot a$$

and, in general, if n is a positive integer,

$$a^n = a \cdot a \cdot \cdots \cdot a$$

where there are n factors, all equal to a on the right-hand side. By definition, $a^0 = 1$. Also, if n is a positive integer and $a \neq 0$, then $a^{-n} = 1/a^n$.

The following rules are indispensable when working with exponents.

Laws of Exponents

If a and b are real numbers and m and n are integers, then

(i) $a^m a^n = a^{m+n}$ (ii) $(a^m)^n = a^{mn}$ (iii) $(ab)^n = a^n b^n$

(iv) $\left(\dfrac{a}{b}\right)^n = \dfrac{a^n}{b^n}$, if $b \neq 0$ (v) If $a \neq 0$, then $\dfrac{a^m}{a^n} = a^{m-n} = \dfrac{1}{a^{n-m}}$.

If $b^n = a$, where b is a positive real number and n is a positive integer, we write $b = \sqrt[n]{a}$ and call b the **principal nth root** of a. If, in addition, m is an integer, then *rational exponents* are defined by $a^{m/n} = \sqrt[n]{a^m} = (\sqrt[n]{a})^m$. The laws of exponents can be extended to rational exponents.

It is also possible to define a unique real number a^x for every real number x (rational or irrational) in such a way that the laws of exponents remain valid. To illustrate, given a number such as a^π, we may use the nonterminating decimal representation 3.14159... for π and consider the number a^3, $a^{3.1}$, $a^{3.14}$, $a^{3.141}$, $a^{3.1415}$,.... We might expect that each successive power gets closer to a^π. This is precisely what happens if a^x is properly defined. However, the definition requires deeper concepts than are available to us, and consequently, it is better to leave it for a more advanced mathematics course such as calculus. Although definitions and proofs are omitted, we shall assume, henceforth, that the laws of exponents are valid for all *real* exponents.

Since to each real number x there corresponds a unique real number a^x, we may define a function as follows.

Definition

> If $a > 0$, then the **exponential function f with base a** is defined by
>
> $$f(x) = a^x$$
>
> where x is any real number.

If $a > 1$ and x_1 and x_2 are real numbers such that $x_1 < x_2$, then it can be shown that $a^{x_1} < a^{x_2}$, that is, $f(x_1) < f(x_2)$. This means that if $a > 1$, then the exponential function f with base a is increasing for all real numbers. It can also be shown that if $0 < a < 1$, then f is decreasing for all real numbers.

Example 1   Sketch the graph of f if $f(x) = 2^x$.

Solution   Coordinates of some points on the graph are listed in the following table.

x	-3	-2	-1	0	1	2	3	4
2^x	$\frac{1}{8}$	$\frac{1}{4}$	$\frac{1}{2}$	1	2	4	8	16

Plotting points and using the fact that f is increasing gives us the sketch in Figure 6.1.

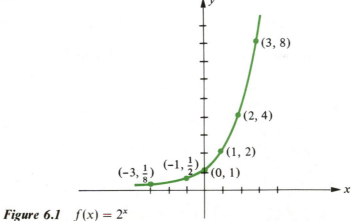

Figure 6.1 $f(x) = 2^x$

The graph in Figure 6.1 is typical of the exponential function with base a if $a > 1$. Since $a^0 = 1$, the y-intercept is always 1. Observe that as x decreases through negative values, the graph approaches the x-axis but never intersects it, since $a^x > 0$ for all x. This means that the x-axis is a **horizontal asymptote** for the graph. As x increases through positive values, the graph rises very rapidly. Indeed, if we begin with $x = 0$ and consider successive unit changes in x, then the corresponding changes in y are 1, 2, 4, 8, 16, 32, 64, and so on. This type of variation is very common in nature and is characteristic of the **exponential law of growth**. In this case f is called a **growth function**. At the end of this section we shall give several practical applications.

Example 2   If $f(x) = (3/2)^x$ and $g(x) = 3^x$, sketch the graphs of f and g on the same coordinate plane.

Solution   The following table displays coordinates of several points on the graphs.

x	-2	-1	0	1	2	3	4
$(\frac{3}{2})^x$	$\frac{4}{9}$	$\frac{2}{3}$	1	$\frac{3}{2}$	$\frac{9}{4}$	$\frac{27}{8}$	$\frac{81}{16}$
3^x	$\frac{1}{9}$	$\frac{1}{3}$	1	3	9	27	81

With the aid of these points we obtain Figure 6.2, where dashes have been used for the graph of f in order to distinguish it from the graph of g.

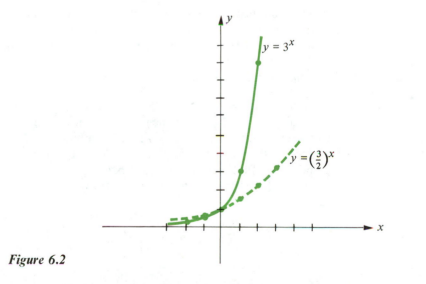

Figure 6.2

Example 2 brings out the fact that if $1 < a < b$, then $a^x < b^x$ for positive values of x and $b^x < a^x$ for negative values of x. In particular, since $\frac{3}{2} < 2 < 3$, this tells us that the graph of $y = 2^x$ in Example 1 lies between the graphs in Example 2.

Example 3   Sketch the graph of the equation $y = (\frac{1}{2})^x$.

Solution   Some points on the graph may be obtained from the following table.

x	-3	-2	-1	0	1	2	3
$(\frac{1}{2})^x$	8	4	2	1	$\frac{1}{2}$	$\frac{1}{4}$	$\frac{1}{8}$

The graph is sketched in Figure 6.3. Since $(\frac{1}{2})^x = 2^{-x}$, the graph is the same as the graph of the equation $y = 2^{-x}$.

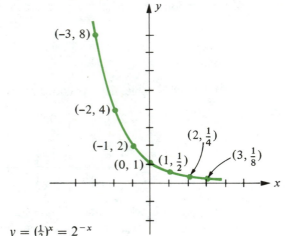

Figure 6.3 $y = (\frac{1}{2})^x = 2^{-x}$

In advanced mathematics and applications, it is often necessary to consider a function f such that $f(x) = a^p$, where p is some expression in x. We do not intend to study such functions in detail; however, let us consider one example.

Example 4   Sketch the graph of f if $f(x) = 2^{-x^2}$.

Solution   Since $f(x) = 1/2^{x^2}$, it follows that if x increases numerically, the corresponding point $(x, f(x))$ on the graph approaches the x-axis. The maximum value of $f(x)$ occurs at $x = 0$. Since f is an even function, the graph is symmetric with respect to the y-axis (see Section 1.5). Several points on the graph are $(0, 1)$, $(1, \frac{1}{2})$, and $(2, \frac{1}{16})$. Plotting and using symmetry gives us the sketch in Figure 6.4. Functions of this type arise in the study of the branch of mathematics called *probability*.

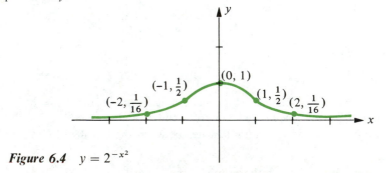

Figure 6.4 $y = 2^{-x^2}$

**Application
(Biology)**   The variation of many physical entities can be described by means of exponential functions. One of the most common examples occurs in the growth of certain populations. As an illustration, it might be observed experimentally that the number of bacteria in a culture doubles every hour. If 1,000 bacteria are present at the start of the experiment, then the experimenter would obtain the readings listed below, where t is the time in hours and $f(t)$ is the bacteria count at time t.

t	0	1	2	3	4
$f(t)$	1,000	2,000	4,000	8,000	16,000

It appears that $f(t) = (1,000)2^t$. This formula makes it possible to predict the number of bacteria present at any time t. For example, at $t = 1.5$ we have

$$f(t) = (1,000)2^{3/2} = 1,000\sqrt{2^3} = 1,000\sqrt{8} \approx 2,828.$$

Exponential growth patterns of this type may also be observed in some human and animal populations.

**Application
(Compound
Interest)**   Compound interest provides another illustration of exponential growth. If a sum of money P (called the **principal**) is invested at a simple interest rate of i percent, then the interest at the end of one interest period is Pi. For example, if $P = \$100$ and i is 8% per year, then the interest at the end of one year is $\$100(0.08)$, or $\$8$. If the interest is reinvested at the end of this period, then the new principal is

$$P + Pi, \quad \text{or} \quad P(1 + i).$$

Note that to find the new principal we multiply the original principal by $(1 + i)$. In the preceding illustration the new principal is $\$100(1.08)$, or $\$108$.

If another time period elapses, then the new principal may be found by multiplying $P(1 + i)$ by $(1 + i)$. Thus, the principal after two time periods is $P(1 + i)^2$. If we reinvest and continue this process, the principal after three periods is $P(1 + i)^3$; after four it is $P(1 + i)^4$; and in general, after n time periods the principal P_n is given by

$$\boxed{P_n = P(1 + i)^n.}$$

Interest accumulated in this way is called **compound interest**. We see that the principal is given in terms of an exponential function whose base is $1 + i$ and exponent is n. The time period may vary, being measured in years, months, weeks, days, or any other suitable unit of time. When this formula for P_n is employed, it must be remembered that i is the interest rate per time period. For example, if the rate is stated as 9% *per year compounded monthly*, then the rate per month is $\frac{9}{12}\%$, or, equivalently, $\frac{3}{4}\%$. In this case, $i = 0.75\% = 0.0075$ and n is the number of months. The sketch in Figure 6.5 illustrates the growth of $\$100$ invested at this rate over a period of 15 years. We have connected the principal amounts by a smooth curve in order to indicate the growth during this time. Due to the complexity of the base, the use of the formula for P_n is extremely tedious unless tables or calculators are available. For those with calculators, several problems on compound interest have been included in the exercises.

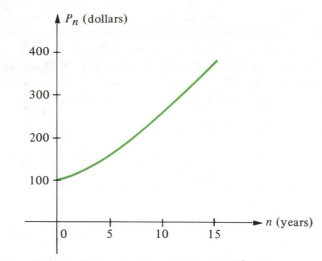

Figure 6.5   *Compound interest:* $P_n = 100(1.0075)^{12n}$

Application (Radioactive Decay)   Certain physical quantities may *decrease* exponentially. In such cases, the base a of the exponential function is between 0 and 1. One of the most common examples is the decay of a radioactive substance. As an illustration, the polonium isotope ^{210}Po has a half-life of approximately 140 days; that is, given any amount, one-half of it will disintegrate in 140 days. If there is initially 20 mg present, then the following table indicates the amount remaining after various intervals of time.

t (days)	0	140	280	420	560
Amount remaining (mg)	20	10	5	2.5	1.25

The sketch in Figure 6.6 illustrates the exponential nature of the disintegration.

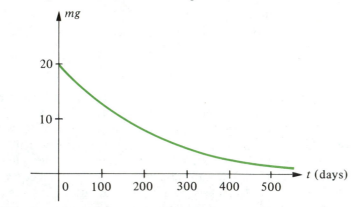

Figure 6.6   *Decay of polonium*

The behavior of an electrical condenser can also be used to illustrate exponential decay. If the condenser is allowed to discharge, the initial rate of discharge is relatively high, but it then tapers off as in the preceding example of radioactive decay.

In calculus and its applications, a certain irrational number, denoted by e, is often used as the base of an exponential function. To five decimal places,

$$e \approx 2.71828.$$

The base e arises naturally in the discussion of many physical phenomena. For this reason, the function f defined by $f(x) = e^x$ is called the **natural exponential function**. Since $2 < e < 3$, the graph of f lies "between" the graphs of the equations $y = 2^x$ and $y = 3^x$. Many hand-held calculators have an e^x key which can be used to approximate values of the natural exponential function. There may also be a key marked y^x which can be used for any positive base y. For those who have access to calculators, we have included some exercises involving e^x and y^x.

EXERCISES 6.1

In each of Exercises 1–24, sketch the graph of the function f.

1 $f(x) = 4^x$

2 $f(x) = 5^x$

3 $f(x) = 10^x$

4 $f(x) = 8^x$

5 $f(x) = 3^{-x}$

6 $f(x) = 4^{-x}$

7 $f(x) = -2^x$

8 $f(x) = -3^x$

9 $f(x) = 4 - 2^{-x}$

10 $f(x) = 2 + 3^{-x}$

11 $f(x) = (2/3)^x$

12 $f(x) = (3/4)^{-x}$

13 $f(x) = (5/2)^{-x}$

14 $f(x) = (4/3)^x$

15 $f(x) = 2^{|x|}$

16 $f(x) = 2^{-|x|}$

17 $f(x) = 2^{x+3}$

18 $f(x) = 3^{x+2}$

19 $f(x) = 2^{3-x}$

20 $f(x) = 3^{-2-x}$

21 $f(x) = 3^{1-x^2}$

22 $f(x) = 2^{-(x+1)^2}$

23 $f(x) = 3^x + 3^{-x}$

24 $f(x) = 3^x - 3^{-x}$

25 If $f(x) = 2^x$ and $g(x) = x^2$, illustrate the difference in the rate of growth of f and g for $x \ge 0$ by sketching the graphs of both functions on the same coordinate plane.

26 Repeat Exercise 25 if $f(x) = 2^{-x}$ and $g(x) = x^{-2}$.

27 The number of bacteria in a certain culture increased from 600 to 1,800 between 7:00 A.M. and 9:00 A.M. Assuming exponential growth, it can be shown, using methods of calculus, that the number $f(t)$ of bacteria t hours after 7:00 A.M. was given by $f(t) = 600(3)^{t/2}$.

(a) Estimate the number of bacteria in the culture at 8:00 A.M.; 10:00 A.M., 11:00 A.M.

(b) Sketch the graph of f from $t = 0$ to $t = 4$.

28 According to Newton's Law of Cooling, the rate at which an object cools is directly proportional to the difference in temperature between the object and the surrounding medium. If a certain object cools from 125° to 100° in 30 minutes when surrounded by air at a temperature of 75°, then it can be shown that its temperature $f(t)$ after t hours of cooling is given by $f(t) = 50(2)^{-2t} + 75$.

(a) If $t = 0$ corresponds to 1:00 P.M., approximate, to the nearest tenth of a degree, the temperature at 2:00 P.M.; 3:30 P.M.; 4:00 P.M.

(b) Sketch the graph of f from $t = 0$ to $t = 4$.

29 The radioactive isotope ^{210}Bi has a half-life of 5 days; that is, the number of radioactive particles will decrease to one-half the number in 5 days. If there are 100 mg of ^{210}Bi present at $t = 0$, then the amount $f(t)$ remaining after t days is given by $f(t) = 100(2)^{-t/5}$.

(a) How much remains after 5 days? 10 days? 12.5 days?

(b) Sketch the graph of f from $t = 0$ to $t = 30$.

30 The number of bacteria in a certain culture at time t is given by $Q(t) = 2(3^t)$, where t is measured in hours and $Q(t)$ in thousands. What is the initial number of bacteria? What is the number after 10 minutes? After 30 minutes? After 1 hour?

31 The half-life of radium is 1,600 years; that is, given any quantity, one-half of it will disintegrate in 1,600 years. If the initial amount is q_0 milligrams, then it can be shown that the quantity $q(t)$ remaining after t years is given by $q(t) = q_0 2^{kt}$. Find k.

32 If 10 grams of salt are added to a certain quantity of water, then the amount $q(t)$ that is undissolved after t minutes is given by $q(t) = 10(\frac{4}{5})^t$. Sketch a graph that shows the value $q(t)$ at any time from $t = 0$ to $t = 10$.

33 If \$1,000 is invested at a rate of 12% per year compounded monthly, what is the principal after 1 month? 2 months? 6 months? 1 year?

34 If a savings fund pays interest at a rate of 10% compounded semiannually, how much money invested now will amount to \$5,000 after one year?

35 If a certain make of automobile is purchased for C dollars, then its trade-in value $v(t)$ at the end of t years is given by $v(t) = 0.78C(0.85)^{t-1}$. If the original cost is \$10,000, calculate, to the nearest dollar, the value after   (a) 1 year;   (b) 4 years;   (c) 7 years.

36 If the value of real estate increases at a rate of 10% per year, then after t years the value V of a house purchased for P dollars is given by $V = P(1.1)^t$. If a house was purchased for \$80,000 in 1980, what will it be worth in 1984?

37 Why was $a < 0$ ruled out in the discussion of a^x?

38 Prove that if $0 < a < 1$ and r and s are rational numbers such that $r < s$, then $a^r > a^s$.

39 How does the graph of $y = a^x$ compare with the graph of $y = -a^x$?

40 If $a > 1$, how does the graph of $y = a^x$ compare with the graph of $y = a^{-x}$?

CALCULATOR EXERCISES 6.1

1 Approximate $3^{\sqrt{2}}$, and compare this number with the successive approximations

$$3^{1.4}, \quad 3^{1.41}, \quad 3^{1.414}, \quad 3^{1.4142}.$$

2 Approximate 2^{π}, and compare this number with the successive approximations

$$2^{3.1}, \quad 2^{3.14}, \quad 2^{3.141}, \quad 2^{3.1415}.$$

In Exercises 3 and 4, use decimal approximations to replace $\square$ by $<$, $>$, or $=$.

3 $(\sqrt{2})^{\sqrt{3}} \square (\sqrt{3})^{\sqrt{2}}$

4 $\pi^{22/7} \square (22/7)^{\pi}$

In Exercises 5 and 6, demonstrate that the given equality is true by expressing each side as a decimal (do not use laws of exponents).

5 (a) $5^{\sqrt{2}}5^{\sqrt{3}} = 5^{\sqrt{2}+\sqrt{3}}$
    (b) $5^{\sqrt{3}}/5^{\sqrt{2}} = 5^{\sqrt{3}-\sqrt{2}}$

6 $(5^{\sqrt{3}})^{\sqrt{2}} = 5^{\sqrt{6}}$

In Exercises 7 and 8, sketch the graph corresponding to $-3 \le x \le 3$ by choosing values of x at intervals of length 0.5 as follows: $x = -3, -2.5, -2, -1.5$, etc.

7 $y = (1.8)^x$

8 $y = (2.3)^{-x^2}$

Solve Exercises 9–12 by using the compound interest formula $P_n = P(1 + i)^n$.

9 If \$1,000 is invested at an interest rate of 6% per year compounded quarterly, find the principal at the end of
   (a) one year.   (b) two years.
   (c) five years.   (d) ten years.
   (*Hint:* $i = \frac{1}{4}(6\%) = 1.5\%$, and, at the end of one year, $n = 4$.)

10 Rework Exercise 9 if the interest rate is 6% per year compounded monthly.

11 If \$10,000 is invested at a rate of 9% per year compounded semi-annually, how long will it take for the principal to exceed
   (a) \$15,000? (b) \$20,000? (c) \$30,000?

12 A certain department store requires its credit card customers to pay interest at the rate of 18% per year compounded monthly on any unpaid bills. If a man buys a $500 television set on credit and then makes no payments for one year, how much does he owe?

13 Sketch the graph of f if $f(x)$ is given by:
(a) e^x 　　　　(b) e^{-x}

(c) $\dfrac{e^x + e^{-x}}{2}$ 　　(d) $\dfrac{2}{e^x + e^{-x}}$

(e) $\dfrac{e^x - e^{-x}}{2}$ 　　(f) $\dfrac{2}{e^x - e^{-x}}$

14 Sketch the graph of the equation $y = e^{-x^2/2}$.

15 Sketch the graph of $y = x(2^x)$.

16 If $f(x) = x^2(5^{\sqrt{x}})$, find $f(1.01) - f(1)$.

17 If $f(x) = (1 + x)^{1/x}$, approximate the following to four decimal places:

$$f(1), \quad f(0.1), \quad f(0.01), \quad f(0.001),$$

$$f(0.0001), \quad f(0.00001).$$

Compare your answers with the value of $e \approx 2.71828$ and arrive at a conjecture.

18 The population of a certain city is increasing at the rate of 5% per year and the present population is 500,000. Using methods developed in calculus, it is estimated that the population after t more years will be approximately $500{,}000e^{0.05t}$. Estimate the population after (a) 10 years; (b) 20 years; (c) 40 years.

19 Under certain conditions, the atmospheric pressure p at altitude h ft is given by

$$p = 29e^{-0.000034h}.$$

What is the pressure at an altitude of 40,000 ft?

20 If one starts with c milligrams of the polonium isotope $^{210}P_0$, the amount remaining after t days

may be approximated by $A = ce^{-0.00495t}$. If the initial amount is 50 milligrams, find, to the nearest hundredth, the amount remaining after (a) 30 days; (b) 180 days; (c) 365 days.

21 Growth of physical quantities are often more stable than that given by $f(t) = ke^{at}$, where t is time. In biology the formula

$$G(t) = ke^{-(Ae^{-Bt})},$$

where A, B and k are positive constants, is used to estimate certain populations. The graph of G is called a **Gompertz growth curve**. Sketch the graph of G for the special case $k = 10$, $A = 1/2$, $B = 1$, and $t \geq 0$, and describe what happens as t increases without bound.

22 The graph of

$$f(x) = a + b(1 - e^{-cx}),$$

where a, b and c are positive constants, may be used to describe certain learning processes. To illustrate, suppose a manufacturer estimates that a new employee can produce 3 items the first day on the job. As the employee becomes more proficient, more items per day can be produced until a certain maximum production is reached. Suppose that after n days on the job, the number $f(n)$ of items produced is approximated by

$$f(n) = 3 + 20(1 - e^{-0.1n}).$$

(a) Estimate the number of items produced on the fifth day; the ninth day; the twenty-fourth day; the thirtieth day.
(b) Sketch the graph of f from $n = 0$ to $n = 30$. (Graphs of this type are called **learning curves**, and are used frequently in education and psychology).
(c) What happens as n increases without bound?

6.2 LOGARITHMS

Throughout this section and the next, it is assumed that a is a positive real number different from 1. *Let us begin by examining the graph of f, where* $f(x) = a^x$ *(see Figure*

6.7 for the case $a > 1$). It appears that every positive real number u is the ordinate of some point on the graph; that is, there is a number v such that $u = a^v$. Indeed, v is the abscissa of the point where the line $y = u$ intersects the graph. Moreover, since f is increasing throughout its domain, the number u can occur as an ordinate only once. A similar situation exists if $0 < a < 1$. This makes the following theorem plausible.

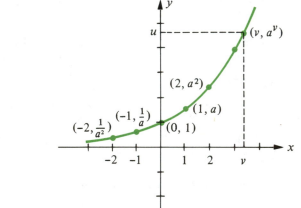

Figure 6.7 $f(x) = a^x, a > 1$

Theorem

For each positive real number u, there is a unique real number v such that

$$a^v = u.$$

A rigorous proof of this theorem requires concepts studied in calculus.

Definition

If u is any positive real number, then the (unique) exponent v such that $a^v = u$ is called the **logarithm of u with base a** and is denoted by $\log_a u$.

A convenient way to memorize this definition is by means of the following statement:

$$v = \log_a u \quad \text{if and only if} \quad a^v = u.$$

As illustrations, we may write

$$3 = \log_2 8 \quad \text{since } 2^3 = 8$$
$$-2 = \log_5 \tfrac{1}{25} \quad \text{since } 5^{-2} = \tfrac{1}{25}$$
$$4 = \log_{10} 10{,}000 \quad \text{since } 10^4 = 10{,}000.$$

The fact that $\log_a u$ is the exponent v such that $a^v = u$ gives us the following important identity:

$$a^{\log_a u} = u.$$

Since $a^r = a^r$ for every real number r, we may use the definition of logarithm with $v = r$ and $u = a^r$ to obtain

$$r = \log_a a^r.$$

In particular, letting $r = 1$ we see that $\log_a a = 1$.

Since $a^0 = 1$, it follows from the definition of logarithm that

$$\log_a 1 = 0.$$

Example 1   In each of the following find s.

(a) $s = \log_4 2$ (b) $\log_5 s = 2$ (c) $\log_s 8 = 3$

Solution

(a)   If $s = \log_4 2$, then $4^s = 2$, and hence, $s = \frac{1}{2}$

(b)   If $\log_5 s = 2$, then $5^2 = s$, and hence, $s = 25$.

(c)   If $\log_s 8 = 3$, then $s^3 = 8$, and hence, $s = \sqrt[3]{8} = 2$. ∎

Example 2   Solve the equation $\log_4 (5 + x) = 3$.

Solution   If $\log_4 (5 + x) = 3$, then

$$5 + x = 4^3 \quad \text{or} \quad 5 + x = 64.$$

Hence, the solution is $x = 59$. ∎

The following laws are fundamental for all work with logarithms, where it is assumed that u and w are positive real numbers.

Laws of Logarithms

(i) $\log_a (uw) = \log_a u + \log_a w$
(ii) $\log_a (u/w) = \log_a u - \log_a w$
(iii) $\log_a (u^c) = c \log_a u$, for every real number c

Proof   To prove (i), we begin by letting

$$r = \log_a u \quad \text{and} \quad s = \log_a w.$$

By the definition of logarithm, this implies that $a^r = u$ and $a^s = w$. Consequently,

$$a^r a^s = uw$$

and hence, by a law of exponents,

$$a^{r+s} = uw.$$

Again using the definition of logarithm, we see that the last equation is equivalent to

$$r + s = \log_a (uw).$$

Substituting for r and s from the first step in the proof gives us

$$\log_a u + \log_a w = \log_a uw.$$

This completes the proof of (i).

To prove (ii), we begin as in the proof of (i), but this time we divide a^r by a^s, obtaining

$$\frac{a^r}{a^s} = \frac{u}{w}, \quad \text{or} \quad a^{r-s} = \frac{u}{w}.$$

The last equation is equivalent to

$$r - s = \log_a (u/w).$$

Substituting for r and s gives us (ii).

Finally, if c is any real number, then using the same notation as above,

$$(a^r)^c = u^c, \quad \text{or} \quad a^{cr} = u^c.$$

According to the definition of logarithm, the last equality implies that

$$cr = \log_a u^c.$$

Substituting for r, we obtain

$$c \log_a u = \log_a u^c.$$

This proves Law (iii).   ■

The following examples illustrate uses of the Laws of Logarithms.

Example 3   If $\log_a 3 = 0.4771$ and $\log_a 2 = 0.3010$, find each of the following.

(a) $\log_a 6$ (b) $\log_a (\tfrac{3}{2})$ (c) $\log_a \sqrt{2}$ (d) $\dfrac{\log_a 3}{\log_a 2}$

Solution

(a)   Since $6 = 2 \cdot 3$, we may use Law (i) to obtain

$$\log_a 6 = \log_a (2 \cdot 3) = \log_a 2 + \log_a 3$$
$$= 0.4771 + 0.3010 = 0.7781.$$

(b) By Law (ii),

$$\log_a \left(\tfrac{3}{2}\right) = \log_a 3 - \log_a 2$$
$$= 0.4771 - 0.3010 = 0.1761.$$

(c) Using Law (iii),

$$\log_a \sqrt{2} = \log_a 2^{1/2} = \left(\tfrac{1}{2}\right)\log_a 2$$
$$= \left(\tfrac{1}{2}\right)(0.3010) = 0.1505.$$

(d) There is no law of logarithms that allows us to simplify $(\log_a 3)/(\log_a 2)$. Consequently, we *divide* 0.4771 by 0.3010, obtaining the approximation 1.585. It is important to notice the difference between this problem and the one stated in part (b). ∎

Example 4 Solve each of the following equations.

(a) $\log_5 (2x + 3) = \log_5 11 + \log_5 3$

(b) $\log_4 (x + 6) - \log_4 10 = \log_4 (x - 1) - \log_4 2$

Solution

(a) Using Law (i), the given equation may be written as

$$\log_5 (2x + 3) = \log_5 (11 \cdot 3) = \log_5 33.$$

Consequently, $2x + 3 = 33$, or $2x = 30$, and therefore, the solution is $x = 15$.

(b) The given equation is equivalent to

$$\log_4 (x + 6) - \log_4 (x - 1) = \log_4 10 - \log_4 2.$$

Applying Law (ii) gives us

$$\log_4 \left(\frac{x + 6}{x - 1}\right) = \log_4 \frac{10}{2} = \log_4 5$$

and hence,

$$\frac{x + 6}{x - 1} = 5.$$

The last equation implies that

$$x + 6 = 5x - 5 \quad \text{or} \quad 4x = 11.$$

Thus, the solution is $x = 11/4$. ∎

Extraneous solutions sometimes occur in the process of solving logarithmic equations, as illustrated in the next example.

Example 5 Solve the equation $2 \log_7 x = \log_7 36$.

Solution Applying Law (iii), we obtain $2 \log_7 x = \log_7 x^2$, and substitution in the given equation leads to

$$\log_7 x^2 = \log_7 36.$$

Consequently, $x^2 = 36$, and hence, either $x = 6$ or $x = -6$. However, $x = -6$ is not a solution of the original equation, since x must be positive in order for $\log_7 x$ to exist. Thus, there is only one solution, $x = 6$. ∎

Sometimes it is necessary to *change the base* of a logarithm by expressing $\log_b u$ in terms of $\log_a u$, for some positive real number b different from 1. This can be accomplished as follows. We begin with the equivalent equations

$$v = \log_b u \quad \text{and} \quad b^v = u.$$

Taking the logarithm, base a, of both sides of the second equation gives us

$$\log_a b^v = \log_a u.$$

Applying Law (iii), we get

$$v \log_a b = \log_a u.$$

Solving for v (that is, $\log_b u$), we obtain formula (i) in the next box.

Change of Base Formulas

$$\text{(i)} \quad \log_b u = \frac{\log_a u}{\log_a b} \qquad \text{(ii)} \quad \log_b a = \frac{1}{\log_a b}$$

To obtain formula (ii) we let $u = a$ in (i) and use the fact that $\log_a a = 1$.

The Laws of Logarithms are often used as in the next example.

Example 6 Express $\log_a \dfrac{x^3 \sqrt{y}}{z^2}$ in terms of the logarithms of x, y, and z.

Solution Using the three Laws of Logarithms,

$$\log_a \frac{x^3 \sqrt{y}}{z^2} = \log_a (x^3 \sqrt{y}) - \log_a z^2$$

$$= \log_a x^3 + \log_a \sqrt{y} - \log_a z^2$$
$$= 3 \log_a x + (\tfrac{1}{2}) \log_a y - 2 \log_a z. \quad ∎$$

The procedure in Example 6 can also be reversed; that is, beginning with the final equation, we can retrace our steps to obtain the original expression (see Exercises 67–70.)

As a final remark, note that there is no general law for expressing $\log_a (u + w)$ in terms of simpler logarithms. It is evident that it does not always equal $\log_a u + \log_a w$, since the latter equals $\log_a (uw)$.

EXERCISES 6.2

Change the equations in Exercises 1–8 to logarithmic form.

1 $4^3 = 64$

2 $3^5 = 243$

3 $2^7 = 128$

4 $5^3 = 125$

5 $10^{-3} = 0.001$

6 $10^{-2} = 0.01$

7 $t^r = s$

8 $v^w = u$

Change the equations in Exercises 9–16 to exponential form.

9 $\log_{10} 1000 = 3$

10 $\log_3 81 = 4$

11 $\log_3 \dfrac{1}{243} = -5$

12 $\log_4 \dfrac{1}{64} = -3$

13 $\log_7 1 = 0$

14 $\log_9 1 = 0$

15 $\log_t r = p$

16 $\log_v w = q$

Find the numbers in Exercises 17–30.

17 $\log_4 (1/16)$

18 $\log_2 32$

19 $\log_{10} 100$

20 $\log_8 64$

21 $10^{\log_{10} 5}$

22 $\log_{10} 0.0001$

23 $\log_7 \sqrt[3]{7}$

24 $10^{2\log_{10} 3}$

25 $\log_{10} (1/10)$

26 $\log_{10} 100{,}000$

27 $\log_{1/2} 8$

28 $\log_3 (1/81)$

29 $3^{4\log_3 2}$

30 $\log_6 \sqrt[5]{6}$

Given $\log_a 7 = 0.8$ and $\log_a 3 = 0.5$, change the expressions in Exercises 31–40 to decimal form.

31 $\log_a (7/3)$

32 $\log_a (3/7)$

33 $\log_a 7^3$

34 $\log_a (3^7)$

35 $\log_a (1/\sqrt{3})$

36 $\log_a \sqrt[4]{3}$

37 $\log_a 63$

38 $(\log_a 7)/(\log_a 3)$

39 $\log_7 a$

40 $(\log_3 a)(\log_a 3)$

Find the solutions of the equations in Exercises 41–58.

41 $\log_3 (x - 4) = 2$

42 $\log_2 (x - 5) = 4$

43 $\log_9 x = 3/2$

44 $\log_4 x = -3/2$

45 $\log_5 x^2 = -2$

46 $\log_{10} x^2 = -4$

47 $\log_2 (x^2 - 5x + 14) = 3$

48 $\log_2 (x^2 - 10x + 18) = 1$

49 $\log_x 7 = 3$

50 $5^{\log_5 x} = 10$

51 $\log_6 (2x - 3) = \log_6 12 - \log_6 3$

52 $2\log_3 x = 3\log_3 5$

53 $\log_2 x - \log_2 (x + 1) = 3 \log_2 4$

54 $\log_5 x + \log_5 (x + 6) = \frac{1}{2}\log_5 9$

55 $\log_{10} x^2 = \log_{10} x$

56 $\log_x 10 = 10$

57 $\frac{1}{2}\log_5 (x - 2) = 3 \log_5 2 - \frac{3}{2}\log_5 (x - 2)$

58 $\log_{10} 5^x = \log_3 1$

In each of Exercises 59–66, express the logarithm in terms of logarithms of x, y, and z.

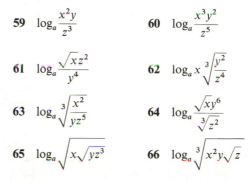

59 $\log_a \dfrac{x^2 y}{z^3}$

60 $\log_a \dfrac{x^3 y^2}{z^5}$

61 $\log_a \dfrac{\sqrt{x}\, z^2}{y^4}$

62 $\log_a x \sqrt[3]{\dfrac{y^2}{z^4}}$

63 $\log_a \sqrt[3]{\dfrac{x^2}{yz^5}}$

64 $\log_a \dfrac{\sqrt{x}\, y^6}{\sqrt[3]{z^2}}$

65 $\log_a \sqrt{x\sqrt{yz^3}}$

66 $\log_a \sqrt[3]{x^2 y \sqrt{z}}$

In each of Exercises 67–70, write the expression as one logarithm.

67 $2\log_a x + \frac{1}{3}\log_a (x - 2) - 5\log_a (2x + 3)$

68 $5\log_a x - \frac{1}{2}\log_a (3x - 4) + 3\log_a (5x + 1)$

69 $\log_a (y^2 x^3) - 2\log_a x\sqrt[3]{y} + 3\log_a \left(\dfrac{x}{y}\right)$

70 $2\log_a \dfrac{y^3}{x} - 3\log_a y + \frac{1}{2}\log_a x^4 y^2$

CALCULATOR EXERCISES 6.2

The LOG key refers to logarithms with base 10. In Exercises 1–6, use this key to demonstrate that the given equality is true by expressing each side as a decimal (do not use Laws of Logarithms).

1 $\log_{10} (2 \cdot 5) = \log_{10} 2 + \log_{10} 5$

2 $\log_{10} (5/2) = \log_{10} 5 - \log_{10} 2$

3 $\log_{10} (2^5) = 5\log_{10} 2$

4 $\log_{10} (2 + 5) \neq \log_{10} 2 + \log_{10} 5$

5 $10^{\log_{10} 5} = 5$

6 $\log_{10} 1 = 0$

If $a = 10$ in the Change of Base Formula (i), then

$$\log_b u = (\log_{10} u)/(\log_{10} b).$$

Use this formula to find the following to four-decimal-place accuracy.

7 $\log_3 8$

8 $\log_9 7$

9 $\log_{17} 412$

10 $\log_\pi \sqrt{5}$

6.3 LOGARITHMIC FUNCTIONS

We next use the concept of logarithm to introduce a new function whose domain is the set of positive real numbers.

Definition

> The function f defined by
>
> $$f(x) = \log_a x$$
>
> for all positive real numbers x is called the **logarithmic function with base a**.

The graph of f is the same as the graph of the equation $y = \log_a x$, which, by the definition of logarithm, is equivalent to

$$x = a^y.$$

In order to find some pairs that are solutions of the preceding equation, we may substitute for y and find the corresponding values of x, as illustrated in the following table.

y	-3	-2	-1	0	1	2	3
x	$\dfrac{1}{a^3}$	$\dfrac{1}{a^2}$	$\dfrac{1}{a}$	1	a	a^2	a^3

If $a > 1$, we obtain the sketch in Figure 6.8. In this case f is an increasing function throughout its domain. If $0 < a < 1$, then the graph has the general shape shown in

Figure 6.9, and hence, f is a decreasing function. Note that for every a under consideration, the region to the left of the y-axis is excluded. There is no y-intercept and the x-intercept is 1.

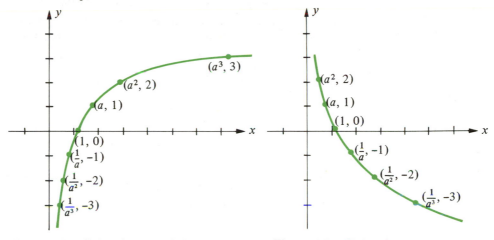

Figure 6.8 $f(x) = \log_a x, a > 1$ **Figure 6.9** $f(x) = \log_a x, 0 < a < 1$

Functions defined by expressions of the form $\log_a p$, where p is some expression in x, often occur in mathematics and its applications. Functions of this type are classified as members of the logarithmic family; however, the graphs may differ from those sketched in Figures 6.8 and 6.9, as is illustrated in the following examples.

Example 1   Sketch the graph of f if $f(x) = \log_3(-x)$, $x < 0$.

Solution   If $x < 0$, then $-x > 0$, and hence, $\log_3(-x)$ is defined. We wish to sketch the graph of the equation $y = \log_3(-x)$, or, equivalently, $3^y = -x$. The following table displays coordinates of some points on the graph, which is sketched in Figure 6.10.

y	-2	-1	0	1	2
x	$-\frac{1}{9}$	$-\frac{1}{3}$	-1	-3	-9

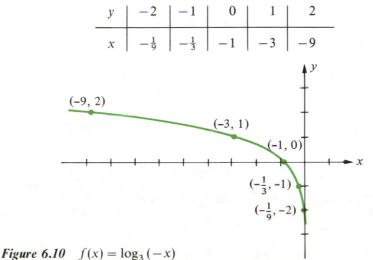

Figure 6.10 $f(x) = \log_3(-x)$

Example 2   Sketch the graph of the equation $y = \log_3 |x|$, $x \neq 0$.

Solution   Since $|x| > 0$ for all $x \neq 0$, there are points on the graph corresponding to negative values of x as well as to positive values. If $x > 0$, then $|x| = x$, and hence, to the right of the y-axis the graph coincides with the graph of $y = \log_3 x$, or, equivalently, $x = 3^y$. If $x < 0$, then $|x| = -x$ and the graph is the same as that of $y = \log_3 (-x)$ (see Example 1). The graph is sketched in Figure 6.11. Note that the graph is symmetric with respect to the y-axis.

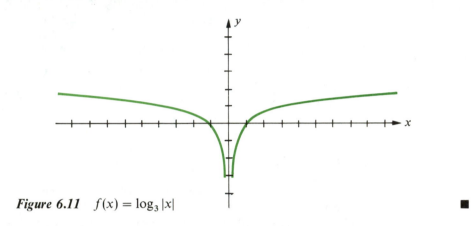

Figure 6.11 $f(x) = \log_3 |x|$ ■

Logarithmic functions occur frequently in applications. Indeed, if two variables u and v are related so that u is an exponential function of v, then v is a logarithmic function of u. As a specific example, if \$1.00 is invested at a rate of 9% per year compounded monthly, then from the discussion in Section 6.1, the principal P after n interest periods is

$$P = (1.0075)^n.$$

The logarithmic form of this equation is

$$n = \log_{1.0075} P.$$

Thus, the number of periods n required for \$1.00 to grow to an amount P is related logarithmically to P.

Another example we considered in Section 6.1 was that of population growth. In particular, the equation for the number N of bacteria in a certain culture after t hours was

$$N = (1000)2^t \quad \text{or} \quad 2^t = N/1000.$$

Changing to logarithmic form, we obtain

$$t = \log_2 (N/1000).$$

Hence, the time t is a logarithmic function of N.

In Section 6.1, we defined the natural exponential function f by means of the equation $f(x) = e^x$. The logarithmic function with base e is called the **natural logarithmic function**. We use **ln x** as an abbreviation for $\log_e x$ and refer to it as the **natural logarithm of x**. Since $e \approx 3$, the graph of $y = \ln x$ is similar in appearance to the graph of $y = \log_3 x$. For natural logarithms, the Laws of Logarithms are written

$$\ln (uv) = \ln u + \ln v, \qquad \ln \frac{u}{v} = \ln u - \ln v, \qquad \ln u^c = c \ln u.$$

Example 3   According to Newton's Law of Cooling, the rate at which an object cools is directly proportional to the difference in temperature between the object and the surrounding medium. Newton's Law can be used to show that under certain conditions the temperature T of an object is given by

$$T = 75e^{-2t},$$

where t is time. Express t as a function of T.

Solution   The given equation may be rewritten

$$e^{-2t} = T/75.$$

Using logarithms with base e yields

$$-2t = \log_e (T/75) = \ln (T/75).$$

Consequently,

$$t = -\tfrac{1}{2} \ln (T/75) \quad \text{or} \quad t = -\tfrac{1}{2}[\ln T - \ln 75]. \qquad \blacksquare$$

We shall not have many occasions to work with natural logarithms in this text. For computational purposes the base 10 is used. Base 10 gives us the system of common logarithms discussed in subsequent sections.

Many hand-held calculators have a key labeled ln x which can be used to approximate values of the natural logarithmic function. Several exercises are included at the end of this section for those who have a calculator of that type.

EXERCISES 6.3

Sketch the graph of f in each of Exercises 1–10.

1 (a) $f(x) = \log_2 x$ (b) $f(x) = \log_4 x$

2 (a) $f(x) = \log_5 x$ (b) $f(x) = \log_{10} x$

3 (a) $f(x) = \log_3 x$

   (b) $f(x) = \log_3 (x - 2)$

4 (a) $f(x) = \log_2 (-x)$
   (b) $f(x) = \log_2 (3 - x)$

5 (a) $f(x) = \log_3 (3x)$ (b) $f(x) = 3 \log_3 x$

6 (a) $f(x) = \log_2 (x^2)$ (b) $f(x) = \log_2 (x^3)$

7 (a) $f(x) = \log_2 \sqrt{x}$ (b) $f(x) = \log_2 \sqrt[3]{x}$

8 (a) $f(x) = \log_2 |x|$ (b) $f(x) = |\log_2 x|$

9 (a) $f(x) = \log_3 (1/x)$
   (b) $f(x) = 1/(\log_3 x)$

10 (a) $f(x) = \log_3 (2 + x)$
    (b) $f(x) = 2 + \log_3 x$

11 What is the geometric relationship between the graphs of $y = \log_a x$ and $y = a^x$? Why does this relationship exist?

12 Describe the relationship of the graph of $y = \ln x$ to the graphs of $y = \log_2 x$ and $y = \log_3 x$.

13 If one begins with q_0 milligrams of pure radium, then the amount q remaining after t years is given by the formula

$$q = q_0(2)^{-t/1600}.$$

Use logarithms with base 2 to solve for t in terms of q and q_0.

14 The number of bacteria in a certain culture at time t is given by

$$N = 10^4(3)^t.$$

Use logarithms with base 3 to solve for t in terms of N.

15 An electrical condenser with initial charge Q_0 is allowed to discharge. After t seconds, the charge Q is given by

$$Q = Q_0 e^{kt}$$

where k is a constant of proportionality. Use natural logarithms to solve for t in terms of Q_0, Q, and k.

16 Under certain conditions the atmospheric pressure p at altitude h is given by

$$p = 29e^{-0.000034h}.$$

Use natural logarithms to solve for h as a function of p.

17 The loudness of sound, as experienced by the human ear, is based upon intensity levels. A formula used for finding the intensity level α that corresponds to a sound intensity I is

$$\alpha = 10\log_{10} (I/I_0) \text{ decibels}$$

where I_0 is a special value of I agreed to be the weakest sound that can be detected by the ear under certain conditions. Find α if:
(a) I is 10 times as great as I_0
(b) I is 1,000 times as great as I_0
(c) I is 10,000 times as great as I_0. (This is the intensity level of the average voice.)

18 The current I at time t in a certain electrical circuit is given by $I = 20e^{-Rt/L}$, where R and L denote the resistance and inductance, respectively. Use natural logarithms to solve for t in terms of the remaining variables.

19 Using the Richter scale, the magnitude R of an earthquake of intensity I may be found by means of the formula $R = \log_{10} (I/I_0)$, where I_0 is a certain minimum intensity. Find R, if an earthquake has intensity
(a) 100 times that of I_0
(b) 10,000 times that of I_0
(c) 100,000 times that of I_0.

20 Refer to Exercise 19. The magnitude of the San Francisco earthquake of 1906 was approximately 8 on the Richter scale. What is the corresponding intensity in terms of I_0?

CALCULATOR EXERCISES 6.3

1 Sketch the graph of

(a) $y = \ln x$ (b) $y = \ln |x|$ (c) $y = |\ln x|$.

2 Sketch the graph of f if $f(x) = x^2 \ln x$.

3 Demonstrate that $\ln e^x = x$ and $e^{\ln x} = x$ for the following values of x.
(a) 1   (b) 3.4   (c) 0.056   (d) 8.143

4 Refer to Calculator Exercise 18 of Section 6.1. For what value of t will the population of the city be 1,000,000?

5 Letting $a = e$ in the change of base formula $\log_b u = (\log_a u)/(\log_a b)$ leads to

$$\log_b u = \frac{\ln u}{\ln b}.$$

Use this formula to approximate

(a) $\log_3 4$ (b) $\log_5 (1.64)$ (c) $\log_7 \sqrt{2}$
(d) $\log_{10} 382$ (e) $\log_{10} (47/62)$.

6 The LOG key on a calculator refers to the logarithmic function with base 10. Use a calculator as an aid to sketching the graph of f if $f(x) = \log_{10} x$.

6.4 COMMON LOGARITHMS

Logarithms with base 10 are useful for certain numerical computations. It is customary to refer to such logarithms as **common logarithms** and to use the symbol **log** x as an abbreviation for $\log_{10} x$.

Base 10 is used in computational work because every positive real number can be written in the **scientific form** $c \cdot 10^k$, where $1 \le c < 10$ and k is an integer.

For example,

$$513 = (5.13)10^2, \qquad 2375 = (2.375)10^3, \qquad 720000 = (7.2)10^5,$$
$$0.641 = (6.41)10^{-1}, \qquad 0.00000438 = (4.38)10^{-6}, \qquad 4.601 = (4.601)10^0.$$

If x is any positive real number and we write

$$x = c \cdot 10^k$$

where $1 \le c < 10$ and k is an integer, then applying (iii) of the Laws of Logarithms gives us

$$\log x = \log c + \log 10^k.$$

Since $\log 10^k = k$ (Why?) we see that

$$\log x = \log c + k.$$

The last equation tells us that to find $\log x$ for any positive real number x it is sufficient to know the logarithms of numbers between 1 and 10. The number $\log c$, where $1 \le c < 10$, is called the **mantissa**, and the integer k is called the **characteristic** of $\log x$.

If $1 \le c < 10$, then since $\log x$ increases as x increases,

$$\log 1 \le \log c < \log 10,$$

or, equivalently, $\qquad\qquad\qquad 0 \le \log c < 1.$

Hence, the mantissa of a logarithm is a number between 0 and 1. When working numerical problems, it is usually necessary to approximate logarithms. For example, it can be shown that

$$\log 2 = 0.3010299957\ldots$$

where the decimal is nonrepeating and nonterminating. We shall round off such logarithms to four decimal places and write

$$\log 2 \approx 0.3010.$$

If a number between 0 and 1 is written as a finite decimal, it is sometimes referred to as a **decimal fraction**. Thus, the equation $\log x = \log c + k$ implies that if x is any positive real number, then *log x may be approximated by the sum of a positive decimal fraction (the mantissa) and an integer k (the characteristic)*. We shall refer to this representation as the **standard form** for $\log x$.

Logarithms of many of the numbers between 1 and 10 have been calculated. Table 1 contains four-decimal-place approximations for logarithms of numbers between 1.00 and 9.99 at intervals of 0.01. This table can be used to find the logarithm of any three-digit number to four-decimal-place accuracy. There exist far more extensive tables which provide logarithms of many additional numbers to much greater accuracy than four decimal places. The use of Table 1 is illustrated in the following examples.

Example 1   Approximate each of the following.

    (a) $\log 43.6$ (b) $\log 43{,}600$ (c) $\log 0.0436$

Solution

    (a)   Since $43.6 = (4.36)10^1$, the characteristic of $\log 43.6$ is 1. Referring to Table 1, we find that the mantissa of $\log 4.36$ may be approximated by 0.6395. Hence, as in the preceding discussion,

$$\log 43.6 \approx 0.6395 + 1 = 1.6395.$$

    (b)   Since $43{,}600 = (4.36)10^4$, the mantissa is the same as in part (a); however, the characteristic is 4. Consequently,

$$\log 43{,}600 \approx 0.6395 + 4 = 4.6395.$$

    (c)   If we write $0.0436 = (4.36)10^{-2}$, then

$$\log 0.0436 = \log 4.36 + (-2).$$

Hence, $\log 0.0436 \approx 0.6395 + (-2).$

We could subtract 2 from 0.6395 and obtain

$$\log 0.0436 \approx -1.3605$$

but this is not standard form, since $-1.3605 = -0.3605 + (-1)$, a number in which the decimal fraction is *negative*. A common error is to write $0.6395 + (-2)$ as -2.6395. This is incorrect, since $-2.6395 = -0.6395 + (-2)$, which is not the same as $0.6395 + (-2)$.   ■

If a logarithm has a negative characteristic, it is customary either to leave it in standard form or to rewrite the logarithm, keeping the decimal part positive. To illustrate the latter technique, led us add and subtract 8 on the right side of the equation

$$\log 0.0436 \approx 0.6395 + (-2).$$

This gives us

$$\log 0.0436 \approx 0.6395 + (8 - 8) + (-2)$$

or $\qquad\qquad \log 0.0436 \approx 8.6395 - 10.$

We could also write

$$\log 0.0436 \approx 18.6395 - 20 = 43.6395 - 45$$

and so on, as long as the *integral part* of the logarithm is -2.

Example 2   Approximate each of the following.

(a) $\log (0.00652)^2$ (b) $\log (0.00652)^{-2}$ (c) $\log (0.00652)^{1/2}$

Solution

(a)   By (iii) of the Laws of Logarithms,

$$\log (0.00652)^2 = 2 \log 0.00652.$$

Since $0.00652 = (6.52)10^{-3}$,

$$\log 0.00652 = \log 6.52 + (-3).$$

Referring to Table 1, we see that $\log 6.52$ is approximately 0.8142, and therefore,

$$\log 0.00652 \approx 0.8142 + (-3).$$

Hence, $\qquad\qquad \log (0.00652)^2 = 2 \log 0.00652$
$$\approx 2 [0.8142 + (-3)]$$
$$= 1.6284 + (-6).$$

The standard form is $0.6284 + (-5)$.

(b)   Again using Law (iii) and the value for $\log 0.00652$ found in part (a),

$$\log (0.00652)^{-2} = -2 \log 0.00652$$
$$\approx -2 [0.8142 + (-3)]$$
$$= -1.6284 + 6.$$

It is important to note that -1.6284 means $-0.6284 + (-1)$, and consequently, the decimal part is negative. To obtain the standard form, we may write

$$-1.6284 + 6 = 6.0000 - 1.6284$$
$$= 4.3716.$$

This shows that the mantissa is 0.3716 and the characteristic is 4.

(c) By Law (iii),

$$\log (0.00652)^{1/2} = (\tfrac{1}{2}) \log 0.00652$$

$$\approx \tfrac{1}{2}[0.8142 + (-3)].$$

If we multiply by 1/2, the standard form is not obtained, since neither number in the resulting sum is the characteristic. In order to avoid this, we may adjust the expression within brackets by adding and subtracting a suitable number. If we use 1 in this way, we obtain

$$\log (0.00652)^{1/2} \approx \tfrac{1}{2}[1.8142 + (-4)]$$
$$= 0.9071 + (-2)$$

which is in standard form. We could also have added and subtracted a number other than 1. For example,

$$\tfrac{1}{2}[0.8142 + (-3)] = \tfrac{1}{2}[17.8142 + (-20)]$$
$$= 8.9071 + (-10).$$ ∎

Table 1 can be used to find an approximation to x if $\log x$ is given, as illustrated in the following example.

Example 3 Find a decimal approximation to x if $\log x$ is as follows.

(a) $\log x = 1.7959$ (b) $\log x = -3.5918$

Solution

(a) The mantissa 0.7959 determines the sequence of digits in x, and the characteristic determines the position of the decimal point. Referring to the *body* of Table 1, we see that the mantissa 0.7959 is the logarithm of 6.25. Since the characteristic is 1, x lies between 10 and 100. Consequently, $x \approx 62.5$.

(b) In order to find x from Table 1, $\log x$ must be written in standard form. In order to change $\log x = -3.5918$ to standard form, we may add and subtract 4, obtaining

$$\log x = (4 - 3.5918) - 4$$
$$= 0.4082 - 4.$$

Referring to Table 1, we see that the mantissa 0.4082 is the logarithm of 2.56. Since the characteristic of $\log x$ is -4, it follows that $x \approx 0.000256$.   ∎

The only logarithms that can be found *directly* from Table 1 are logarithms of numbers that contain at most three nonzero digits. If *four* nonzero digits are involved, then it is possible to obtain an approximation by using the method of linear interpolation described for trigonometric functions in Chapter Two. We shall illustrate the method with examples.

Example 4 Approximate log 572.6.

Solution   It is convenient to arrange our work as follows:

$$1.0\left\{0.6\left\{\begin{matrix}\log 572.0 \approx 2.7574\\ \log 572.6 = ?\end{matrix}\right\}d\right\}0.0008$$
$$\log 573.0 \approx 2.7582$$

where we have indicated differences by appropriate symbols alongside the braces. This leads to the proportion

$$\frac{d}{0.0008} = \frac{0.6}{1.0} = \frac{6}{10} \quad \text{or} \quad d = \left(\frac{6}{10}\right)(0.0008) = 0.00048 \approx 0.0005.$$

Hence,

$$\log 572.6 \approx 2.7574 + 0.0005 = 2.7579.$$

Another way of working this type of problem is to reason that since 572.6 is 6/10 of the way from 572.0 to 573.0, then log 572.6 is (approximately) 6/10 of the way from 2.7574 to 2.7582. Hence,

$$\log 572.6 \approx 2.7574 + (\tfrac{6}{10})(0.0008) \approx 2.7574 + 0.0005 = 2.7579. \qquad \blacksquare$$

Example 5 Approximate log 0.003678.

Solution   We begin by arranging our work as in the solution of Example 4. Thus,

$$10\left\{8\left\{\begin{matrix}\log 0.003670 \approx 0.5647 + (-3)\\ \log 0.003678 = ?\end{matrix}\right\}d\right\}0.0011.$$
$$\log 0.003680 \approx 0.5658 + (-3)$$

Since we are only interested in ratios, we have used the numbers 8 and 10 on the left side because their ratio is the same as the ratio of 0.000008 to 0.000010. This leads to the proportion

$$\frac{d}{0.0011} = \frac{8}{10} = 0.8 \quad \text{or} \quad d = (0.0011)(0.8) = 0.00088 \approx 0.0009.$$

Hence,

$$\log 0.003678 \approx [0.5647 + (-3)] + 0.0009$$
$$= 0.5656 + (-3). \qquad \blacksquare$$

If a number x is written in scientific form $x = c \cdot 10^k$, where $1 \leq c < 10$, then before Table 1 is used to find $\log x$ by interpolation, c should be rounded off to three decimal places. Another way of saying this is that x should be rounded off to four **significant figures**. Some examples will help to clarify the procedure. If $x = 36.4635$, we round off to 36.46 before approximating $\log x$. The number 684,279 should be rounded off to 684,300. For a decimal such as 0.096202 we write 0.09620, and so on. The reason for doing this is that Table 1 does not guarantee more than four-digit accuracy, since the mantissas that appear in it are approximations. This means that if *more* than four-digit accuracy is required in a problem, then Table 1 cannot be used. If, in more extensive tables, the logarithm of a number containing n digits can be found directly, then interpolation is allowed for numbers involving $n + 1$ digits, and numbers should be rounded off accordingly.

The method of interpolation can also be used to find x when we are given $\log x$. If we use Table 1, then x may be found to four significant figures, as illustrated in the next example.

Example 6   Find x to four significant figures if $\log x = 1.7949$.

Solution   The mantissa 0.7949 does not appear in Table 1, but it can be isolated between adjacent entries, namely the mantissas corresponding to 6.230 and 6.240. We shall arrange our work as follows:

$$0.1\left\{ {}^{r}\left\{\begin{matrix}\log 62.30 \approx 1.7945 \\ \log x \quad\; = 1.7949\end{matrix}\right\}0.0004 \atop \log 62.40 \approx 1.7952 \right\}0.0007.$$

This leads to the proportion

$$\frac{r}{0.1} = \frac{0.0004}{0.0007} = \frac{4}{7} \quad\text{or}\quad r = (0.1)\left(\frac{4}{7}\right) \approx 0.06.$$

Hence,

$$x \approx 62.30 + 0.06 = 62.36. \qquad\blacksquare$$

If we are given $\log x$, then the number x is called the **antilogarithm** of $\log x$. In Example 6, the antilogarithm of $\log x = 1.7949$ is $x \approx 62.36$. Sometimes the notation antilog $(1.7949) \approx 62.63$ is used.

If a hand-held calculator with a log key is used to determine common logarithms, then the standard form for $\log x$ is obtained only if $x \geq 1$. For example, to find $\log 463$ on a typical calculator we enter 463 and press the log key, obtaining the standard form

However, if we find log 0.0463 in similar fashion, then the following number appears on the display panel:

This is not the standard form for the logarithm, but is similar to that which occurred in the solutions to Example 1(c) and Example 3(b). To find the standard form we could add 2 to the logarithm (using a calculator), obtaining 0.665580991, and then append -2. Thus,

$$\log 0.0463 \approx 0.665580991 - 2.$$

EXERCISES 6.4

In Exercises 1–16, use Table 1 and Laws of Logarithms to approximate the common logarithms of the given numbers. If a calculator with a log key is available, compare your answers with those obtained by means of the calculator.

1 347; 0.00347; 3.47

2 86.2; 8,620; 0.862

3 0.54; 540; 540,000

4 208; 2.08; 20,800

5 60.2; 0.0000602; 602

6 5; 0.5; 0.0005

7 $(44.9)^2$; $(44.9)^{1/2}$; $(44.9)^{-2}$

8 $(1810)^4$; $(1810)^{40}$; $(1810)^{1/4}$

9 $(0.943)^3$; $(0.943)^{-3}$; $(0.943)^{1/3}$

10 $(0.017)^{10}$; $10^{0.017}$; $10^{1.43}$

11 $(638)(17.3)$

12 $\dfrac{(2.73)(78.5)}{621}$

13 $\dfrac{(47.4)^3}{(29.5)^2}$

14 $\dfrac{(897)^4}{\sqrt{17.8}}$

15 $\sqrt[3]{20.6}(371)^3$

16 $\dfrac{(0.0048)^{10}}{\sqrt{0.29}}$

In Exercises 17–30, use Table 1 to find a decimal approximation to x. If a suitable calculator is available, compare your approximations with those obtained by means of the calculator.

17 $\log x = 3.6274$

18 $\log x = 1.8965$

19 $\log x = 0.9469$

20 $\log x = 0.5729$

21 $\log x = 5.2095$

22 $\log x = 6.7300 - 10$

23 $\log x = 9.7348 - 10$

24 $\log x = 7.6739 - 10$

25 $\log x = 8.8306 - 10$

26 $\log x = 4.9680$

27 $\log x = 2.2765$

28 $\log x = 3.0043$

29 $\log x = -1.6253$

30 $\log x = -2.2118$

31 Chemists use a number denoted by pH to describe quantitatively the acidity or basicity of solutions. By definition,

$$pH = -\log [H^+]$$

where $[H^+]$ is the hydrogen ion concentration in moles per liter. Given the following, with the indicated $[H^+]$, approximate the pH of each substance.

(a) vinegar: $[H^+] \approx 6.3 \times 10^{-3}$

(b) carrots: $[H^+] \approx 1.0 \times 10^{-5}$

(c) sea water: $[H^+] \approx 5.0 \times 10^{-9}$

32 Approximate the hydrogen ion concentration $[H^+]$ in each of the following substances. (Refer to Exercise 31 and use the closest entry in Table 1 to approximate $[H^+]$.)

(a) apples: pH ≈ 3.0 (b) beer: pH ≈ 4.2

(c) milk: pH ≈ 6.6

33 A solution is considered acidic if $[H^+] > 10^{-7}$ or basic if $[H^+] < 10^{-7}$. What are the corresponding inequalities involving pH?

34 Many solutions have a pH between 1 and 14. What is the corresponding range of the hydrogen ion content $[H^+]$?

35 The sound intensity level formula considered in Exercise 17 of Section 6.3 may be written

$$\alpha = 10 \log (I/I_0).$$

Find α if I is 285,000 times as great as I_0.

36 A sound intensity level of 140 decibels produces pain in the average human ear. Approximately how many times greater than I_0 must I be in order for α to reach this level? (Refer to Exercise 35 and use the nearest entry in Table 1 to find the approximation.)

Use linear interpolation to approximate the common logarithms of the numbers in Exercises 37–48.

37 25.48

38 421.6

39 5363

40 0.3817

41 0.001259

42 69,450

43 123,400

44 0.0212

45 0.7786

46 1.203

47 384.7

48 54.44

In Exercises 49–60, use linear interpolation to approximate x.

49 $\log x = 1.4437$

50 $\log x = 3.7455$

51 $\log x = 4.6931$

52 $\log x = 0.5883$

53 $\log x = 9.1664 - 10$

54 $\log x = 8.3902 - 10$

55 $\log x = 3.8153 - 6$

56 $\log x = 5.9306 - 9$

57 $\log x = 0.1358$

58 $\log x = 5.0409$

59 $\log x = -2.8712$

60 $\log x = -1.8164$

6.5 EXPONENTIAL AND LOGARITHMIC EQUATIONS

The variables in certain equations appear as exponents or logarithms, as illustrated in the following examples.

Example 1   Solve the equation $3^x = 21$.

Solution   Taking the common logarithm of both sides and using (iii) of the Laws of Logarithms, we obtain

$$\log (3^x) = \log 21$$
$$x \log 3 = \log 21$$
$$x = \frac{\log 21}{\log 3}.$$

If an approximation is desired, we may use Table 1 to obtain

$$x \approx \frac{1.3222}{0.4771} \approx 2.77$$

where the last number is obtained by dividing 1.3222 by 0.4771. A partial check on the solution is to note that, since $3^2 = 9$ and $3^3 = 27$, the number x such that $3^x = 21$ should lie between 2 and 3, somewhat closer to 3 than to 2. ∎

Example 2 Solve $5^{2x+1} = 6^{x-2}$.

Solution Taking the common logarithm of both sides and using (iii) of the Laws of Logarithms, we obtain

$$(2x+1)\log 5 = (x-2)\log 6.$$

We may now solve for x as follows:

$$2x\log 5 + \log 5 = x\log 6 - 2\log 6$$
$$2x\log 5 - x\log 6 = -\log 5 - 2\log 6$$
$$x(2\log 5 - \log 6) = -(\log 5 + \log 6^2)$$
$$x = \frac{-(\log 5 + \log 36)}{2\log 5 - \log 6}$$
$$= \frac{-\log(5 \cdot 36)}{\log 5^2 - \log 6}$$
$$= \frac{-\log 180}{\log(25/6)}.$$

If an approximation to the solution is desired, we may proceed as in Example 1. ∎

Example 3 Solve the equation $\log(5x-1) - \log(x-3) = 2$.

Solution The given equation may be written as

$$\log \frac{5x-1}{x-3} = 2.$$

Using the definition of logarithm with $a = 10$ gives us

$$\frac{5x-1}{x-3} = 10^2.$$

Consequently,

$$5x - 1 = 10^2(x-3) = 100x - 300, \quad \text{or} \quad 299 = 95x.$$

Hence,
$$x = \frac{299}{95}.$$ ∎

Example 4 Solve the equation $\dfrac{5^x - 5^{-x}}{2} = 3$.

Solution   Multiplying both sides of the given equation first by 2 and then by 5^x gives
us

$$5^x - 5^{-x} = 6$$

$$5^{2x} - 1 = 6(5^x)$$

which may be written $(5^x)^2 - 6(5^x) - 1 = 0.$

Letting $u = 5^x$ gives us the quadratic equation

$$u^2 - 6u - 1 = 0$$

in the variable u. Applying the Quadratic Formula,

$$u = \frac{6 \pm \sqrt{36 + 4}}{2} = 3 \pm \sqrt{10}$$

that is, $5^x = 3 \pm \sqrt{10}$. Since 5^x is never negative, the number $3 - \sqrt{10}$ must be discarded; therefore,

$$5^x = 3 + \sqrt{10}.$$

Taking the common logarithm of both sides and using (iii) of the Laws of Logarithms,

$$x \log 5 = \log (3 + \sqrt{10}) \quad \text{or} \quad x = \frac{\log (3 + \sqrt{10})}{\log 5}.$$

To obtain an approximate solution we may write $3 + \sqrt{10} \approx 6.16$ and use Table 1. This gives us

$$x \approx \frac{\log 6.16}{\log 5} \approx \frac{0.7896}{0.6990} \approx 1.13.$$ ■

EXERCISES 6.5

Find the solutions of the equations in Exercises 1–20.

1 $10^x = 7$

2 $5^x = 8$

3 $4^x = 3$

4 $10^x = 6$

5 $3^{4-x} = 5$

6 $(1/3)^x = 100$

7 $3^{x+4} = 2^{1-3x}$

8 $4^{2x+3} = 5^{x-2}$

9 $2^{-x} = 8$

10 $2^{-x^2} = 5$

11 $\log x = 1 - \log (x - 3)$

12 $\log (5x + 1) = 2 + \log (2x - 3)$

13 $\log (x^2 + 4) - \log (x + 2) = 3 + \log (x - 2)$

14 $\log (x - 4) - \log (3x - 10) = \log (1/x)$

15 $\log (x^2) = (\log x)^2$

16 $\log \sqrt{x} = \sqrt{\log x}$

17 $\log (\log x) = 2$

18 $\log \sqrt{x^3 - 9} = 2$

19 $x^{\sqrt{\log x}} = 10^8$

20 $\log (x^3) = (\log x)^3$

In Exercises 21–24, solve for x in terms of y.

21 $y = \dfrac{10^x + 10^{-x}}{2}$

22 $y = \dfrac{10^x - 10^{-x}}{2}$

23 $y = \dfrac{10^x - 10^{-x}}{10^x + 10^{-x}}$

24 $y = \dfrac{1}{10^x - 10^{-x}}$

In Exercises 25–28, use natural logarithms to solve for x in terms of y.

25 $y = \dfrac{e^x - e^{-x}}{2}$

26 $y = \dfrac{e^x + e^{-x}}{2}$

27 $y = \dfrac{e^x - e^{-x}}{e^x + e^{-x}}$

28 $y = \dfrac{e^x + e^{-x}}{e^x - e^{-x}}$

29 The current i in a certain electrical circuit is given by

$$i = \frac{E}{R}(1 - e^{-Rt/L}).$$

Use natural logarithms to solve for t in terms of the remaining symbols.

30 If a sum of money P_0 is invested at an interest rate of $100r$ percent per year, compounded m times per year, then the principal P at the end of t years is given by

$$P = P_0\left(1 + \frac{r}{m}\right)^{mt}.$$

Solve for t in terms of the other symbols.

31 In Exercise 17 of Section 6.3, we considered the sound intensity level formula

$$\alpha = 10 \log (I/I_0).$$

(a) Solve for I in terms of α and I_0.
(b) Show that a one-decibel rise in the intensity level corresponds to a 26% increase in the intensity.

32 The chemical formula $pH = -\log [H^+]$ was introduced in Exercise 31 of Section 6.4. Solve for $[H^+]$ in terms of pH.

CALCULATOR EXERCISES 6.5

Use natural logarithms to approximate the solutions of the equations in Exercises 1–4.

1 $5^x = 7$ (*Hint:* $\ln 5^x = \ln 7$, or $x \ln 5 = \ln 7$.)

2 $4^{-x} = 10$

3 $e^{-x^2} = 0.163$

4 $e^{-2x+1} = 5^x$.

5 How long will it take money to double if it is invested at a rate of 6% per year compounded monthly?

6 If \$10,000 is invested at an interest rate of 8% per year compounded quarterly, when will the principal exceed \$20,000? (*Hint:* Use Exercise 30.)

7 A certain radioactive substance decays according to the formula $q(t) = q_0 e^{-0.0063t}$, where q_0 is the initial amount of the substance and t is the time in days. Use natural logarithms to approximate its half-life, that is, the number of days it takes for half of the substance to decay.

8 The air pressure $p(h)$, in lb/in^2, at an altitude of h feet above sea level may be approximated by

$$p(h) = 14.7e^{-0.0000385h}.$$

At approximately what altitude h is the air pressure
(a) $10\,lb/in^2$?
(b) one-half its value at sea level?

9 The graph of $G(t) = 10e^{-(1/2)e^{-t}}$ is a Gompertz growth curve. (See Calculator Exercise 21 of Section 6.1.) Approximate, to the nearest thousandth, the value of t such that $G(t) = 8$.

10 The formula $f(n) = 3 + 20(1 - e^{-0.1n})$ may be used to estimate certain learning processes. (See Calculator Exercise 22 of Section 6.1.) Approximate, to the nearest hundredth, the value of n such that $f(n) = 13$.

6.6 COMPUTATIONS WITH LOGARITHMS

The importance of logarithms for numerical computations has diminished in recent years because of the development of computers and hand-held calculators. However, since mechanical devices are not always available, it is worthwhile to have some familiarity with the use of logarithms for solving arithmetic problems. At the same time, practice in working numerical problems leads to a deeper understanding of logarithms and logarithmic functions. The following examples illustrate some computational techniques.

Example 1   Approximate $N = \dfrac{(59700)(0.0163)}{41.7}$.

Solution   Using Laws of Logarithms and Table 1 leads to

$$\begin{aligned}
\log N &= \log 59700 + \log 0.0163 - \log 41.7 \\
&\approx 4.7760 + (0.2122 - 2) - (1.6201) \\
&= 4.9882 - 3.6201 \\
&= 1.3681.
\end{aligned}$$

Referring to Table 1 for the antilogarithm, we have, to three significant figures,

$$N \approx 23.3. \qquad\blacksquare$$

Example 2   Approximate $N = \sqrt[3]{56.11}$ to four significant figures.

Solution   Writing $N = (56.11)^{1/3}$ and using (iii) of the Laws of Logarithms gives us

$$\log N = \tfrac{1}{3}\log 56.11.$$

To find $\log 56.11$, we interpolate from Table 1 as follows:

$$10\left\{\begin{array}{l} 1\left\{\begin{array}{l}\log 56.10 \approx 1.7490 \\ \log 56.11 = \text{?}\end{array}\right\}d \\ \log 56.20 \approx 1.7497\end{array}\right\}0.0007$$

$$\frac{d}{0.0007} = \frac{1}{10}$$

$$d = 0.00007 \approx 0.0001.$$

Hence, $\log 56.11 \approx 1.7490 + 0.0001 = 1.7491$

and therefore, $\log N \approx \tfrac{1}{3}(1.7491) \approx 0.5830.$

The antilogarithm may be found by interpolation from Table 1 as follows.

$$0.01 \left\{ r \begin{cases} \log 3.820 \approx 0.5821 \\ \log N \quad \approx 0.5830 \end{cases} \right\} 9 \right\} 11$$
$$\log 3.830 \approx 0.5832$$

$$\frac{r}{0.01} = \frac{9}{11}$$

$$r = \frac{9}{11}(0.01) \approx 0.008.$$

Consequently, $N \approx 3.820 + 0.008 = 3.828.$ ■

If we were interested in only *three* significant figures, then the interpolations in Example 2 could have been avoided. In the remaining examples we shall, for simplicity, work only with three-digit numbers.

Example 3   Approximate $N = \dfrac{(1.32)^{10}}{\sqrt[5]{0.0268}}$.

Solution   Using Laws of Logarithms and Table 1,

$$\begin{aligned}
\log N &= 10 \log 1.32 - \tfrac{1}{5} \log 0.0268 \\
&\approx 10(0.1206) - \tfrac{1}{5}(3.4281 - 5) \\
&= 1.206 - 0.6856 + 1 \\
&= 1.5204.
\end{aligned}$$

Finding the antilogarithm (to three significant figures), we obtain

$$N \approx 33.1.$$ ■

Example 4   Find x if $x^{2.1} = 6.5$.

Solution   Taking the common logarithm of both sides and using (iii) of the Laws of Logarithms gives us

$$(2.1) \log x = \log 6.5.$$

Hence, $$\log x = \frac{\log 6.5}{2.1}$$

and by the definition of logarithm,

$$x = 10^{(\log 6.5)/(2.1)}.$$

If an approximation to x is desired, then from the second equation above we have

$$\log x = \frac{\log 6.5}{2.1} \approx \frac{0.8129}{2.1} \approx 0.3871.$$

Using Table 1, the antilogarithm (to three significant figures) is

$$x \approx 2.44.$$ ∎

Example 5 Approximate $N = \dfrac{69.3 + \sqrt[3]{56.1}}{\log 807}$.

Solution   Since we have no formula for the logarithm of a sum, the two terms in the numerator must be *added* before the logarithm can be found. From Example 2, $\sqrt[3]{56.1} \approx 3.8$, and hence, the numerator is approximately 73.1. Using Table 1, we see that

$$\log 807 \approx 2.9069 \approx 2.91.$$

Hence, the given expression may be approximated by

$$N \approx \frac{73.1}{2.91}.$$

It is now an easy matter to find N, either by using logarithms or by long division. It is left to the reader to verify that $N \approx 25.1$. ∎

EXERCISES 6.6

Use logarithms to approximate the numbers in Exercises 1–20 to three significant figures. If a calculator is available, compare your answers with those obtained by means of the calculator.

1 $(638)(57.2)$

2 $(0.0178)(0.00729)$

3 $\dfrac{35,900}{8,430}$

4 $\dfrac{3.14}{63.2}$

5 $(4.21)^{10}$

6 $(0.712)^6$

7 $\sqrt[5]{0.517}$

8 $\sqrt[4]{2.23}$

9 $\dfrac{(26.7)^3(1.48)}{(67.4)^2}$

10 $\dfrac{(3.04)^3}{\sqrt{1.12(86.6)}}$

11 $\sqrt{1.65}\,\sqrt[3]{(70.8)^2}$

12 $\left[\dfrac{(11.1)^3}{\sqrt[5]{4.17}}\right]^{-1/2}$

13 $\sqrt{\dfrac{0.563}{(0.105)^3}}$

14 $\sqrt[5]{\dfrac{(124)^2}{(9.83)^3}}$

15 $10^{-3.14}$

16 $(100)^{0.523}$

17 $(4.12)^{0.220}$

18 $\sqrt{8.46\sqrt{3.07}}$

19 $\dfrac{\log 37.4}{\log 6.19}$

20 $\dfrac{56.8 + \log(7.13)}{\sqrt[10]{4.42}}$

Use interpolation in Table 1 to approximate the numbers in Exercises 21–26 to four significant figures.

21 $(2.461)^5$

22 $1/(33.89)^4$

23 $\sqrt[10]{0.5138}$

24 $\sqrt[5]{(17.04)^2}$

25 $(5.375)^{2/3}$

26 $(1776)^{11}$

27 The area A of a triangle with sides a, b, and c may be calculated from the formula $A = \sqrt{s(s-a)(s-b)(s-c)}$, where s is one-half the perimeter. Use logarithms to approximate the area of a triangle with sides 12.6, 18.2, and 14.1.

28 The volume V of a right circular cone of altitude h and radius of base r is $V = \frac{1}{3}\pi r^2 h$. Use logarithms to approximate the volume of a cone of radius 2.43 cm and altitude 7.28 cm.

29 The formula used in physics to approximate the period T (seconds) of a simple pendulum of length L (feet) is $T = 2\pi\sqrt{L/(32.2)}$. Approximate the period of a pendulum 33 inches long.

30 The pressure p (pounds per cubic foot) and volume v (cubic feet) of a certain gas are related by the formula $pv^{1.4} = 600$. Approximate the pressure if $v = 8.22$ cubic feet.

6.7 REVIEW

Concepts

Define or discuss the following.

1 The exponential function with base a

2 The natural exponential function

3 The logarithm of u with base a

4 The natural logarithmic function

5 The Laws of Logarithms

6 The logarithmic function with base a

7 Common logarithms

8 Mantissa

9 Characteristic

Exercises

Find the numbers in Exercises 1–6.

1 $\log_2 (1/16)$

2 $\log_5 \sqrt[3]{5}$

3 $6^{\log_6 4}$

4 $10^{3\log 2}$

5 $\log 1,000,000$

6 $\ln e$

In Exercises 7–16, sketch the graph of f.

7 $f(x) = 3^{x+2}$

8 $f(x) = (3/5)^x$

9 $f(x) = (3/2)^{-x}$

10 $f(x) = 3^{-2x}$

11 $f(x) = 3^{-x^2}$

12 $f(x) = 1 - 3^{-x}$

13 $f(x) = \log_6 x$

14 $f(x) = \log_3 (x^2)$

15 $f(x) = 2\log_3 x$

16 $f(x) = \log_2 (x+4)$

Find the solutions of the equations in Exercises 17–24.

17 $\log_8 (x-5) = 2/3$

18 $\log_4 (x+1) = 2 + \log_4 (3x-2)$

19 $2\log_3 (x+3) - \log_3 (x+1) = 3\log_3 2$

20 $\log \sqrt[4]{x+1} = 1/2$

21 $2^{5-x} = 6$

22 $3^{x^2} = 7$

23 $2^{5x+3} = 3^{2x+1}$

24 $5^{\log_5 (x+1)} = 3$

25 Express $\log x^4 \sqrt[3]{y^2/z}$ in terms of logarithms of x, y, and z.

26 Express $\log (x^2/y^3) + 4\log y - 6\log \sqrt{xy}$ as one logarithm.

Solve the equations in Exercises 27 and 28 for x in terms of y.

27 $y = \dfrac{10^x + 10^{-x}}{10^x - 10^{-x}}$

28 $y = \dfrac{1}{10^x + 10^{-x}}$

Use linear interpolation to approximate logarithms in Exercises 29–32.

29 $\log 47.82$

30 $\log 0.001347$

31 log 300,600

32 log 0.2143

Use linear interpolation to approximate x in Exercises 33–36.

33 $\log x = 2.4995$

34 $\log x = 1.5045$

35 $\log x = 8.7970 - 10$

36 $\log x = -1.3146$

Use logarithms to approximate the numbers in Exercises 37–40.

37 $\dfrac{(38.2)^3}{\sqrt{4.67}}$

38 $\sqrt[5]{\dfrac{21.8}{62.2}}$

39 $(5.16)^{2.1}$

40 $(1.01)^{44}$

TOPICS IN ANALYTIC GEOMETRY

Plane geometry includes the study of figures such as lines, circles, and triangles which lie in a plane. Theorems are proved by reasoning deductively from postulates. In analytic geometry, plane geometric figures are investigated by introducing a coordinate system and then using equations and formulas of various types. If the study of analytic geometry were to be summarized by means of one statement, perhaps the following would be appropriate: "Given an equation, find its graph, and conversely, given a graph, find its equation." In this chapter we shall apply coordinate methods to several basic plane figures.

7.1 CIRCLES

In Section 1.3, we proved that the circle in a coordinate plane with center $C(h, k)$ and radius r is the graph of the equation

$$(x - h)^2 + (y - k)^2 = r^2.$$

Squaring and simplifying, we obtain an equation of the form

$$x^2 + y^2 + ax + by + c = 0$$

where a, b, and c are real numbers. Conversely, if we begin with such an equation, it is always possible, by completing the squares in x and y, to obtain an equation of the form

$$(x - h)^2 + (y - k)^2 = d.$$

The method will be illustrated in Example 1. If $d > 0$, then the graph is a circle with center (h, k) and radius $r = \sqrt{d}$. If $d = 0$, then, since $(x - h)^2 \geq 0$ and $(y - k)^2 \geq 0$, the only solution of the equation is (h, k) and hence the graph consists of only one point. Finally, if $d < 0$, the equation has no real solutions and there is no graph.

Example 1   Find the center and radius of the circle with equation

$$x^2 + y^2 - 4x + 6y - 3 = 0.$$

Solution   We begin by arranging the equation as follows:

$$(x^2 - 4x) + (y^2 + 6y) = 3.$$

Next, we complete the squares by adding appropriate numbers within the parentheses. Of course, to obtain equivalent equations we must add the numbers to *both* sides of the equation. In order to complete the square for an expression of the form $x^2 + ax$, we add the square of half the coefficient of x, that is, $(a/2)^2$, to both sides of the equation. Similarly, for $y^2 + by$ we add $(b/2)^2$ to both sides. This leads to

$$(x^2 - 4x + 4) + (y^2 + 6y + 9) = 3 + 4 + 9$$

or $$(x - 2)^2 + (y + 3)^2 = 16.$$

Hence, by the preceding discussion, the center is $(2, -3)$ and the radius is 4. ■

In the next example we use the following fundamental principle of analytic geometry:

> A point $P(x_1, y_1)$ is on the graph of an equation in x and y if and only if the pair (x_1, y_1) is a solution of the equation.

Example 2   Find an equation of the circle that contains the points $A(-1, 7)$, $B(3, 9)$, and the origin $O(0, 0)$. What is the center and radius of the circle?

Solution   The circle is sketched in Figure 7.1. If we choose a, b, and c appropriately, then the equation has the form $x^2 + y^2 + ax + by + c = 0$. Moreover, since the

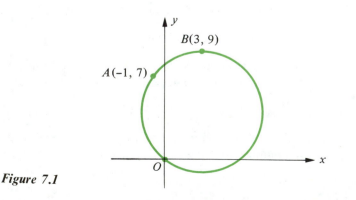

Figure 7.1

circle passes through the origin, $(0,0)$ is a solution, that is,

$$0^2 + 0^2 + a \cdot 0 + b \cdot 0 + c = 0$$

and consequently, $c = 0$. Therefore, an equation for the circle is of the form

$$x^2 + y^2 + ax + by = 0.$$

Since A and B are on the circle, $(-1, 7)$ and $(3, 9)$ are solutions of this equation; that is,

$$1 + 49 - a + 7b = 0 \quad \text{and} \quad 9 + 81 + 3a + 9b = 0.$$

Simplifying, we see that the pair (a, b) must be a solution of *both* of the equations

$$a - 7b = 50 \quad \text{and} \quad a + 3b = -30.$$

Solving the first equation for a and substituting in the second equation, we obtain $(7b + 50) + 3b = -30$, or $10b = -80$. Consequently, $b = -8$. Since $a = 7b + 50$, we have $a = 7(-8) + 50 = -6$. Substitution of these numbers for a and b in $x^2 + y^2 + ax + by = 0$ gives us

$$x^2 + y^2 - 6x - 8y = 0.$$

Completing the squares, we obtain

$$(x^2 - 6x + 9) + (y^2 - 8y + 16) = 9 + 16$$

or

$$(x - 3)^2 + (y - 4)^2 = 25.$$

Hence, the center is $C(3, 4)$ and the radius is 5. ∎

EXERCISES 7.1

In each of Exercises 1–6, find an equation of the circle which satisfies the stated conditions.

1 Center $C(3, -4)$, radius 2

2 Center $C(5, 0)$, radius 5

3 Center $C(6, -2)$, tangent to the line $x = 3$

4 Endpoints of diameter $A(-1, 1)$, $B(4, -6)$

5 Circumscribed about the right triangle with vertices $A(-1, 2)$, $B(2, -3)$, and $C(7, 0)$ (*Hint:* The center of the circle is the midpoint of the hypotenuse.)

6 Passing through the three points $A(-2, 1)$, $B(5, 1)$, and $C(5, -3)$

In each of Exercises 7–16, find the center and radius of the circle with the given equation.

7 $x^2 + y^2 + 2x - 10y + 10 = 0$

8 $x^2 + y^2 - 8x + 4y + 15 = 0$

9 $x^2 + y^2 - 6y + 5 = 0$

10 $x^2 + y^2 + 14x + 46 = 0$

11 $x^2 + y^2 - 10x + 8y = 0$

12 $x^2 + y^2 + 2y = 0$

13 $4x^2 + 4y^2 + 8x - 8y + 7 = 0$

14 $2x^2 + 2y^2 + 8x + 7 = 0$

15 $3x^2 + 3y^2 - 3x + 2y + 1 = 0$

16 $9x^2 + 9y^2 + 12x - 6y + 4 = 0$

In Exercises 17 and 18, use the method of Example 2 to find an equation for the circle that circumscribes the triangle with the given vertices.

17 $A(-2, 1), B(-4, -1), C(1, 2)$

18 $A(-3, 1), B(5, 5), C(-3, 9)$

19 Show that the center of the circle given by $x^2 + y^2 + ax + by + c = 0$ is on the line $y = x$ if and only if $a = b$.

20 Show that the graph of $x^2 + y^2 + ax + by + c = 0$ contains the origin if and only if $c = 0$.

7.2 LINES

Let us first introduce several fundamental concepts pertaining to lines. All lines referred to are considered to be in a coordinate plane.

Definition

> If l is a line that is not parallel to the y-axis, and if $P_1(x_1, y_1)$ and $P_2(x_2, y_2)$ are distinct points on l, then the **slope m** of l is given by
>
> $$m = \frac{y_2 - y_1}{x_2 - x_1}.$$
>
> If l is parallel to the y-axis, then the slope is not defined.

The numerator $y_2 - y_1$ in the formula for m is sometimes called the **rise** from P_1 to P_2. It measures the vertical change in direction in proceeding from P_1 to P_2 and may be positive, negative, or zero. The denominator $x_2 - x_1$ is called the **run** from P_1 to P_2. It measures the amount of horizontal change in going from P_1 to P_2. The run may be positive or negative, but is never zero, because l is not parallel to the y-axis. Using this terminology,

$$\text{slope of } l = \frac{\text{rise from } P_1 \text{ to } P_2}{\text{run from } P_1 \text{ to } P_2}.$$

In finding the slope of a line it is immaterial which point is labeled P_1 and which is labeled P_2, since

$$\frac{y_2 - y_1}{x_2 - x_1} = \frac{y_1 - y_2}{x_1 - x_2}.$$

Consequently, we may as well assume that the points are labeled so that $x_1 < x_2$, as in Figure 7.2. In this event $x_2 - x_1 > 0$, and hence, the slope is positive, negative, or zero, depending on whether $y_2 > y_1, y_2 < y_1,$ or $y_2 = y_1$. The slope of the line shown in (i) of Figure 7.2 is positive, whereas the slope of the line shown in (ii) of the figure is negative.

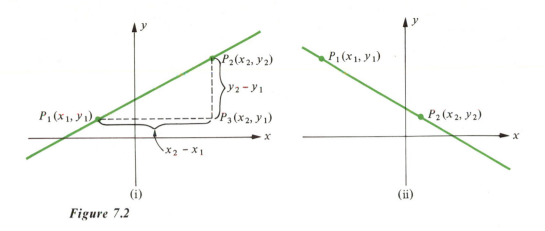

Figure 7.2

A **horizontal line** is a line that is parallel to the x-axis. Note that a line is horizontal if and only if its slope is 0. A **vertical line** is a line that is parallel to the y-axis. The slope of a vertical line is undefined.

Example 1   Sketch the lines through the following pairs of points and find their slopes.

(a) $A(-1, 4)$ and $B(3, 2)$

(b) $A(2, 5)$ and $B(-2, -1)$

(c) $A(4, 3)$ and $B(-2, 3)$

(d) $A(4, -1)$ and $B(4, 4)$

Solution   The lines are sketched in Figure 7.3. Using the definition of slope gives us

(a) $m = \dfrac{2 - 4}{3 - (-1)} = \dfrac{-2}{4} = -\dfrac{1}{2}$

(b) $m = \dfrac{5 - (-1)}{2 - (-2)} = \dfrac{6}{4} = \dfrac{3}{2}$

(c) $m = \dfrac{3 - 3}{-2 - 4} = \dfrac{0}{-6} = 0$

(d)   The slope is undefined, since the line is vertical. This is also seen by noting that if the formula for m is used, the denominator is zero.   ■

It is important to note that the definition of slope is independent of the two points that are chosen on l, for if other points $P_1'(x_1', y_1')$ and $P_2'(x_2', y_2')$ are used, then, as in Figure 7.4, the triangle with vertices P_1', P_2', and P_3' (x_2', y_1') is similar to the triangle with vertices P_1, P_2, $P_3(x_2, y_1)$. Since the ratios of corresponding sides are equal, it follows that

$$\frac{y_2 - y_1}{x_2 - x_1} = \frac{y_2' - y_1'}{x_2' - x_1'}.$$

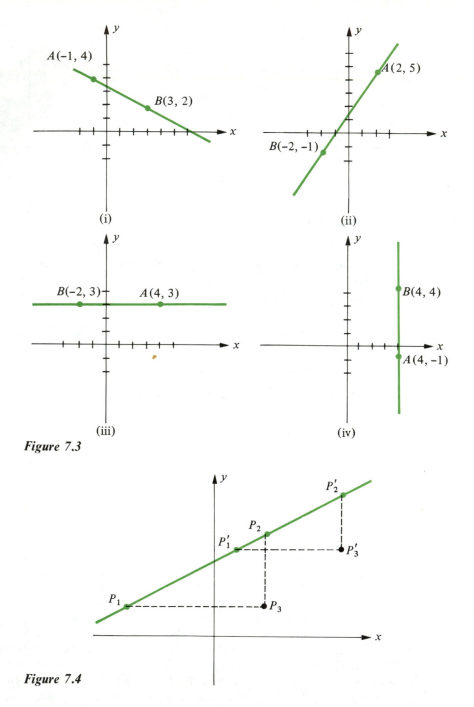

Figure 7.3

Figure 7.4

Example 2   Construct a line through $P(2, 1)$ that has slope   (a) $5/3$;   (b) $-5/3$.

Solution   If the slope of a line is a/b, where b is positive, then for every change of b units in the horizontal direction, the line rises or falls $|a|$ units, depending on whether a is positive or negative, respectively. If $P(2, 1)$ is on the line and $m = 5/3$, we can obtain another point on the line by starting at P and moving 3 units to the right and 5 units upward. This gives us the point $Q(5, 6)$, and the line is determined (see (i) of Figure 7.5). Similarly, if $m = -5/3$, we move 3 units to the right and 5 units downward, obtaining $Q(5, -4)$, as in (ii) of Figure 7.5.

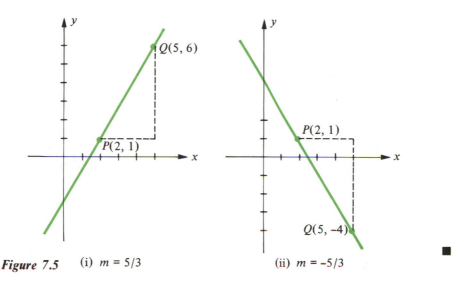

Figure 7.5   (i) $m = 5/3$ (ii) $m = -5/3$

Theorem

(i)   The graph of the equation $x = a$ is a vertical line with x-intercept a.

(ii) The graph of the equation $y = b$ is a horizontal line with y-intercept b.

Proof

The equation $x = a$, where a is a real number, may be considered as an equation in two variables x and y, since we can write it in the form

$$x + (0)y = a.$$

Some typical solutions of the equation are $(a, -2), (a, 1)$, and $(a, 3)$. Evidently, all solutions of the equation consist of pairs of the form (a, y), where y may have any value and a is fixed. It follows that the graph of $x = a$ is a line parallel to the y-axis with x-intercept a, as illustrated in Figure 7.6. This proves (i). A similar argument can be used to show that the graph of $y = b$ is a line parallel to the x-axis with y-intercept b, as shown in Figure 7.6. ■

Let us now find an equation of a line l through a point $P_1(x_1, y_1)$ with slope m (only one such line exists). If $P(x, y)$ is any point with $x \neq x_1$ (see Figure 7.7), then P is on l if and only if the slope of the line through P_1 and P is m, that is, if and only if

$$\frac{y - y_1}{x - x_1} = m.$$

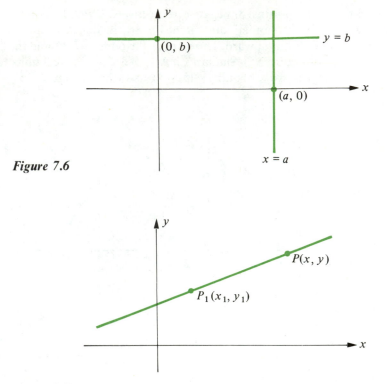

Figure 7.6

Figure 7.7

This equation may be written in the form

$$y - y_1 = m(x - x_1).$$

Note that (x_1, y_1) is also a solution of the last equation, and hence, the points on l are precisely the points that correspond to the solutions. This equation for l is referred to as the **point-slope form**. Our discussion may be summarized as follows:

Point-Slope Form for the Equation of a Line

> An equation for the line through the point $P(x_1, y_1)$ with slope m is
>
> $$y - y_1 = m(x - x_1).$$

Example 3   Find an equation of the line through the points $A(1, 7)$ and $B(-3, 2)$.

Solution   The slope m of the line is

$$m = \frac{7 - 2}{1 - (-3)} = \frac{5}{4}.$$

Using the coordinates of A in the point-slope form gives us

$$y - 7 = \frac{5}{4}(x - 1)$$

which is equivalent to

$$4y - 28 = 5x - 5 \quad \text{or} \quad 5x - 4y + 23 = 0.$$

The same equation would have been obtained if the coordinates of points B had been substituted in the point-slope form. ∎

The point-slope form may be rewritten as $y = mx - mx_1 + y_1$, which is of the form

$$y = mx + b$$

where $b = -mx_1 + y_1$. The real number b is the y-intercept of the graph, as may be seen by setting $x = 0$. Since the equation $y = mx + b$ displays the slope m and y-intercept b of l, it is called the **slope-intercept form** for the equation of a line. Conversely, if we start with $y = mx + b$, we may write

$$y - b = m(x - 0).$$

Comparing with the point-slope form, we see that the graph is a line with slope m and passing through the point $(0, b)$. This gives us the next result.

Slope-Intercept Form for the Equation of a Line

> The graph of the equation $y = mx + b$ is a line having slope m and y-intercept b.

The work we have done shows that every line is the graph of an equation of the form

$$ax + by + c = 0$$

where a, b, and c are real numbers, and a and b are not both zero. We call such an equation a **linear equation** in x and y. Let us show, conversely, that the graph of $ax + by + c = 0$, where a and b are not both zero, is always a line. On the one hand, if $b \neq 0$, we may solve for y, obtaining

$$y = (-a/b)x + (-c/b)$$

which, by the slope-intercept form, is an equation of a line with slope $-a/b$ and y-intercept $-c/b$. On the other hand, if $b = 0$ but $a \neq 0$, then we may solve for x, obtaining $x = -c/a$, which is the equation of a vertical line with x-intercept $-c/a$. This establishes the following important theorem.

Theorem

> The graph of a linear equation $ax + by + c = 0$ is a line, and conversely, every line is the graph of a linear equation.

For simplicity, we shall often use the terminology *the line* $ax + by + c = 0$, instead of the more accurate phrase *the line with equation* $ax + by + c = 0$.

Example 4   Sketch the graph of $2x - 5y = 8$.

Solution   From the previous theorem we know the graph is a line, and hence, it is sufficient to find two points on the graph. Let us find the x- and y-intercepts. Substituting $y = 0$ in the given equation, we obtain the x-intercept 4. Substituting $x = 0$, we see that the y-intercept is $-8/5$. This leads to the graph in Figure 7.8.

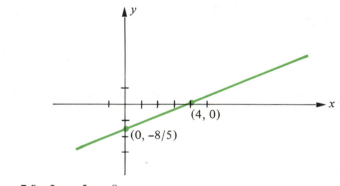

Figure 7.8 $2x - 5y = 8$

Another method of solution is to express the given equation in slope-intercept form. To do this, we begin by isolating the term involving y on one side of the equals sign, obtaining

$$5y = 2x - 8.$$

Next, dividing both sides by 5 gives us

$$y = \frac{2}{5}x + \left(\frac{-8}{5}\right)$$

which is of the form $y = mx + b$. Hence, the slope is $m = 2/5$ and the y-intercept is $b = -8/5$. We may then sketch a line through the point $(0, -8/5)$ with slope $2/5$. ∎

It will be shown in the next section that *two nonvertical lines are parallel if and only if they have the same slope*. We shall use this fact in the next example.

Example 5 Find an equation of a line through the point $(5, -7)$ which is parallel to the line $6x + 3y - 4 = 0$.

Solution Let us express the given equation in slope-intercept form. We begin by writing

$$3y = -6x + 4$$

and then divide both sides by 3, obtaining

$$y = -2x + \frac{4}{3}.$$

The last equation is in slope-intercept form with $m = -2$, and hence, the slope is -2. Since parallel lines have the same slope, the required line must have slope -2. Applying the point-slope form gives us

$$y + 7 = -2(x - 5)$$

or, equivalently,

$$y + 7 = -2x + 10 \quad \text{or} \quad 2x + y - 3 = 0. \qquad \blacksquare$$

EXERCISES 7.2

In each of Exercises 1–6, plot the points A and B and find the slope of the line through A and B.

1 $A(-3, 8)$, $B(-2, 16)$

2 $A(7, -1)$, $B(-4, 9)$

3 $A(\frac{1}{3}, \frac{2}{3})$, $B(-\frac{3}{2}, \frac{1}{2})$

4 $A(-5, -2)$, $B(6, 4)$

5 $A(5, 0)$, $B(-3, 2)$

6 $A(0, -4)$, $B(8, 3)$

7 Use slopes to show that $A(-4, -1)$, $B(2, 3)$, $C(1, -3)$, and $D(7, 1)$ are vertices of a parallelogram.

8 Use slopes to show that $A(-3, -9)$, $B(1, -1)$, and $C(4, 5)$ lie on a straight line.

In each of Exercises 9–22, find an equation for the line satisfying the given conditions.

9 Through $A(5, -2)$; slope $1/3$

10 Through $B(-3, 7)$; slope -2

11 Through $A(-8, -3)$ and $B(2, -5)$

12 Through $P(4, -1)$ and $Q(-6, 3)$

13 Slope -4, y-intercept 7

14 Slope $3/4$, x-intercept 5

15 x-intercept -3, y-intercept 7

16 Through $A(-7, -8)$; y-intercept 0

17 Through $A(7, -3)$, parallel to the (a) x-axis
    (b) y-axis

18 Through $A(-8, 2)$, perpendicular to the (a) y-axis (b) x-axis

19 Bisecting the second and fourth quadrants

20 Coinciding with the y-axis

21 Through $A(-4, 10)$, parallel to the line through $B(0, 5)$ and $C(-8, -8)$

22 Through $P(3/2, -1/4)$, parallel to the line with equation $2x + 4y = 5$

23 Find equations for the medians of the triangle with vertices $A(-4, -3)$, $B(2, 3)$, and $C(5, -1)$.

24 If $A(x_1, y_1)$, $B(x_2, y_2)$, $C(x_3, y_3)$, and $D(x_4, y_4)$ are vertices of an arbitrary quadrilateral, prove that the line segments joining the midpoints of adjacent sides form a parallelogram.

In each of Exercises 25–34, use the slope-intercept form to find the slope and y-intercept of the line with the given equation and sketch the graph.

25 $2x - 5y + 10 = 0$ **26** $2y - 3x = 4$

27 $3x + 5y = 0$ **28** $6x = 1 - 2y$

29 $y + 2 = 0$ **30** $3y = 8$

31 $5x = 20 - 6y$ **32** $9x - 4y = 0$

33 $y = 0$ **34** $x = (2/3)y + 4$

35 If a line l has nonzero x- and y-intercepts a and b, respectively, prove that an equation for l is

$$\frac{x}{a} + \frac{y}{b} = 1.$$

(This is called the **intercept form** for the equation of a line.) Express the equation $4x - 2y = 6$ in intercept form.

36 Prove that an equation of the line through $P_1(x_1, y_1)$ and $P_2(x_2, y_2)$ is

$$(y - y_1)(x_2 - x_1) = (y_2 - y_1)(x - x_1).$$

(This is called the **two-point form** for the equation of a line.) Use the two-point form to find an equation of the line through $A(7, -1)$ and $B(4, 6)$.

7.3 FURTHER PROPERTIES OF LINES

The concept of *inclination*, introduced in the next definition, is fundamental for the further study of lines.

Definition

> If l is a line that is not parallel to the x-axis, and if P_1 is the point of intersection of l and the x-axis, then the **inclination** of l is the smallest angle α through which the x-axis must be rotated in a counterclockwise direction about P_1 in order to coincide with l. If l is parallel to the x-axis, then $\alpha = 0°$.

If l is not horizontal then $0° < \alpha < 180°$. The line shown in (i) of Figure 7.9 illustrates the case $0° < \alpha < 90°$ and that in (ii) illustrates $90° < \alpha < 180°$. It follows from plane geometry that two lines are parallel if and only if they have the same inclination.

Theorem

> If a line has slope m and inclination α, then $m = \tan \alpha$.

Proof If the line is horizontal, then $m = 0$, $\alpha = 0°$, and, since $0 = \tan 0°$, the theorem is true.

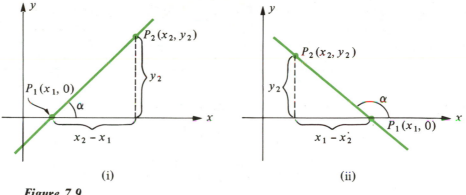

Figure 7.9

If the line is not horizontal, let x_1 be the x-intercept and consider any point $P_2(x_2, y_2)$ on the line, where $y_2 > 0$. If $x_1 < x_2$, then referring to the triangle in (i) of Figure 7.9,

$$\tan \alpha = \frac{y_2}{x_2 - x_1} = m.$$

If $x_2 < x_1$, then from (ii) of Figure 7.9,

$$\tan (180° - \alpha) = \frac{y_2}{x_1 - x_2}.$$

However, by Exercise 35 in Section 3.6, $\tan (180° - \alpha) = -\tan \alpha$, and hence, we again obtain $\tan \alpha = m$. This completes the proof. ∎

Corollary

> Two lines with slopes m_1 and m_2 are parallel if and only if $m_1 = m_2$.

Proof

If the lines have inclinations α_1 and α_2, then they are parallel if and only if $\alpha_1 = \alpha_2$, or, equivalently, $\tan \alpha_1 = \tan \alpha_2$. The corollary now follows from the theorem. ∎

Example 1

(a) Find the slope m of a line whose inclination is $120°$.

(b) Find the inclination α of a line whose slope is $7/10$.

Solution

(a) By the preceding theorem, $m = \tan 120° = -\sqrt{3}$.

(b) Since $\tan \alpha = 0.7$, $\alpha = \tan^{-1} (0.7)$. If an approximation is desired, then using Table 2, $\alpha \approx 35°$. ∎

The next theorem provides conditions for testing perpendicularity of lines.

Theorem

> Two nonvertical lines with slopes m_1 and m_2 are perpendicular if and only if $m_1 m_2 = -1$.

Proof

If α_1 and α_2 denote the inclinations of the lines, then

$$m_1 = \tan \alpha_1 \quad \text{and} \quad m_2 = \tan \alpha_2.$$

We may assume, without loss of generality, that $\alpha_2 > \alpha_1$, as illustrated in Figure 7.10. If θ is the angle indicated in the figure, then

$$\alpha_2 = \alpha_1 + \theta, \quad \text{or} \quad \theta = \alpha_2 - \alpha_1.$$

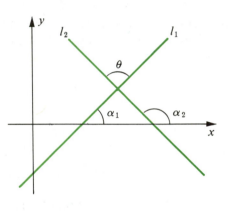

Figure 7.10

Applying the subtraction formula for the tangent function,

$$\tan \theta = \tan (\alpha_2 - \alpha_1) = \frac{\tan \alpha_2 - \tan \alpha_1}{1 + \tan \alpha_1 \tan \alpha_2}$$

or
$$\tan \theta = \frac{m_2 - m_1}{1 + m_1 m_2}.$$

By definition, the lines are perpendicular if and only if $\theta = 90°$, or, equivalently, $\tan \theta$ is undefined. However, by the preceding formula, $\tan \theta$ is undefined if and only if $1 + m_1 m_2 = 0$, or $m_1 m_2 = -1$, which is what we wished to prove. Although we have referred to Figure 7.10, a similar argument may be used regardless of the magnitudes of α_1 and α_2, or where the lines intersect. ∎

Another way of stating this theorem is to say that l_1 and l_2 are perpendicular if and only if $m_1 = -1/m_2$; that is, m_1 and m_2 are negative reciprocals of one another.

Example 2   Prove that the triangle with vertices $A(-1, -3), B(6, 1)$, and $C(2, -5)$ is a right triangle.

Solution   If m_1 denotes the slope of the line through B and C, and if m_2 denotes the slope of the line through A and C, then

$$m_1 = \frac{1 - (-5)}{6 - 2} = \frac{3}{2}, \qquad m_2 = \frac{-3 - (-5)}{-1 - 2} = -\frac{2}{3}.$$

Since $m_1 m_2 = -1$, the angle at C is a right angle.   ■

Example 3   Find an equation for the perpendicular bisector l of the line segment from $A(1, 7)$ to $B(-3, 2)$.

Solution   The given points and the perpendicular bisector are shown in Figure 7.11. The slope of the line through A and B is

$$m = \frac{7 - 2}{1 - (-3)} = \frac{5}{4}$$

and hence, by the last theorem, the slope of l is $-4/5$. Applying the midpoint formula, we see that the midpoint of AB is $(-1, 9/2)$. Using the point-slope form, an equation for l is

$$y - \frac{9}{2} = -\frac{4}{5}(x + 1).$$

Multiplying both sides by 10 and simplifying gives us

$$8x + 10y - 37 = 0.$$

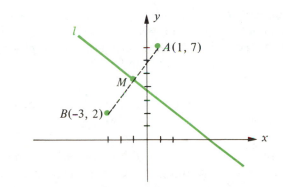

Figure 7.11   ■

We shall conclude this section by deriving a formula that may be used to find the angle between two lines in a coordinate plane. If the lines are parallel, then by definition the angle between them is $0°$. If the lines intersect, label the line of larger inclination l_2 and the line of smaller inclination l_1. Denoting the inclinations of l_1 and l_2 by α_1 and α_2, respectively, it follows that $\alpha_2 > \alpha_1$. The angle θ between l_1 and l_2 is defined by $\theta = \alpha_2 - \alpha_1$, as illustrated in Figure 7.12.

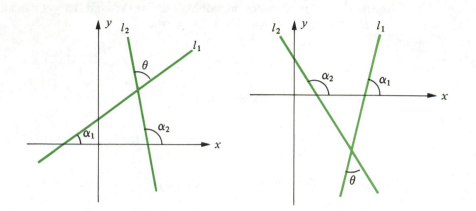

Figure 7.12

Assuming that none of the angles are right angles,

$$\tan\theta = \tan(\alpha_2 - \alpha_1) = \frac{\tan\alpha_2 - \tan\alpha_1}{1 + \tan\alpha_2 \tan\alpha_1}$$

or

$$\tan\theta = \frac{m_2 - m_1}{1 + m_2 m_1}$$

where m_1 and m_2 are the slopes of l_1 and l_2, respectively. If $\theta = 90°$, the lines are perpendicular, which, for nonvertical lines, is equivalent to $m_1 m_2 = -1$. If either line is vertical, then the formula for $\tan\theta$ cannot be employed. In this latter case, the fact that $\theta = \alpha_2 - \alpha_1$ should be used to find θ.

Example 4   Find the tangent of the angle between the lines $3x - 4y = 8$ and $5x + y - 7 = 0$.

Solution   The slopes of the lines are $3/4$ and -5. (Why?) Setting $m_2 = -5$, $m_1 = 3/4$, and applying the last formula gives us

$$\tan\theta = \frac{-5 - (3/4)}{1 + (-5)(3/4)} = \frac{23}{11}.$$

An approximation to θ may be found by means of Table 2. To the nearest degree, $\theta \approx 64°$.   ■

EXERCISES 7.3

In Exercises 1 and 2, find the inclination of the line that has the given slope.

1 (a) -1 (b) $\sqrt{3}/3$

   (c) 2 (d) $\tan 20°$

2 (a) 1 (b) $\sqrt{3}$

   (c) -4 (d) $\cot 55°$

In Exercises 3 and 4, find the slope of the line with the given inclination.

3 (a) $0°$ (b) $120°$

   (c) $\arctan 1$ (d) $\arctan 4/3$

4 (a) $135°$ (b) $5\pi/6$

   (c) $\arcsin 1/2$ (d) $\arctan 1/2$

5 Prove that the following points are vertices of a rectangle: $A(6, 15)$, $B(11, 12)$, $C(-1, -8)$, $D(-6, -5)$.

6 Prove that the points $A(1, 4)$, $B(6, -4)$, and $C(-15, -6)$ are vertices of a right triangle.

In each of Exercises 7–10, find an equation for the lines satisfying the given conditions.

7 Through $A(7, -3)$, perpendicular to the line with equation $2x - 5y = 8$.

8 Through $A(-4, 8)$, perpendicular to the line through $B(5, -1)$ and $C(-2, -3)$.

9 Through $A(-7, 2)$, parallel to the line through $B(0, 4)$ and $C(-6, -6)$.

10 Through $P(-3/4, -1/2)$, parallel to the line with equation $x + 3y = 1$.

11 Find an equation for the perpendicular bisector of the line segment from $A(3, -1)$ to $B(-2, 6)$.

12 Find an equation for the perpendicular bisector of the line segment from the origin to $P(-5, 6)$.

13 Find equations for the altitudes of the triangle with vertices $A(-3, 2), B(5, 4)$, and $C(3, -8)$, and find the point at which they intersect.

14 Find equations for the medians of the triangle in Exercise 13, and find their point of intersection.

15 Find the tangent of the angle between lines whose slopes are

    (a) 4 and 2/3   (b) -3 and -5.

16 Approximate, to the nearest degree, the angle between the lines having equations $6x - 2y - 3 = 0$ and $3x + 8y + 1 = 0$.

17 Approximate, to the nearest degree, the interior angles of the triangle with vertices $A(1, 6)$, $B(-3, -2)$, and $C(4, 4)$.

18 Given the triangle of Exercise 17, determine the slope of the bisector of the angle at vertex A.

19 Find the slope of a line through the point $P(4, -5)$ which makes an angle of $30°$ with the line having equation $3x + y - 18 = 0$.

20 If the slope of a line l_1 is 1/2, find the slope of a line l_2 such that the angle between l_1 and l_2 is $135°$.

7.4 CONIC SECTIONS

Each of the geometric figures to be discussed in this and the next three sections can be obtained by intersecting a double-napped right circular cone with a plane. For this reason, they are called **conic sections**, or simply **conics**. If, as in (i) of Figure 7.13, the plane cuts entirely across one nappe of the cone and is not perpendicular to the axis, then the curve of intersection is called an **ellipse**. If the plane is perpendicular to the axis of the cone, a *circle* results. If the plane does not cut across one entire nappe and does not intersect both nappes, as illustrated in (ii) of Figure 7.13, then the curve of intersection is a

parabola. If the plane cuts through both nappes of the cone, as in (iii) of the figure, then the resulting figure is called a **hyperbola**.

By changing the position of the plane and the shape of the cone, conics can be made to vary considerably. For certain positions of the plane, there result what are called **degenerate conics**. For example, if the plane intersects the cone only at the vertex, then the conic consists of one point. If the axis of the cone lies on the plane, then a pair of intersecting lines is obtained. Finally, if we begin with the parabolic case, as in (ii) of Figure 7.13, and move the plane parallel to its initial position until it coincides with one of the generators of the cone, a line results.

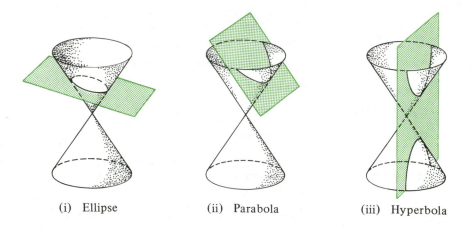

(i) Ellipse   (ii) Parabola   (iii) Hyperbola

Figure 7.13

The conic sections were studied extensively by the early Greek mathematicians, who used the methods of Euclidean geometry. They discovered the properties that enable us to define conics in terms of points (foci) and lines (directrices) in the plane of the conic. Reconciliation of the latter definitions with the previous discussion requires proofs that we shall not go into here.

A remarkable fact about conic sections is that although they were studied thousands of years ago, they are far from obsolete. Indeed, they are important tools for present-day investigations in outer space and for the study of the behavior of atomic particles. It is shown in physics that if a mass moves under the influence of what is called an *inverse square force field*, then its path may be described by means of a conic section. Examples of inverse square fields are gravitational and electromagnetic fields. Planetary orbits are elliptical. If the ellipse is very "flat," the curve resembles the path of a comet. The hyperbola is useful for describing the path of an alpha particle in the electric field of the nucleus of an atom. The interested person can find many other applications of conic sections.

7.5 PARABOLAS

Parabolas are very useful in applications of mathematics to the physical world. For example, it can be shown that if a projectile is fired and it is assumed that it is acted upon only by the force of gravity (that is, air resistance and other outside factors are ignored), then the path of the projectile is parabolic. Properties of parabolas are used in the design of mirrors for telescopes and searchlights. They are also employed in the design of field microphones used in television broadcasts of football games. These are only a few of many physical applications.

Definition

> A **parabola** is the set of all points in a plane equidistant from a fixed point F (the **focus**) and a fixed line l (the **directrix**) in the plane.

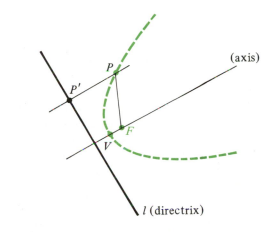

Figure 7.14

We shall assume that F is not on l, for otherwise the parabola degenerates into a line. If P is any point in the plane and P' is the point on l determined by a line through P which is perpendicular to l, then by definition P is on the parabola if and only if $d(P, F) = d(P, P')$. A typical situation is illustrated in Figure 7.14, where the dashes indicate possible positions of P. The line through F, perpendicular to the directrix, is called the **axis** of the parabola. The point V on the axis, halfway from F to l, is called the **vertex** of the parabola.

In order to obtain a simple equation for a parabola, let us choose the y-axis along the axis of the parabola, with the origin at the vertex V, as illustrated in Figure 7.15. In this case, the focus F has coordinates $(0, p)$ for some real number $p \neq 0$, and the equation of the directrix is $y = -p$. By the Distance Formula, a point $P(x, y)$ is on the parabola if and only if

$$\sqrt{(x - 0)^2 + (y - p)^2} = \sqrt{(x - x)^2 + (y + p)^2}.$$

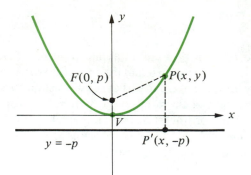

Figure 7.15 $x^2 = 4py$

Squaring both sides gives us

$$(x - 0)^2 + (y - p)^2 = (y + p)^2$$

or
$$x^2 + y^2 - 2py + p^2 = y^2 + 2py + p^2$$

which simplifies to
$$x^2 = 4py.$$

The last equation is called the **standard form** for the equation of a parabola with focus at $F(0, p)$ and directrix $y = -p$. If $p > 0$, the parabola **opens upward,** as in Figure 7.15; whereas if $p < 0$, the parabola **opens downward**.

An analogous situation exists if the axis of the parabola is taken along the x-axis. If the vertex is $V(0, 0)$, the focus is $F(p, 0)$, and the directrix has equation $x = -p$ (see Figure 7.16), then using the same type of argument we obtain the **standard form**

$$y^2 = 4px.$$

If $p > 0$, the parabola opens to the right, as in Figure 7.16, whereas if $p < 0$, it opens to the left.

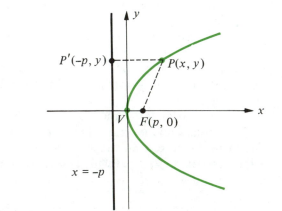

Figure 7.16 $y^2 = 4px$

Example 1 Find the focus and directrix of the parabola having equation $y^2 = -6x$, and sketch the graph.

Solution The equation is in the standard form $y^2 = 4px$ with $4p = -6$, and hence, $p = -3/2$. Consequently, the focus is $F(-3/2, 0)$ and the equation of the directrix is $x = 3/2$. The graph is sketched in Figure 7.17.

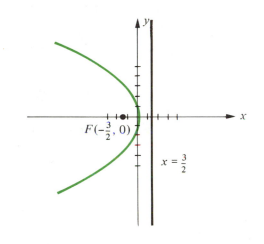

Figure 7.17 $y^2 = -6x$ ■

Example 2 Find an equation of the parabola that has vertex at the origin, opens upward, and passes through the point $P(-3, 7)$.

Solution According to our previous discussion, the general form of the equation is given by $x^2 = 4py$. If P is on the parabola, then $(-3, 7)$ is a solution of the equation. Hence, we must have $(-3)^2 = 4p(7)$, or $p = 9/28$. Substitution for p leads to the desired equation $x^2 = (9/7)y$, or $7x^2 = 9y$.   ■

It is worth noting that each of the graphs we have discussed is symmetric to one of the coordinate axes. For example, the graph of $x^2 = 4py$ in Figure 7.15 is symmetric with respect to the y-axis, since the equation is unchanged if x is replaced by $-x$. Similarly, the graph of $y^2 = 4px$ in Figure 7.16 is symmetric with respect to the x-axis, since the equation is unchanged if y is replaced by $-y$.

It is not difficult to extend our work to the case in which the axis of the parabola is parallel to one of the coordinate axes. In Figure 7.18, we have taken the vertex at the point $V(h, k)$, the focus at $F(h, k + p)$, and the directrix $y = k - p$. As before, the point $P(x, y)$ is on the parabola if and only if $d(P, F) = d(P, P')$, that is, if and only if

$$\sqrt{(x - h)^2 + (y - k - p)^2} = \sqrt{(x - x)^2 + (y - k + p)^2}.$$

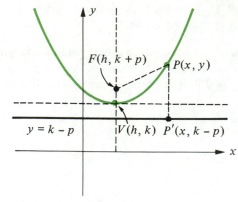

Figure 7.18 $(x - h)^2 = 4p(y - k)$

We leave it to the reader to show that the equation simplifies to the following.

Standard Equation of a Parabola (vertical axis)

$$(x - h)^2 = 4p(y - k)$$

Note the manner in which the standard equation displays the vertex (h, k) of the parabola. Squaring the left side and simplifying leads to an equation of the form

$$y = ax^2 + bx + c$$

where a, b, and c are real numbers. Conversely, given such an equation, we may complete the square in x to arrive at the standard form. Consequently, if $a \neq 0$, then the graph of $y = ax^2 + bx + c$ is a parabola with a vertical axis.

We may obtain the following in similar fashion:

Standard Equation of a Parabola (horizontal axis)

$$(y - k)^2 = 4p(x - h)$$

where, as before, the vertex is (h, k). This parabola opens to the right or left as p is positive or negative, respectively.

Example 3   Find an equation of the parabola with vertex $(4, -1)$, with axis parallel to the y-axis, and which passes through the origin.

Solution   The standard equation is

$$(x - 4)^2 = 4p(y + 1).$$

If the origin is on the parabola, then $(0, 0)$ is a solution of this equation, and hence, $(0 - 4)^2 = 4p(0 + 1)$. Consequently, $16 = 4p$ and $p = 4$. The desired equation is, therefore,

$$(x - 4)^2 = 16(y + 1). \qquad \blacksquare$$

Example 4   Discuss and sketch the graph of the equation

$$2y = x^2 + 8x + 22.$$

Solution   By our previous remarks, the graph of the equation is a parabola with a vertical axis. Writing

$$x^2 + 8x = 2y - 22$$

we complete the square on the left by adding 16 to both sides. This gives us

$$x^2 + 8x + 16 = 2y - 6.$$

The last equation may be written

$$(x + 4)^2 = 2(y - 3)$$

which is a standard equation of a parabola, with $h = -4$, $k = 3$, and $p = 1/2$. Hence, the vertex is $V(-4, 3)$. Since $p = 1/2 > 0$, the parabola opens upward with focus at $F(-4, 7/2)$. The equation of the directrix is $y = k - p$, or $y = 5/2$. The parabola is sketched in Figure 7.19.

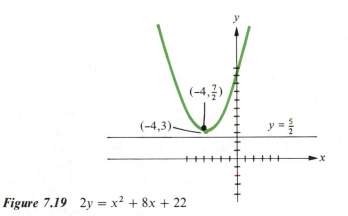

Figure 7.19 $2y = x^2 + 8x + 22$

EXERCISES 7.5

In each of Exercises 1–16, find the focus and directrix of the parabola with the given equation, and sketch the graph.

1   $y^2 = 12x$

2   $y^2 = -20x$

3   $x^2 = -8y$

4   $x^2 = 5y$

5   $4y^2 = -5x$

6   $4y^2 = x$

7   $9x^2 = y$

8   $7x^2 = 3y$

9   $(y + 3)^2 = 4(x - 1)$

10   $6(x - 5)^2 = 8 - y$

11   $y^2 - 4y - 2x - 4 = 0$

12   $y^2 + 14y + 4x + 45 = 0$

13   $4x^2 + 40x + y + 106 = 0$

14   $y^2 - 20y + 100 = 6x$

15 $y^2 + 20x = 10$

16 $4x^2 + 4x + 4y + 1 = 0$

In each of Exercises 17–22, find an equation for the parabola that satisfies the given conditions.

17 Focus $(-6, 0)$, directrix $x = 6$

18 Focus $(0, 3)$, directrix $y = -3$

19 Focus $(2, 5)$, directrix $y = -1$

20 Focus $(-4, 1)$, directrix $y = 5$

21 Vertex at the origin, symmetric to the y-axis, and passing through the point $A(3, -2)$

22 Vertex $V(1, -4)$, axis parallel to the x-axis, and passing through $A(-6, 7)$

23 A searchlight reflector is designed so that a cross section through its axis is a parabola and the light source is at the focus. Find the focus if the reflector is 3 feet across at the opening and 1 foot deep.

24 Prove that the point on a parabola that is closest to the focus is the vertex.

7.6 ELLIPSES

An ellipse may be defined as follows:

Definition

> An **ellipse** is the set of all points in a plane, the sum of whose distances from two fixed points in the plane (the **foci**) is constant.

The orbits of planets in the solar system are elliptical, with the sun at one of the foci. This is only one of many important applications of ellipses.

There is an easy way to construct an ellipse on paper. Begin by inserting two thumbtacks in the paper at points labeled F and F' and fastening the ends of a piece of string to the thumbtacks. Now loop the string around a pencil and draw it taut at point P, as in Figure 7.20. If the string is then kept taut while the pencil is moved, the sum of the distances $d(F, P)$ and $d(F', P)$ will always be the length of the string and hence constant. The pencil will, therefore, trace out a figure that resembles an ellipse with foci at F and F'. By varying the positions of F and F' but keeping the length of string fixed, the shape of the ellipse can be made to change considerably. If F and F' are far apart, in the sense that $d(F, F')$ is almost the same as the length of the string, then the ellipse is quite flat. On the other hand, if $d(F, F')$ is close to zero, the ellipse is almost circular. Indeed, if $F = F'$, a circle is obtained.

By introducing suitable coordinate systems we may derive simple equations for ellipses. Let us choose the x-axis as the line through the two foci F and F', with the origin at the midpoint of the segment $F'F$. This point is called the **center** of the ellipse. If F has coordinates $(c, 0)$, where $c > 0$, then, as shown in Figure 7.21, F' has coordinates $(-c, 0)$, and hence, the distance between F and F' is $2c$. Let the constant sum of the distances of P, from F and F' be denoted by $2a$, where, in order to get points that are not on the x-axis, we must have $2a > 2c$, that is, $a > c$. (Why?) By definition, $P(x, y)$ is on the ellipse if and only if

$$d(P, F) + d(P, F') = 2a$$

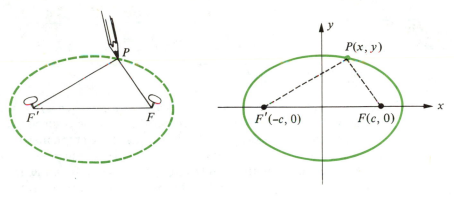

Figure 7.20   **Figure 7.21**

or, by the Distance Formula,

$$\sqrt{(x-c)^2 + (y-0)^2} + \sqrt{(x+c)^2 + (y-0)^2} = 2a.$$

Writing this equation as

$$\sqrt{(x-c)^2 + y^2} = 2a - \sqrt{(x+c)^2 + y^2}$$

and squaring both sides, we obtain

$$x^2 - 2cx + c^2 + y^2 = 4a^2 - 4a\sqrt{(x+c)^2 + y^2} + x^2 + 2cx + c^2 + y^2$$

which simplifies to

$$a\sqrt{(x+c)^2 + y^2} = a^2 + cx.$$

Squaring both sides gives us

$$a^2(x^2 + 2cx + c^2 + y^2) = a^4 + 2a^2cx + c^2x^2$$

which may be written in the form

$$x^2(a^2 - c^2) + a^2y^2 = a^2(a^2 - c^2).$$

Dividing both sides by $a^2(a^2 - c^2)$ leads to

$$\frac{x^2}{a^2} + \frac{y^2}{a^2 - c^2} = 1.$$

For convenience, we let

$$\boxed{b^2 = a^2 - c^2 \qquad \text{where } b > 0}$$

obtaining the following equation.

Equation of an Ellipse

$$\frac{x^2}{a^2} + \frac{y^2}{b^2} = 1$$

Since $c > 0$ and $b^2 = a^2 - c^2$, it follows that $a^2 > b^2$ and hence $a > b$. The equation we have derived is called the **standard form** for the equation of an ellipse with foci on the x-axis and center at the origin. The x-intercepts of the graph may be found by setting $y = 0$. Doing so gives us $x^2/a^2 = 1$, or $x^2 = a^2$, and consequently, the x-intercepts are a and $-a$. The corresponding points $V(a, 0)$ and $V'(-a, 0)$ on the graph are called the **vertices** of the ellipse, and the line segment $V'V$ is referred to as the **major axis**. The y-intercepts are b and $-b$. The segment from $M'(0, -b)$ to $M(0, b)$ is called the **minor axis** of the ellipse. Note that the major axis is longer than the minor axis, since $a > b$.

Applying tests for symmetry, we see that the ellipse is symmetric to both the x-axis and the y-axis. It is also symmetric with respect to the origin, since substitution of $-x$ for x and $-y$ for y does not change the equation.

Example 1   Discuss and sketch the graph of the equation

$$4x^2 + 18y^2 = 36.$$

Solution   To obtain the standard form, we divide both sides of the given equation by 36 and simplify. This leads to

$$\frac{x^2}{9} + \frac{y^2}{2} = 1$$

which is in standard form with $a^2 = 9$ and $b^2 = 2$. Thus, $a = 3$ and $b = \sqrt{2}$, and hence, the endpoints of the major axis are $(\pm 3, 0)$ and the endpoints of the minor axis are $(0, \pm\sqrt{2})$. Since $b^2 = a^2 - c^2$, we have

$$c^2 = a^2 - b^2 = 9 - 2 = 7, \quad \text{or} \quad c = \sqrt{7}.$$

Consequently, the foci are $(\pm\sqrt{7}, 0)$. The graph is sketched in Figure 7.22.

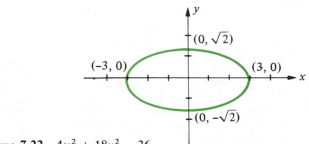

Figure 7.22 $4x^2 + 18y^2 = 36$

Example 2   Find an equation of the ellipse with vertices $(\pm 4, 0)$ and foci $(\pm 2, 0)$.

Solution   Since $a = 4$ and $c = 2$,

$$b^2 = a^2 - c^2 = 16 - 4 = 12.$$

Substitution in the standard form gives us

$$\frac{x^2}{16} + \frac{y^2}{12} = 1.$$

Multiplying both sides by 48 leads to $3x^2 + 4y^2 = 48$.   ∎

It is sometimes convenient to choose the major axis of an ellipse along the y-axis. If the foci are $(0, \pm c)$, then by the same type of argument used previously we obtain the following **standard form** for the equation of an ellipse with foci on the y-axis and center at the origin:

Equation of an Ellipse

$$\frac{x^2}{b^2} + \frac{y^2}{a^2} = 1$$

where $a > b$. As before, the connection between a, b, and c is given by $b^2 = a^2 - c^2$, or, equivalently, by $c^2 = a^2 - b^2$. In this case, the vertices are $V(0, a)$ and $V'(0, -a)$. The endpoints of the minor axis are $M(b, 0)$ and $M'(-b, 0)$. A typical graph is sketched in Figure 7.23.

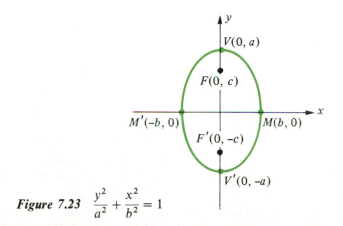

Figure 7.23 $\dfrac{y^2}{a^2} + \dfrac{x^2}{b^2} = 1$

The preceding discussion shows that an equation of an ellipse with center at the origin and foci on a coordinate axis may always be written in the form

$$\frac{x^2}{p} + \frac{y^2}{q} = 1 \quad \text{or} \quad qx^2 + py^2 = pq$$

where p and q are positive. If $p > q$, then the major axis lies on the x-axis, whereas if $q > p$, then the major axis is on the y-axis. It is unnecessary to memorize these facts, since in any given problem the major axis can be determined by examining the x- and y-intercepts.

Example 3   Sketch the graph of the equation $9x^2 + 4y^2 = 25$.

Solution   The graph is an ellipse with center at the origin and foci on one of the coordinate axes. To find the x-intercepts, we let $y = 0$, obtaining $9x^2 = 25$, or $x = \pm 5/3$. Similarly, to find the y-intercepts, we let $x = 0$, obtaining $4y^2 = 25$, or $y = \pm 5/2$.

This enables us to sketch the ellipse (see Figure 7.24). Since $5/3 < 5/2$, the major axis is on the y-axis.

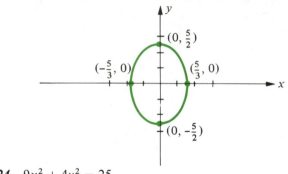

Figure 7.24 $9x^2 + 4y^2 = 25$

EXERCISES 7.6

In each of Exercises 1–8, sketch the graph of the equation and give coordinates of the vertices and foci.

1 $\dfrac{x^2}{49} + \dfrac{y^2}{25} = 1$ **2** $\dfrac{x^2}{16} + \dfrac{y^2}{9} = 1$

3 $9x^2 + y^2 = 36$ **4** $y^2 + 25x^2 = 25$

5 $3x^2 + 4y^2 = 12$ **6** $x^2 + 4y^2 = 16$

7 $4x^2 + 9y^2 = 1$ **8** $3y^2 + x^2 = 9$

In each of Exercises 9–14, find an equation for the ellipse satisfying the given conditions.

9 Vertices $V(0, \pm 8)$, foci $F(0, \pm 5)$

10 Vertices $V(\pm 10, 0)$, foci $F(\pm 6, 0)$

11 Vertices $V(\pm 5, 0)$, length of minor axis 3

12 Foci $F(0, \pm 3)$, length of minor axis 2

13 Vertices $V(0, \pm 10)$, passing through $(4, 3)$

14 Center at the origin, symmetric with respect to both axes, passing through $A(-6, 1)$ and $B(2, -3)$.

In each of Exercises 15 and 16, find the points of intersection of the graphs of the given equations. Sketch both graphs on the same coordinate axes, showing points of intersection.

15 $\begin{cases} x^2 + 4y^2 = 20 \\ x + 2y = 6 \end{cases}$

16 $\begin{cases} x^2 + 4y^2 = 36 \\ x^2 + y^2 = 12 \end{cases}$

17 An arch of a bridge is semielliptical, with its major axis horizontal. The base of the arch is 30 feet across, and the highest part of the arch is 10 feet above the horizontal roadway. Find the height of the arch 6 feet from the center of the base.

18 If a square with sides parallel to the coordinate axes is inscribed in the ellipse with equation

$x^2/a^2 + y^2/b^2 = 1$, express the area A of the square in terms of a and b.

19 The **eccentricity** of an ellipse is defined as the ratio $(\sqrt{a^2 - b^2})/a$. If a is fixed and b varies, describe the general shape of the ellipse when the eccentricity is close to 1, and when it is close to zero.

20 Derive the standard form $x^2/b^2 + y^2/a^2 = 1$.

7.7 HYPERBOLAS

The definition of hyperbola is similar to that of an ellipse. The only change is that, instead of using the *sum* of distances from two fixed points, we use the *difference*.

Definition

> A **hyperbola** is the set of all points in a plane, the difference of whose distances from two fixed points in the plane (the **foci**) is a positive constant.

To find a simple equation for a hyperbola, we choose a coordinate system with foci at $F(c, 0)$ and $F'(-c, 0)$, and denote the (constant) distance by $2a$. Referring to Figure 7.25, we see that a point $P(x, y)$ is on the hyperbola if and only if either one of the following is true:

$$d(P, F) - d(P, F') = 2a$$
(*)
$$d(P, F') - d(P, F) = 2a.$$

For hyperbolas (unlike ellipses), we need $a < c$ in order to obtain points on the hyperbola which are not on the x-axis, for if P is such a point, then from Figure 7.25 we see that

$$d(P, F) < d(F', F) + d(P, F')$$

since the length of one side of a triangle is always less than the sum of the lengths of the other two sides. Similarly,

$$d(P, F') < d(F', F) + d(P, F).$$

Equivalent forms for the previous two inequalities are

$$d(P, F) - d(P, F') < d(F', F)$$
$$d(P, F') - d(P, F) < d(F', F).$$

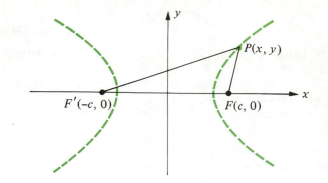

Figure 7.25

From the equations labeled (∗) and the fact that $d(F', F) = 2c$, the latter inequalities imply that $2a < 2c$, or $a < c$.

Equations (∗) may be replaced by the single equation

$$|d(P, F) - d(P, F')| = 2a.$$

It then follows from the Distance Formula that an equation of the hyperbola is given by

$$|\sqrt{(x - c)^2 + (y - 0)^2} - \sqrt{(x + c)^2 + (y - 0)^2}| = 2a.$$

Employing the type of simplification procedure used to derive an equation for an ellipse, we arrive at the equivalent equation

$$\frac{x^2}{a^2} - \frac{y^2}{c^2 - a^2} = 1.$$

For convenience, we let

$$\boxed{b^2 = c^2 - a^2 \qquad \text{where } b > 0}$$

in the preceding equation, obtaining

**Equation of
a Hyperbola**

$$\boxed{\frac{x^2}{a^2} - \frac{y^2}{b^2} = 1.}$$

This equation is called the **standard form** for the equation of a hyperbola with foci on the x-axis and center at the origin. By the tests for symmetry we see that the graph is symmetric with respect to both axes and the origin. The x-intercepts are $\pm a$. The corresponding points $V(a, 0)$ and $V'(-a, 0)$ are called the **vertices**, and the line segment $V'V$ is known as the **transverse axis** of the hyperbola. There are no y-intercepts, since the equation $-y^2/b^2 = 1$ has no solution.

If the equation $x^2/a^2 - y^2/b^2 = 1$ is solved for y, we obtain

$$y = \pm \frac{b}{a}\sqrt{x^2 - a^2}.$$

Hence, there are no points (x, y) on the graph if $x^2 - a^2 < 0$, that is, if $-a < x < a$. However, there *are* points $P(x, y)$ on the graph if $x \ge a$ or $x \le -a$. In order to arrive at a precise description of the graph, it is necessary to investigate the position of the point $P(x, y)$ on the hyperbola when x is numerically very large. If $x \ge a$, we may write the last equation in the form

$$y = \pm \frac{b}{a}x \sqrt{1 - \frac{a^2}{x^2}}.$$

It follows that if x is large (in comparison to a), the radicand is close to 1, and hence, the ordinate y of the point $P(x, y)$ on the hyperbola is close to either $(b/a)x$ or $-(b/a)x$. This means that the point $P(x, y)$ is close to the line with equation $y = (b/a)x$ when y is positive, or the line with equation $y = -(b/a)x$ when y is negative. As x increases (or decreases), we say that the point $P(x, y)$ *approaches* one of these lines. A corresponding situation exists when $x \le -a$. The lines with equations

$$y = \pm \frac{b}{a}x$$

are called the **asymptotes** of the hyperbola under discussion. The asymptotes serve as an excellent guide for sketching the graph. This is illustrated in Figure 7.26, where we have represented the asymptotes by dashed lines and indicated the manner in which the points on the hyperbola approach the asymptotes as x increases or decreases. The two curves that make up the hyperbola are called the **branches** of the hyperbola.

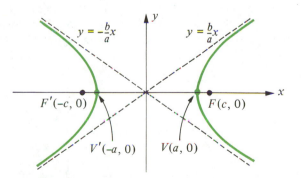

Figure 7.26

A convenient way to sketch the asymptotes is first to plot the vertices $V(a, 0)$ and $V'(-a, 0)$ and the points $W(0, b)$ and $W'(0, -b)$ (see Figure 7.27). The line segment $W'W$ of length $2b$ is called the **conjugate axis** of the hyperbola. If horizontal and vertical lines are drawn through the endpoints of the conjugate and transverse axes, respectively, then the diagonals of the resulting rectangle have slopes b/a and $-b/a$.

Consequently, by extending these diagonals, we obtain the asymptotes. The hyperbola is then sketched as in Figure 7.27, using the asymptotes as a guide.

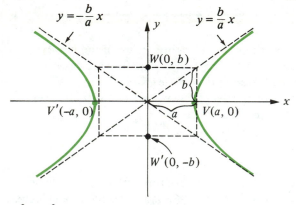

Figure 7.27 $\dfrac{x^2}{a^2} - \dfrac{y^2}{b^2} = 1$

Example 1   Discuss and sketch the graph of the equation

$$9x^2 - 4y^2 = 36.$$

Solution   Dividing both sides by 36, we have

$$\dfrac{x^2}{4} - \dfrac{y^2}{9} = 1$$

which is in the preceding standard form with $a^2 = 4$ and $b^2 = 9$. Hence, $a = 2$ and $b = 3$. The vertices $(\pm 2, 0)$ and the endpoints $(0, \pm 3)$ of the conjugate axis determine a rectangle whose diagonals (extended) give us the asymptotes. The graph of the equation is sketched in Figure 7.28. The equations of the asymptotes,

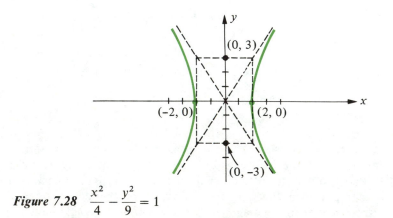

Figure 7.28 $\dfrac{x^2}{4} - \dfrac{y^2}{9} = 1$

$y = \pm\frac{3}{2}x$, may be found by referring to the graph, or to the equations $y = \pm(b/a)x$. Since

$$c^2 = a^2 + b^2 = 4 + 9 = 13$$

the foci are $(\pm\sqrt{13}, 0)$. ∎

The preceding example indicates that for hyperbolas it is not always true that $a > b$, as was the case for ellipses. Indeed, we may have $a < b$, $a > b$, or $a = b$.

Example 2 Find an equation, the foci, and the asymptotes of the hyperbola that has vertices $(\pm 3, 0)$ and passes through the point $P(5, 2)$.

Solution Substituting $a = 3$ in the standard form, we obtain the equation

$$\frac{x^2}{9} - \frac{y^2}{b^2} = 1.$$

If $(5, 2)$ is a solution of this equation, then

$$\frac{25}{9} - \frac{4}{b^2} = 1.$$

Solving for b^2 gives us $b^2 = 9/4$, and hence, the desired equation is

$$\frac{x^2}{9} - \frac{4y^2}{9} = 1$$

or, equivalently, $x^2 - 4y^2 = 9$.

Since $c^2 = a^2 + b^2 = 9 + (9/4) = 45/4$, it follows that $c = \sqrt{45/4} = 3\sqrt{5}/2$. Hence, the foci are $(\pm\frac{3}{2}\sqrt{5}, 0)$. Substituting for b and a in $y = \pm(b/a)x$ and simplifying, we obtain equations $y = \pm\frac{1}{2}x$ of the asymptotes. ∎

If the foci of a hyperbola are the points $(0, \pm c)$ on the y-axis, then it can be shown that an equation for the hyperbola is

Equation of a Hyperbola

$$\frac{y^2}{a^2} - \frac{x^2}{b^2} = 1.$$

This equation is called the **standard form** for the equation of a hyperbola with foci on the y-axis and center at the origin. The numbers a, b, and c are again related by means of the equation $b^2 = c^2 - a^2$. The points $V(0, a)$ and $V'(0, -a)$ are the vertices of the hyperbola, and the endpoints of the conjugate axis are now $W(b, 0)$ and $W'(-b, 0)$. The asymptotes are found, as before, by using the diagonals of the rectangle determined by these points and lines parallel to the coordinate axes. The graph is sketched in Figure 7.29. The equations of the asymptotes are

$$y = \pm \frac{a}{b}x.$$

Note the difference between these equations and the equations $y = \pm (b/a)x$ used previously.

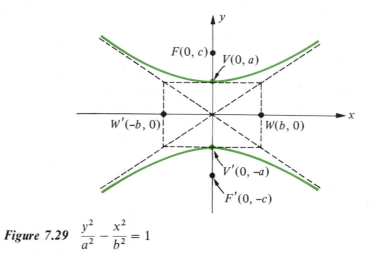

Figure 7.29 $\dfrac{y^2}{a^2} - \dfrac{x^2}{b^2} = 1$

Example 3   Discuss and sketch the graph of the equation

$$4y^2 - 2x^2 = 1.$$

Solution   The standard form is

$$\frac{y^2}{1/4} - \frac{x^2}{1/2} = 1.$$

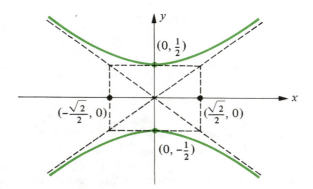

Figure 7.30 $4y^2 - 2x^2 = 1$

Thus, $a^2 = 1/4$, $b^2 = 1/2$, and $c^2 = 1/4 + 1/2 = 3/4$. Consequently, $a = 1/2$ $b = \sqrt{2}/2$, and $c = \sqrt{3}/2$. The vertices are $(0, \pm 1/2)$, and the foci are $(0, \pm \sqrt{3}/2)$. The graph is sketched in Figure 7.30. Equations of the asymptotes are $y = \pm (\sqrt{2}/2)x$. ∎

EXERCISES 7.7

In Exercises 1–10, sketch the graph of the equation, find the coordinates of the vertices and foci, and equations for the asymptotes.

1 $\dfrac{x^2}{49} - \dfrac{y^2}{25} = 1$ **2** $\dfrac{y^2}{16} - \dfrac{x^2}{9} = 1$

3 $\dfrac{y^2}{49} - \dfrac{x^2}{25} = 1$ **4** $\dfrac{x^2}{16} - \dfrac{y^2}{9} = 1$

5 $y^2 - 9x^2 = 36$ **6** $x^2 - 5y^2 = 25$

7 $x^2 - y^2 = 1$ **8** $4y^2 - 4x^2 = 1$

9 $16x^2 - 36y^2 = 1$ **10** $3x^2 - y^2 = -3$

In Exercises 11–16, find an equation for the hyperbola satisfying the given conditions.

11 Foci $F(\pm 8, 0)$, vertices $V(\pm 5, 0)$

12 Foci $F(0, \pm 4)$, vertices $V(0, \pm 1)$

13 Foci $F(0, \pm 3)$, length of conjugate axis 2

14 Vertices $V(\pm 6.0)$, passing through $P(10, 4)$

15 Vertices $V(\pm 10, 0)$, equations of asymptotes $y = \pm \frac{1}{2}x$

16 Foci $F(0, \pm 9)$, equations of asymptotes $y = \pm \frac{1}{5}x$

In each of Exercises 17 and 18, find the points of intersection of the graphs of the given equations and sketch both graphs on the same coordinate axes, showing points of intersection.

17 $\begin{cases} y^2 - 4x^2 = 16 \\ y - x = 4 \end{cases}$ **18** $\begin{cases} x^2 - y^2 = 4 \\ y^2 - 3x = 0 \end{cases}$

19 The graphs of the equations

$$\frac{x^2}{a^2} - \frac{y^2}{b^2} = 1 \quad \text{and} \quad \frac{x^2}{a^2} - \frac{y^2}{b^2} = -1$$

are called **conjugate hyperbolas**. Sketch the graphs of both equations on the same coordinate system with $a = 2$ and $b = 5$. Describe the relationship between the two graphs.

20 Show how to obtain the equation

$$\frac{x^2}{a^2} - \frac{y^2}{c^2 - a^2} = 1$$

from the equation

$$|\sqrt{(x - c)^2 + (y - 0)^2} - \sqrt{(x + c)^2 + (y - 0)^2}| = 2a.$$

7.8 TRANSLATION OF AXES

If a and b are coordinates of two points A and B, respectively, on a coordinate line l, the distance between A and B was defined in Chapter One by $d(A, B) = |b - a|$. If we wish to take into account the direction of l, then we use the *directed distance* $\overline{AB}$ from A to B, defined as follows.

Definition of Directed Distance

$$\overline{AB} = b - a$$

Since $\overline{BA} = a - b$, we have $\overline{AB} = -\overline{BA}$. If the positive direction on l is to the right, then B is to the right of A if and only if $\overline{AB} > 0$, and is to the left of A if and only if $\overline{AB} < 0$. If C is any other point on l with coordinate c, it follows that

$$\overline{AC} = \overline{AB} + \overline{BC}$$

since $(c - a) = (b - a) + (c - b)$. We shall use this formula for directed distances to develop formulas for **translation of axes** in two dimensions.

Suppose that $C(h, k)$ is an arbitrary point in an xy-coordinate plane. Let us introduce a new $x'y'$-coordinate system with origin O' at C such that the x'- and y'- axes are parallel to, and have the same unit lengths and positive directions as, the x- and y- axes, respectively. A typical situation of this type is illustrated in Figure 7.31, where, for simplicity, we have placed C in the first quadrant. We shall use primes on letters to denote coordinates of points in the $x'y'$-coordinate system, in order to distinguish them from coordinates with respect to the xy-coordinate system. Thus, the point $P(x, y)$ in the xy-system will be denoted by $P(x', y')$ in the $x'y'$-system. If we label projections of P on the various axes, as indicated in Figure 7.31, and let A and B denote projections of C on the x- and y-axes, respectively, then, using formulas for directed distances,

$$x = \overline{OQ} = \overline{OA} + \overline{AQ} = \overline{OA} + \overline{O'Q'} = h + x'$$
$$y = \overline{OR} = \overline{OB} + \overline{BR} = \overline{OB} + \overline{O'R'} = k + y'.$$

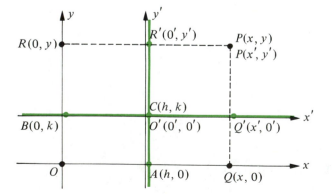

Figure 7.31

To summarize, if (x, y) are the coordinates of a point P relative to the xy-coordinate system, and if (x', y') are the coordinates of P relative to an $x'y'$-coordinate system with origin at the point $C(h, k)$ of the xy-system, then we have the following.

Translation of Axes Formulas

$$\boxed{\begin{array}{ll} \text{(a)} & x = x' + h, \quad y = y' + k \\ \text{(b)} & x' = x - h, \quad y' = y - k \end{array}}$$

These formulas enable us to go from either coordinate system to the other. Their major use is to change the form of equations of graphs. To be specific, if, in the xy-plane, a certain collection of points is the graph of an equation in x and y, then, to find an equation in x' and y' which has the same graph in the $x'y'$-plane, we may substitute $x' + h$ for x and $y' + k$ for y in the given equation. Conversely, if a set of points in the $x'y'$-plane is the graph of an equation in x' and y', then, to find the corresponding equation in x and y, we substitute $x - h$ for x' and $y - k$ for y'.

As a simple illustration of the preceding remarks, the equation

$$(x')^2 + (y')^2 = r^2$$

has, for its graph in the $x'y'$-plane, a circle of radius r with center at the origin O'. Using the translation of axes formulas $x' = x - h, y' = y - k$ we see that an equation for this circle in the xy-plane is

$$(x - h)^2 + (y - k)^2 = r^2$$

which is in agreement with the formula for a circle of radius r with center at $C(h, k)$ in the xy-plane.

As another illustration, we know that

$$(x')^2 = 4py'$$

is an equation of a parabola with vertex at the origin O' of the $x'y'$-plane. Applying translation of axes formulas, it follows that

$$(x - h)^2 = 4p(y - k)$$

is an equation of the same parabola in the xy-plane. This agrees with the formula in Section 7.5, which was derived for a parabola with vertex at the point $V(h, k)$ in the xy-plane.

It should now be evident how this technique can be applied to all the conics. For example, the graph of

$$\frac{(x')^2}{a^2} + \frac{(y')^2}{b^2} = 1$$

is an ellipse with center at O' in the $x'y'$-plane, as illustrated in Figure 7.32. According to translation of axes formulas, its equation relative to the xy-coordinate system is

$$\frac{(x - h)^2}{a^2} + \frac{(y - k)^2}{b^2} = 1.$$

This is called a **standard form** for the equation of an ellipse with center (h, k). A similar situation exists for hyperbolas.

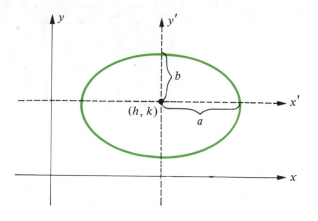

Figure 7.32 $\dfrac{(x')^2}{a^2} + \dfrac{(y')^2}{b^2} = 1$ or $\dfrac{(x-h)^2}{a^2} + \dfrac{(y-k)^2}{b^2} = 1$

In certain cases, given an equation in x and y, we may, by a proper translation of axes, obtain a simpler equation in x' and y' which has the same graph. In particular, this is true for an equation in x and y of the form

$$Ax^2 + Cy^2 + Dx + Ey + F = 0$$

where the coefficients are real numbers. The graph of this equation is a conic, except for the degenerate cases in which points, lines, or no graphs are obtained. We shall not give a general proof of this fact but will, instead, illustrate the procedure by means of examples.

Example 1   Discuss and sketch the graph of the equation

$$16x^2 + 9y^2 + 64x - 18y - 71 = 0.$$

Solution   In order to determine the origin of a new $x'y'$-coordinate system that will enable us to simplify the given equation, we begin by writing the given equation in the form

$$16(x^2 + 4x) + 9(y^2 - 2y) = 71.$$

Next, we complete the squares for the expressions within parentheses, obtaining

$$16(x^2 + 4x + 4) + 9(y^2 - 2y + 1) = 71 + 64 + 9.$$

Note that by adding 4 to the expression within the first parentheses, we have added 64 to the left side of the equation and hence must compensate by adding 64 to the right side. Similarly, by adding 1 to the expression within the second parentheses, 9 is added to the left side; consequently, 9 must also be added to the right side. The last equation may be written

$$16(x + 2)^2 + 9(y - 1)^2 = 144.$$

Dividing by 144, we obtain

$$\frac{(x + 2)^2}{9} + \frac{(y - 1)^2}{16} = 1$$

which is of the form

$$\frac{(x')^2}{9} + \frac{(y')^2}{16} = 1$$

where $x' = x + 2$ and $y' = y - 1$. This shows that if we let $h = -2$ and $k = 1$ in the translation of axes formulas we obtain the given equation. Since the graph of $(x')^2/9 + (y')^2/16 = 1$ is an ellipse with center at the origin O' in the $x'y'$-plane, it follows that the given equation is an ellipse with center $C(-2, 1)$ in the xy-plane and with axes parallel to the coordinate axes. The graph is sketched in Figure 7.33.

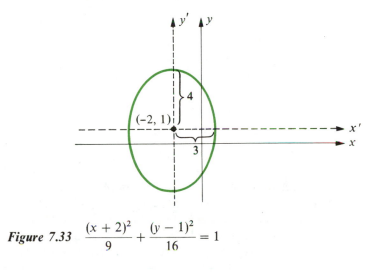

Figure 7.33 $\dfrac{(x + 2)^2}{9} + \dfrac{(y - 1)^2}{16} = 1$ ■

Example 2   Discuss and sketch the graph of the equation

$$9x^2 - 4y^2 - 54x - 16y + 29 = 0.$$

Solution   As in Example 1, we arrange our work as follows:

$$9(x^2 - 6x) - 4(y^2 + 4y) = -29$$
$$9(x^2 - 6x + 9) - 4(y^2 + 4y + 4) = -29 + 81 - 16$$
$$9(x - 3)^2 - 4(y + 2)^2 = 36$$
$$\frac{(x - 3)^2}{4} - \frac{(y + 2)^2}{9} = 1.$$

If we substitute $h = 3$ and $k = -2$ in the translation of axes formulas, then the given equation reduces to a standard form for the equation of a hyperbola, namely,

$$\frac{(x')^2}{4} - \frac{(y')^2}{9} = 1.$$

By translating the x- and y-axes to the new origin $C(3, -2)$, we obtain the sketch shown in Figure 7.34.

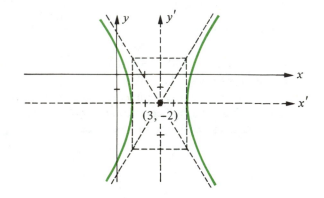

$(3, -2)$

Figure 7.34 $\quad \dfrac{(x - 3)^2}{4} - \dfrac{(y + 2)^2}{9} = 1$ ∎

Example 3 Discuss and sketch the graph of the equation

$$2y = x^2 + 8x + 22.$$

Solution This example is the same as Example 4 of Section 7.5, where we completed the square in x and obtained the equation $(x + 4)^2 = 2(y - 3)$. By the methods of the present section, if we let $h = -4$ and $k = 3$ in the translation of axes formulas, then the given equation reduces to the standard form $(x')^2 = 2y'$ of a parabola with vertex at O'. Consequently, a translation of axes to the new origin $C(-4, 3)$ leads to the sketch shown in Figure 7.19. ∎

Although we have only considered special examples, our methods are perfectly general. If, in the equation

$$Ax^2 + Cy^2 + Dx + Ey + F = 0$$

A and C are equal and not zero, then the graph, when it exists, is a circle, or, in exceptional cases, a point. If A and C are unequal but have the same sign, then, by completing squares and properly translating axes, we obtain an equation whose graph, when it exists, is an ellipse (or a point). If A and C have opposite signs, an equation of a hyperbola is obtained, or possibly, in the degenerate case, two intersecting straight lines. Finally, if either A or C (but not both) is zero, the graph is a parabola, or, in certain cases, a pair of parallel straight lines.

EXERCISES 7.8

Discuss and sketch the graph of each of the equations in Exercises 1–26, after making a suitable translation of axes.

1 $(y + 3)^2 = 12(x - 1)$

2 $(x - 8)^2 = -4(y + 2)$

3 $\dfrac{(x + 5)^2}{16} + \dfrac{(y - 4)^2}{9} = 1$

4 $8(x + 3)^2 + (y - 6)^2 = 32$

5 $\dfrac{(x - 2)^2}{36} - \dfrac{(y + 7)^2}{49} = 1$

6 $\dfrac{(y - 2)^2}{9} - (x + 4)^2 = 1$

7 $4(x + 2)^2 + (y - 2)^2 = 1$

8 $(x + 1)^2 + 9y^2 = 36$

9 $16y^2 - 100(x - 3)^2 = 1600$

10 $(x - 7)^2 - (y + 5)^2 = 1$

11 $4x^2 + y^2 + 24x - 10y + 45 = 0$

12 $9x^2 + 16y^2 + 36x + 96y + 36 = 0$

13 $9x^2 + y^2 - 108x - 4y + 319 = 0$

14 $x^2 + 4y^2 - 2x = 0$

15 $2x^2 - 5y + 8x + 58 = 0$

16 $y^2 + 2x - 16y + 66 = 0$

17 $y^2 - 4x^2 + 6y - 40x - 107 = 0$

18 $25y^2 - 9x^2 - 100y - 54x + 10 = 0$

19 $9x^2 - y^2 - 36x + 12y - 9 = 0$

20 $4y^2 - x^2 + 32y - 8x + 49 = 0$

21 $y = |x - 5| - 4$

22 $x + 2 = \sqrt{(y - 1)^2}$

23 $x = 3 + (y - 6)^3$

24 $(x - 7)^3 - y - 2 = 0$

25 $2y + 10 - (x + 2)^4 = 0$

26 $(y + 7)(x - 5) = 1$

27 Find an equation of the hyperbola with foci $(h \pm c, k)$ and vertices $(h \pm a, k)$, where $0 < a < c$ and $c^2 = a^2 + b^2$.

28 Find an equation of the hyperbola with vertices $(h, k \pm a)$ and asymptotes $y - k = \pm(a/b)(x - h)$, where $b > 0$.

7.9 ROTATION OF AXES

The $x'y'$-coordinate system discussed in Section 7.8 may be thought of as having been obtained by moving the origin O of the xy-system to a new position $C(h, k)$ while, at the same time, not changing the positive directions of the axes or the units of length. We shall now introduce a new coordinate system by keeping the origin O fixed and rotating the x- and y-axes about O to another position denoted by x' and y'. A transformation of this type will be referred to as a **rotation of axes**.

Let us consider a rotation of axes and, as shown in Figure 7.35, let ϕ denote the angle through which the positive x-axis must be rotated in order to coincide with the positive x'-axis. If (x, y) are the coordinates of a point P relative to the xy-plane, then, as before, (x', y') will denote its coordinates relative to the new $x'y'$-coordinate system. Let the projections of P on the various axes be denoted as in Figure 7.35, and let θ denote angle POQ'. If $p = d(O, P)$, then

$$x' = p \cos \theta, \qquad\qquad y' = p \sin \theta$$
$$x = p \cos (\theta + \phi), \qquad y = p \sin (\theta + \phi).$$

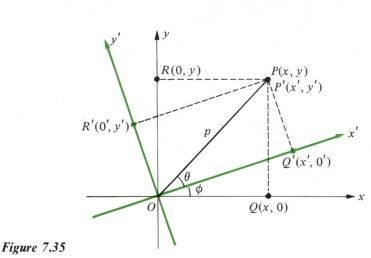

Figure 7.35

Applying addition formulas gives us

$$x = p \cos \theta \cos \phi - p \sin \theta \sin \phi$$
$$y = p \sin \theta \cos \phi + p \cos \theta \sin \phi.$$

Since $p \cos \theta = x'$ and $p \sin \theta = y'$, these equations reduce to formulas (a) in the following.

Rotation of Axes Formulas

> (a) $x = x' \cos \phi - y' \sin \phi, \quad y = x' \sin \phi + y' \cos \phi$
> (b) $x' = x \cos \phi + y \sin \phi, \quad y' = -x \sin \phi + y \cos \phi$

The equations in (b) may be obtained by solving those in (a) for x' and y'.

Example 1   The graph of the equation $xy = 1$, or, equivalently, $y = 1/x$, is sketched in Figure 7.36. If the coordinate axes are rotated through an angle of $45°$, find the equation of the graph relative to the new $x'y'$-coordinate system.

Solution   Letting $\phi = 45°$ in the rotation of axes formulas,

$$x = x'(\sqrt{2}/2) - y'(\sqrt{2}/2) = (\sqrt{2}/2)(x' - y')$$
$$y = x'(\sqrt{2}/2) + y'(\sqrt{2}/2) = (\sqrt{2}/2)(x' + y').$$

Substituting for x and y in the equation $xy = 1$ gives us

$$(\sqrt{2}/2)(x' - y') \cdot (\sqrt{2}/2)(x' + y') = 1.$$

This reduces to
$$\frac{(x')^2}{2} - \frac{(y')^2}{2} = 1$$

which is the standard equation of a hyperbola with vertices $(\pm \sqrt{2}, 0)$ on the x'-axis. Note that the asymptotes for the hyperbola have equations $y' = \pm x'$ in the new system. These correspond to the original x- and y-axes.

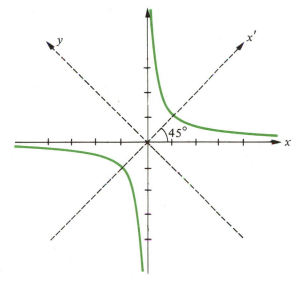

Figure 7.36

Example 1 illustrates a method for eliminating a term of an equation which contains the product xy. This method can be used to transform the following **general quadratic equation in x and y**:

$$Ax^2 + Bxy + Cy^2 + Dx + Ey + F = 0$$

where $B \neq 0$, into an equation in x' and y' which contains no $x'y'$ term. Let us prove that this may always be done. If we rotate the axes through an angle ϕ, then substituting the expressions in (a) of the rotation of axes formulas for x and y gives us

$$A(x' \cos \phi - y' \sin \phi)^2$$
$$+ B(x' \cos \phi - y' \sin \phi)(x' \sin \phi + y' \cos \phi)$$
$$+ C(x' \sin \phi + y' \cos \phi)^2 + D(x' \cos \phi - y' \sin \phi)$$
$$+ E(x' \sin \phi + y' \cos \phi) + F = 0.$$

The last equation may be written in the form

$$A'(x')^2 + B'x'y' + C'(y')^2 + D'x' + E'y' + F = 0$$

where the coefficient B' of $x'y'$ is given by

$$B' = 2(C - A)\sin\phi\cos\phi - B(\cos^2\phi - \sin^2\phi).$$

In order to eliminate the $x'y'$ term, we must select ϕ such that

$$2(C - A)\sin\phi\cos\phi + B(\cos^2\phi - \sin^2\phi) = 0.$$

Using the double-angle formulas of Chapter Three, the last equation may be written

$$(C - A)\sin 2\phi + B\cos 2\phi = 0$$

which is equivalent to

$$\boxed{\cot 2\phi = \frac{A - C}{B}, \text{ where } B \neq 0.}$$

Thus, to eliminate the xy term in the given equation, we may choose ϕ such that $\cot 2\phi = (A - C)/B$ and then employ the rotation of axes formulas. The resulting equation will contain no $x'y'$ term and, therefore, can be analyzed by previous methods. This proves that if the graph of the general quadratic equation in x and y exists, it is a conic (except for degenerate cases).

Example 2   Discuss and sketch the graph of the equation

$$41x^2 - 24xy + 34y^2 - 25 = 0.$$

Solution   Using the notation preceding this example, we have $A = 41$, $B = -24$, and $C = 34$. We wish to determine ϕ such that

$$\cot 2\phi = \frac{A - C}{B} = \frac{41 - 34}{-24} = -\frac{7}{24}.$$

Since $\cot 2\phi$ is negative, we may choose 2ϕ such that $90° < 2\phi < 180°$, and consequently, $\cos 2\phi = -7/25$. (Why?) We now use the half-angle formulas of Chapter Three with $v = 2\phi$. Since $45° < \phi < 90°$, this gives us

$$\sin\phi = \sqrt{\frac{1 - \cos 2\phi}{2}} = \sqrt{\frac{1 - (-7/25)}{2}} = \frac{4}{5}$$

$$\cos\phi = \sqrt{\frac{1 + \cos 2\phi}{2}} = \sqrt{\frac{1 + (-7/25)}{2}} = \frac{3}{5}.$$

It follows that the desired rotation of axes formulas are

$$x = \frac{3}{5}x' - \frac{4}{5}y', \quad y = \frac{4}{5}x' + \frac{3}{5}y'.$$

We leave it to the reader to show that, after substituting for x and y in the given equation and simplifying, we obtain the equation

$$(x')^2 + 2(y')^2 = 1.$$

Thus, the graph is an ellipse with vertices at $(\pm 1, 0)$ on the x'-axis. Since $\tan \phi = \sin \phi / \cos \phi = (4/5)/(3/5) = 4/3$, we obtain $\phi = \tan^{-1}(4/3)$. If an approximation is desired, then, by Table 2, $\phi \approx 53°8'$. The graph is sketched in Figure 7.37.

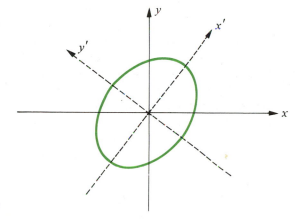

Figure 7.37

EXERCISES 7.9

After a suitable rotation of axes, describe and sketch the graph of each of the equations in Exercises 1–8.

1 $32x^2 - 72xy + 53y^2 = 80$

2 $7x^2 - 48xy - 7y^2 = 225$

3 $11x^2 + 10\sqrt{3}xy + y^2 = 4$

4 $x^2 - xy + y^2 = 3$

5 $5x^2 - 8xy + 5y^2 = 9$

6 $11x^2 - 10\sqrt{3}xy + y^2 = 20$

7 $16x^2 - 24xy + 9y^2 - 60x - 80y + 100 = 0$

8 $64x^2 - 240xy + 225y^2 + 1020x - 544y = 0$

9 Prove that, except for degenerate cases, the graph of the general quadratic equation in x and y is
(a) a parabola if $B^2 - 4AC = 0$.
(b) an ellipse if $B^2 - 4AC < 0$.
(c) a hyperbola if $B^2 - 4AC > 0$.

10 Use the results of Exercise 9 to determine the type of conic in Exercises 1–8.

7.10 POLAR COORDINATES

We have previously specified points in a plane in terms of rectangular coordinates, using the ordered pair (a, b) to denote the point whose directed distances from the x- and y-axes are b and a, respectively. Another important method for representing points is by means of **polar coordinates**. In this case, we again use ordered pairs; however, one of the numbers represents the measure of an angle. In order to introduce a system of polar coordinates in a plane, we begin with a fixed point O (called the **origin**, or **pole**) and a directed half-line (called the **polar axis**) with endpoint O. Next, we consider any point P in the plane different from O. If, as illustrated in Figure 7.38, $r = d(O, P)$, and θ denotes the measure of any angle determined by the polar axis and OP, then r and θ are called **polar coordinates** of P and the symbols (r, θ) or $P(r, \theta)$ are used to denote P. As usual, θ is considered positive if the angle is generated by a counterclockwise rotation of the polar axis, and negative if the rotation is clockwise. Either radians or degrees may be used for the measure of θ. Since there are many angles with the same terminal side, the polar coordinates of a point are not unique. For example, $(3, \pi/4)$, $(3, 9\pi/4)$, and $(3, -7\pi/4)$ all represent the same point (see Figure 7.39). We shall also allow r to be negative. In this event, instead of measuring $|r|$ units along the terminal side of the angle θ, we measure along the half-line with endpoint O which has direction opposite to that of the terminal side. Figure 7.40 contains illustrations for the pairs $(-3, 5\pi/4)$ and $(-3, -3\pi/4)$. Finally, we agree that the pole O has polar coordinates $(0, \theta)$ for *any* θ. An assignment of ordered pairs of the form (r, θ) to points in a plane will be referred to as a **polar coordinate system**, and the plane will be called an $r\theta$-plane.

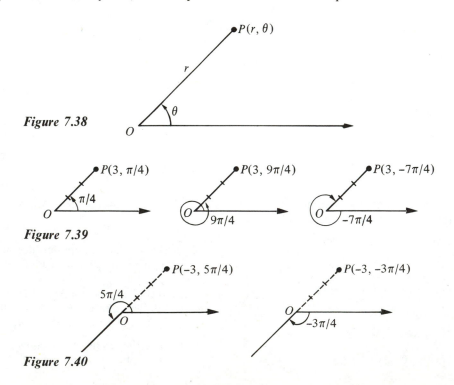

Figure 7.38

Figure 7.39

Figure 7.40

In a manner analogous to that used in our work with equations in x and y, we now consider **polar equations**, that is, equations in r and θ. A solution of such an equation is an ordered pair (a, b) that leads to equality when a is substituted for r and b for θ. The graph is the set of all points (in an $r\theta$-plane) that correspond to the solutions. Although many polar equations contain trigonometric expressions, their graphs will differ from those discussed in Chapter Two, since points are plotted in a *polar* coordinate system instead of a rectangular coordinate system.

Example 1   Sketch the graph of the equation $r = 4\sin\theta$.

Solution   The following table contains some solutions of the equation.

θ	0	$\pi/6$	$\pi/4$	$\pi/3$	$\pi/2$	$2\pi/3$	$3\pi/4$	$5\pi/6$	π
r	0	2	$2\sqrt{2}$	$2\sqrt{3}$	4	$2\sqrt{3}$	$2\sqrt{2}$	2	0

We know that in rectangular coordinates, the graph of the given equation consists of sine waves of amplitude 4 and period 2π. However, if polar coordinates are used, then the points that correspond to the pairs in the table appear to lie on a circle of radius 2, and we draw the graph accordingly (see Figure 7.41). The proof that the graph is a circle will be given in Example 4. Additional points obtained by letting θ vary from π to 2π lie on the same circle. For example, the solution $(-2, 7\pi/6)$ gives us the same point as $(2, \pi/6)$; the point corresponding to $(-2\sqrt{2}, 5\pi/4)$ is the same as that obtained from $(2\sqrt{2}, \pi/4)$; and so on. Because of the periodicity of the sine function, if we let θ increase through all real numbers, we obtain the same points over and over.

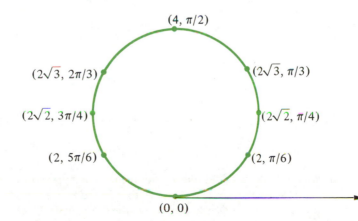

Figure 7.41 $r = 4\sin\theta$

Example 2   Sketch the graph of the equation $r = 2 + 2\cos\theta$.

Solution   Since the cosine function decreases from 1 to -1 as θ varies from 0 to π, it follows that r decreases from 4 to 0 in this θ-interval. The following table exhibits some solutions of the given equation.

θ	0	$\pi/6$	$\pi/4$	$\pi/3$	$\pi/2$	$2\pi/3$	$3\pi/4$	$5\pi/6$	π
r	4	$2 + \sqrt{3}$	$2 + \sqrt{2}$	3	2	1	$2 - \sqrt{2}$	$2 - \sqrt{3}$	0

If θ increases from π to 2π, then $\cos\theta$ increases from -1 to 1, and consequently, r increases from 0 to 4. Plotting points and connecting them with a smooth curve leads to the sketch shown in Figure 7.42, where we have used polar coordinate graph paper which displays lines through O at various angles and circles with centers at the pole. The graph is called a **cardioid**. The same graph may be obtained by taking other intervals for θ.

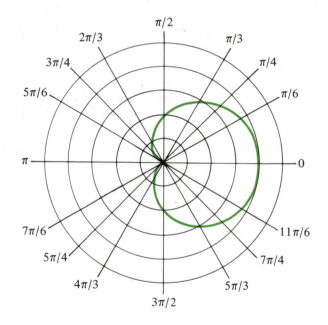

Figure 7.42 $r = 2 + 2\cos\theta$ ∎

Example 3   Sketch the graph of the equation $r = a\sin 2\theta$, where $a > 0$.

Solution   Instead of tabulating solutions, let us reason as follows. If θ increases from 0 to $\pi/4$, then 2θ varies from 0 to $\pi/2$, and hence, $\sin 2\theta$ increases from 0 to 1. It follows that r increases from 0 to a in the θ-interval $[0, \pi/4]$. If we next let θ increase from $\pi/4$ to $\pi/2$, then 2θ changes from $\pi/2$ to π. Consequently, r decreases from a to 0 in the θ-interval $[\pi/4, \pi/2]$. (Why?) The corresponding points on the graph constitute a "loop," as illustrated in Figure 7.43. We shall leave it to the reader to show that as θ increases from $\pi/2$ to π, a similar loop is obtained directly *below* the first loop. (Note that for this range of θ we have $\pi < 2\theta < 2\pi$, and hence, sin 2θ is negative.) Similar loops are obtained for the θ-intervals $[\pi, 3\pi/2]$ and $[3\pi/2, 2\pi]$. We have plotted only those points on the graph which correspond to the largest numerical values of r. The graph is called a **four-leaved rose**.

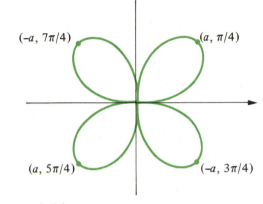

Figure 7.43 $r = a \sin 2\theta$

Many other interesting graphs result from polar equations. Some are included in the exercises at the end of this section. Polar coordinates are very useful in applications involving circles with centers at the origin or lines that pass through the origin, since the equations that have these graphs may be written in the simple forms $r = k$ or $\theta = k$ for some fixed number k. (Verify!)

Let us now superimpose an xy-plane on an $r\theta$-plane in such a way that the positive x-axis coincides with the polar axis. Any point P in the plane may then be assigned rectangular coordinates (x, y) or polar coordinates (r, θ). It is not difficult to obtain formulas that specify the relationship between the two coordinate systems. Thus, if $r > 0$, we have a situation similar to that illustrated in (i) of Figure 7.44, whereas if $r < 0$, we have that shown in (ii), where, for later purposes, we have also plotted the point P' that has polar coordinates $(|r|, \theta)$ and rectangular coordinates $(-x, -y)$. Although we have pictured θ as an acute angle, the discussion that follows is valid for all angles. On the one hand, if $r > 0$ as in (i) of Figure 7.44, then we obtain the following.

Relationship between Polar and Rectangular Coordinates

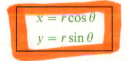

$$x = r \cos \theta$$
$$y = r \sin \theta$$

On the other hand, if $r < 0$, then referring to (ii) of Figure 7.44 and using the fact that $|r| = -r$, we have

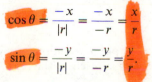

$$\cos \theta = \frac{-x}{|r|} = \frac{-x}{-r} = \frac{x}{r}$$

$$\sin \theta = \frac{-y}{|r|} = \frac{-y}{-r} = \frac{y}{r}.$$

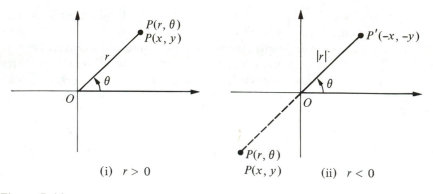

Figure 7.44

Multiplication by r produces $x = r\cos\theta$, $y = r\sin\theta$, and hence, these formulas hold whether r is positive or r is negative. If $r = 0$, then the point is the pole and we again see that the formulas are true. The following are further consequences of our discussion.

$$\tan\theta = \frac{y}{x}, \quad r^2 = x^2 + y^2$$

It is possible to use the formulas we have obtained to change the rectangular coordinates of a point to polar coordinates and vice versa. A more important use is for transforming a polar equation to an equation in x and y and vice versa, as illustrated in the next two examples.

Example 4   Find an equation in x and y which has the same graph as $r = 4\sin\theta$.

Solution   The given equation was considered in Example 1. It is convenient to multiply both sides by r, obtaining $r^2 = 4r\sin\theta$. Since $r^2 = x^2 + y^2$, and $r\sin\theta = y$, we obtain $x^2 + y^2 = 4y$. The last equation is equivalent to $x^2 + (y - 2)^2 = 4$, whose graph is a circle of radius 2 with center at $(0, 2)$ in the xy-plane.   ■

Example 5   Find the general polar equation of a straight line.

Solution   We know that every straight line in an xy-coordinate system is the graph of a linear equation $Ax + By + C = 0$. Substituting $r\cos\theta$ for x and $r\sin\theta$ for y leads to the polar equation

$$r(A\cos\theta + B\sin\theta) + C = 0.$$ ■

The graph of a polar equation may be symmetric with respect to the x-axis, the y-axis, or the origin. It is left to the reader to show that if a substitution listed in the following table does not change the solutions of a polar equation, then the graph has the indicated symmetry.

Tests for Symmetry

Substitution	Symmetry
$-\theta$ for θ	x-axis
$-r$ for r	origin
$\pi - \theta$ for θ	y-axis

To illustrate, since $\cos(-\theta) = \cos\theta$, the graph of the equation in Example 2 (see Figure 7.42) is symmetric with respect to the x-axis. Since $\sin(\pi - \theta) = \sin\theta$, the graph in Example 1 is symmetric with respect to the y-axis. The graph in Example 3 is symmetric to both axes and the origin. Other tests for symmetry may be stated; however, those listed above are among the easiest to apply.

EXERCISES 7.10

graph on test

Sketch the graphs of the equations in Exercises 1–18.

1 $r = 5$

2 $\theta = \pi/4$

3 $\theta = -\pi/6$

4 $r = -2$

5 $r = 4\cos\theta$

6 $r = -2\sin\theta$

7 $r = 4(1 - \sin\theta)$ (cardioid)

8 $r = 1 + 2\cos\theta$ (limaçon)

9 $r = a\cos 3\theta$ (three-leaved rose)

10 $r = a\sin 4\theta$ (eight-leaved rose)

11 $r^2 = a^2\cos 2\theta$ (lemniscate)

12 $r = a\sin^2(\tfrac{1}{2}\theta)$ (cardioid)

13 $r = 4\csc\theta$

14 $r = -3\sec\theta$

15 $r = 2 - \cos\theta$ (limaçon)

16 $r = 2 + 2\sec\theta$ (conchoid)

17 $r = 2^\theta, \theta \geq 0$ (spiral)

18 $r\theta = 1, \theta > 0$ (spiral)

In Exercises 19–26, find a polar equation that has the same graph as the given equation.

19 $x = -3$

20 $y = 2$

21 $x^2 + y^2 = 16$

22 $x^2 = 8y$

23 $y = 6$

24 $y = 6x$

25 $x^2 - y^2 = 16$

26 $9x^2 + 4y^2 = 36$

In Exercises 27–34, find an equation in x and y which has the same graph as the given polar equation.

27 $r\cos\theta = 5$

28 $r\sin\theta = -2$

29 $r - 6\sin\theta = 0$

30 $r = 2(1 + \cos\theta)$

31 $r = a$

32 $\theta = \pi/4$

33 $r = \tan\theta$

34 $r = 4\sec\theta$

35 If $P_1(r_1, \theta_1)$ and $P_2(r_2, \theta_2)$ are points in an $r\theta$-plane, use the Law of Cosines of Section 4.2 to prove that

$$d(P_1, P_2)^2 = r_1^2 + r_2^2 - 2r_1r_2\cos(\theta_2 - \theta_1).$$

36 Prove that the graph of the polar equation $r = a\sin\theta + b\cos\theta$ is a circle, and find its center and radius.

7.11   POLAR EQUATIONS OF CONICS

The following theorem provides another means for describing the conic sections.

Theorem

> Let F be a fixed point and l a fixed line in a plane. The set of all points P in the plane such that the ratio $d(P,F)/d(P,Q)$ is a positive constant e, where $d(P,Q)$ is the distance from P to l, is a conic section. Moreover, the conic is a parabola if $e = 1$, an ellipse if $0 < e < 1$, or a hyperbola if $e > 1$.

The constant e is called the **eccentricity** of the conic. It will be seen that the point F is a focus of the conic. The line l is called a **directrix**. We shall prove the theorem for $e \le 1$ and leave the case $e > 1$ as an exercise.

If $e = 1$, then $d(P,F) = d(P,Q)$ and, by definition, a parabola with focus F and directrix l is obtained.

Suppose next that $0 < e < 1$. It is convenient to introduce a polar coordinate system in the plane with F as the pole and with l perpendicular to the polar axis at the point $D(d, 0)$, where $d > 0$. If $P(r, \theta)$ is a point in the plane such that $d(P,F)/d(P,Q) = e < 1$, then referring to Figure 7.45 we see that P lies to the left of l. Let C be the projection of P on the polar axis. Since $d(P,F) = r$ and $d(P,Q) = \overline{FD} - \overline{FC} = d - r\cos\theta$, it follows that P satisfies the condition in the theorem if and only if

$$\frac{r}{d - r\cos\theta} = e$$

or, equivalently, $r = de - er\cos\theta.$

Solving for r gives us $r = \dfrac{de}{1 + e\cos\theta}.$

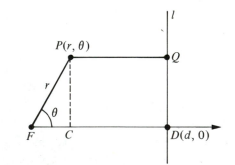

$P(r, \theta)$

Q

r

θ

F C

$D(d, 0)$

l

Figure 7.45

This is a polar equation of the graph. Actually, the same equation is obtained if $e = 1$; however, in this event there is no point (r, θ) on the graph if $1 + \cos\theta = 0$.

The rectangular equation corresponding to $r = de - er\cos\theta$ is

$$\pm\sqrt{x^2 + y^2} = de - ex.$$

Squaring both sides and rearranging terms leads to

$$(1 - e^2)x^2 + 2de^2 x + y^2 = d^2 e^2.$$

Completing the square in the previous equation and simplifying, we obtain

$$\left(x + \frac{de^2}{1 - e^2}\right)^2 + \frac{y^2}{1 - e^2} = \frac{d^2 e^2}{(1 - e^2)^2}.$$

Finally, dividing both sides by $d^2 e^2/(1 - e^2)^2$ gives us a standard form for the equation of an ellipse with center at the point $(-de^2/(1 - e^2), 0)$ and where

$$a^2 = \frac{d^2 e^2}{(1 - e^2)^2}, \quad b^2 = \frac{d^2 e^2}{1 - e^2}.$$

Since
$$c^2 = a^2 - b^2 = \frac{d^2 e^4}{(1 - e^2)^2} = \left(\frac{de^2}{1 - e^2}\right)^2$$

we see that $c = de^2/(1 - e^2)$. This proves that F is a focus of the ellipse. It also follows that $e = c/a$. A similar proof may be given for the case $e > 1$.

It can be shown, conversely, that every conic that is not a circle may be described by means of the statement given in the theorem. This gives us a formulation of conic sections which is equivalent to the approach used previously. Since the theorem includes all three types of conics, it is sometimes regarded as a definition for the conic sections.

If, instead of having l intersect the polar axis at $D(d, 0)$, we had used the point $(-d, 0)$ to the *left* of F, then the resulting polar equation would be

$$r = \frac{de}{1 - e\cos\theta}.$$

Other sign changes occur if d is allowed to be negative.

If l is taken *parallel* to the polar axis through one of the points $(d, \pi/2)$ or $(d, 3\pi/2)$, then the corresponding equations would contain $\sin\theta$ instead of $\cos\theta$. The proofs of these facts are left to the reader.

The following theorem summarizes our discussion.

Theorem

A polar equation having one of the forms

$$r = \frac{de}{1 \pm e\cos\theta}, \quad r = \frac{de}{1 \pm e\sin\theta}$$

is a conic section. Moreover, the conic is a parabola if $e = 1$, an ellipse if $0 < e < 1$, or a hyperbola if $e > 1$.

Example 1   Describe and sketch the graph of the equation

$$r = \frac{10}{3 + 2\cos\theta}.$$

Solution   Dividing numerator and denominator of the given fraction by 3 gives us

$$r = \frac{\dfrac{10}{3}}{1 + \dfrac{2}{3}\cos\theta}$$

which has one of the forms stated in the preceding theorem with $e = 2/3$. Thus, the graph is an ellipse with focus F at the pole and major axis along the polar axis. The endpoints of the major axis may be found by setting θ equal to 0 and π. This gives us $V(2,0)$ and $V'(10, \pi)$. Hence, $2a = d(V', V) = 12$, or $a = 6$. The center of the ellipse is the midpoint of the segment $V'V$, namely $(4, \pi)$. Using the fact that $e = c/a$, we obtain $c = ae = 6(2/3) = 4$. Hence, $b^2 = a^2 - c^2 = 36 - 16 = 20$; that is, the semi-minor axis has length $\sqrt{20}$. The graph is sketched in Figure 7.46, where, for reference, we have superimposed a rectangular coordinate system on the polar system.

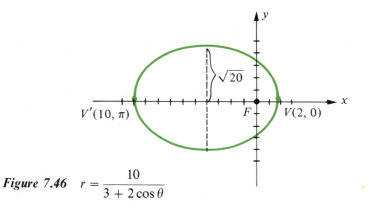

Figure 7.46 $r = \dfrac{10}{3 + 2\cos\theta}$

Example 2   Describe and sketch the graph of the equation

$$r = \frac{10}{2 + 3\sin\theta}.$$

Solution   To express the equation in one of the proper forms, we divide numerator and denominator of the given fraction by 2, obtaining

$$r = \frac{5}{1 + \dfrac{3}{2}\sin\theta}.$$

Thus, $e = 3/2$ and the graph is a hyperbola with a focus at the pole. The expression $\sin \theta$ tells us that the transverse axis is perpendicular to the polar axis. To find the vertices, we let θ equal $\pi/2$ and $3\pi/2$ in the given equation. This gives us the points $V(2, \pi/2)$ and $V'(-10, 3\pi/2)$, and hence, $2a = d(V, V') = 8$, or $a = 4$. The points $(5, 0)$ and $(5, \pi)$ on the graph can be used to get a rough estimate of the lower branch of the hyperbola. The upper branch is obtained by symmetry, as illustrated in Figure 7.47. If more accuracy or additional information is desired, we may calculate

$$c = ae = 4\left(\frac{3}{2}\right) = 6$$

and $\qquad b^2 = c^2 - a^2 = 36 - 16 = 20.$

Asymptotes may then be constructed in the usual way.

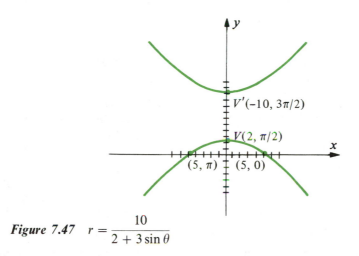

Figure 7.47 $\quad r = \dfrac{10}{2 + 3 \sin \theta}$

EXERCISES 7.11

In each of Exercises 1–10, identify and sketch the graph of the given equation.

1 $\quad r = \dfrac{12}{6 + 2 \sin \theta}$

2 $\quad r = \dfrac{12}{6 - 2 \sin \theta}$

3 $\quad r = \dfrac{12}{2 - 6 \cos \theta}$

4 $\quad r = \dfrac{12}{2 + 6 \cos \theta}$

5 $\quad r = \dfrac{3}{2 + 2 \cos \theta}$

6 $\quad r = \dfrac{3}{2 - 2 \sin \theta}$

7 $\quad r = \dfrac{4}{\cos \theta - 2}$

8 $\quad r = \dfrac{4 \sec \theta}{2 \sec \theta - 1}$

9 $\quad r = \dfrac{6 \csc \theta}{2 \csc \theta + 3}$

10 $\quad r = \csc \theta (\csc \theta - \cot \theta)$

11–20 Find rectangular equations for the graphs in Exercises 1–10.

In each of Exercises 21–26, express the given equation in polar form and then find the eccentricity and an equation for the directrix.

21 $y^2 = 4 - 4x$ **22** $x^2 = 1 - 2y$

23 $3y^2 - 16y - x^2 + 16 = 0$

24 $5x^2 + 9y^2 = 32x + 64$

25 $8x^2 + 9y^2 + 4x = 4$

26 $4x^2 - 5y^2 + 36y - 36 = 0$

In each of Exercises 27–32, find a polar equation of the conic with focus at the pole and the given eccentricity and equation of directrix.

27 $e = 1/3, \ r = 2 \sec \theta$ **28** $e = 2/5, \ r = 4 \csc \theta$

29 $e = 4, \ r = -3 \csc \theta$ **30** $e = 3, \ r = -4 \sec \theta$

31 $e = 1, \ r \cos \theta = 5$ **32** $e = 1, \ r \sin \theta = -2$

33   Find a polar equation of the parabola with focus at the pole and vertex $(4, \pi/2)$.

34   Find a polar equation of the ellipse with eccentricity 2/3, a vertex at $(1, 3\pi/2)$, and a focus at the pole.

35   Prove the theorem of this section for the case $e > 1$.

36   Derive the formulas $r = de/(1 \pm e \sin \theta)$ discussed in this section.

7.12   PLANE CURVES AND PARAMETRIC EQUATIONS

The graph of an equation $y = f(x)$, where the domain of the function f is an interval I, is often called a *plane curve*. However, to use this as a definition is unnecessarily restrictive, since it rules out most of the conic sections and many other useful graphs. The following statement is satisfactory for most applications.

Definition

> A **plane curve** is a set C of ordered pairs of the form
>
> $$(f(t), g(t))$$
>
> where f and g are functions defined on an interval I.

For simplicity, we often refer to a plane curve as a **curve**. The **graph** of C is the set of all points $P(t) = (f(t), g(t))$ in a rectangular coordinate system obtained by letting t vary through I. Each $P(t)$ is referred to as a point on the curve. We shall use the term *curve* interchangeably with *graph of a curve*. Sometimes it is convenient to think that the point $P(t)$ traces the curve C as t varies through the interval I. This is especially true in applications for which t represents time and $P(t)$ is the position of a moving particle at time t.

The graphs of several curves are sketched in Figure 7.48 for the case where I is a closed interval $[a, b]$. If, as in (i) of the figure, $P(a) \neq P(b)$, then $P(a)$ and $P(b)$ are called the **endpoints** of C. Note that the curve illustrated in (i) intersects itself in the sense that two different values of t give rise to the same point. If $P(a) = P(b)$, as illustrated in (ii) of Figure 7.48, then C is called a **closed curve**. If $P(a) = P(b)$ and C does not intersect itself at any other point, as illustrated in (iii) of the figure, then C is called a **simple closed curve**.

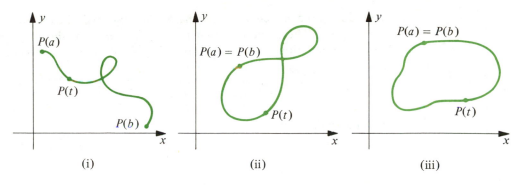

Figure 7.48

If C is the curve of the previous definition, then the equations

$$x = f(t), \quad y = g(t)$$

where t is in I, are called **parametric equations** for C, and t is called a **parameter**. As t varies through I, the point $P(x, y)$ traces the curve. It is sometimes possible to eliminate the parameter and obtain a rectangular equation for C.

Example 1   Describe and sketch the graph of the curve

$$C = \{(2t, t^2 - 1): -1 \le t \le 2\}.$$

Solution   In this example, $f(t) = 2t$, $g(t) = t^2 - 1$, and parametric equations for C are

$$x = 2t, \quad y = t^2 - 1, \qquad \text{where } -1 \le t \le 2.$$

These equations can be used to tabulate coordinates for points $P(x, y)$ on C, as in the following table.

t	-1	$-\frac{1}{2}$	0	$\frac{1}{2}$	1	$\frac{3}{2}$	2
x	-2	-1	0	1	2	3	4
y	0	$-\frac{3}{4}$	-1	$-\frac{3}{4}$	0	$\frac{5}{4}$	3

Plotting points leads to the sketch in Figure 7.49. A precise description of the graph may be obtained by eliminating the parameter. Solving the first parametric equation for t, we obtain $t = x/2$, and substitution in the second equation yields

$$y = \left(\frac{x}{2}\right)^2 - 1, \quad \text{or} \quad y + 1 = \frac{1}{4}x^2.$$

The graph of the last equation is a parabola with vertical axis and vertex at the point $(0, -1)$. The curve C is that part of the parabola shown in Figure 7.49. Parametric equations of curves are not unique. The curve C of this example is also given by

$$C = \{(t^3, \tfrac{1}{4}t^6 - 1): \quad \sqrt[3]{-2} \leq t \leq \sqrt[3]{4}\}$$

or by many other expressions.

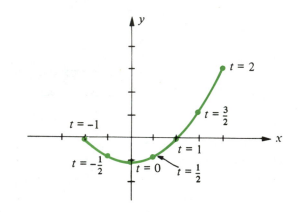

Figure 7.49 $x = 2t, \; y = t^2 - 1; \; -1 \leq t \leq 2$

Example 2   Describe the graph of the curve C having parametric equations $x = \cos t$, $y = \sin t$, where $0 \leq t \leq 2\pi$.

Solution   Eliminating the parameter gives us $x^2 + y^2 = 1$, and hence, points on C are on the unit circle with center at the origin. As t increases from 0 to 2π, $P(t)$ starts at the point $A(1, 0)$ and traverses the circle once in the counterclockwise direction. In this example, the parameter may be interpreted geometrically as the length of arc from A to P.   ■

Example 3   Find parametric equations for the line of slope m through the point (x_1, y_1).

Solution   By the point-slope form, an equation for the line is

$$y - y_1 = m(x - x_1).$$

If we let $x - x_1 = t$, then $P(x, y)$ is on the line if and only if $y - y_1 = mt$. It follows that parametric equations for the line are

$$x = x_1 + t, \quad y = y_1 + mt$$

where t varies through $\mathbb{R}$. As in Example 2, other equations could be used. For example, if we use $5t^3$ in place of t above, then the parametric equations $x = x_1 + 5t^3$, $y = y_1 + 5mt^3$ would describe the line. ∎

Example 4   The curve traced by a fixed point P on the circumference of a circle as the circle rolls along a straight line in a plane is called a **cycloid**. Find parametric equations for a cycloid.

Solution   Suppose that the circle has radius a and that it rolls along (and above) the x-axis in the positive direction. If one position of P is the origin, then Figure 7.50 displays part of the curve and a possible position of the circle. Let C denote the center of the circle and T the point of tangency with the x-axis. We introduce a parameter t as the radian measure of angle TCP. Since $\overline{OT}$ is the distance the circle has rolled, $\overline{OT} = at$. Consequently, the coordinates of C are (at, a). If we consider an $x'y'$-coordinate system with origin at $C(at, a)$, and if $P(x', y')$ denotes the point P relative to this system, then by the translation of axes formulas of Section 7.8 with $h = at$ and $k = a$,

$$x = at + x', \quad y = a + y'.$$

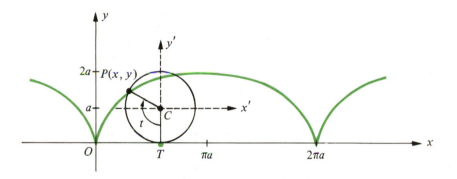

Figure 7.50

If, as in Figure 7.51, θ denotes an angle in standard position on the $x'y'$-system, then $\theta = (3\pi/2) - t$. Hence,

$$x' = a\cos\theta = a\cos(3\pi/2 - t) = -a\sin t$$
$$y' = a\sin\theta = a\sin(3\pi/2 - t) = -a\cos t$$

and substitution in $x = at + x'$, $y = a + y'$ gives us parametric equations for the cycloid, namely,

$$x = a(t - \sin t), \quad y = a(1 - \cos t)$$

where t varies through $\mathbb{R}$.

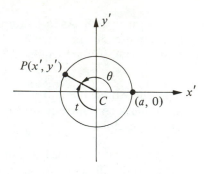

Figure 7.51   ■

If $a < 0$, then the graph is the inverted cycloid that results if the circle rolls *below* the x-axis. This curve has a number of important physical properties. In particular, suppose that a thin wire passes through two fixed points A and B, as illustrated in Figure 7.52, and that the shape of the wire can be changed by bending it in any manner. Suppose, further, that a bead is allowed to slide along the wire and the only force acting on the bead is gravity. We now ask which of all the possible paths will allow the bead to slide from A to B in the least amount of time. It is natural to conjecture that the desired path is the straight line segment from A to B; however, this is not the correct answer. It can be proved, using methods of advanced calculus, that the path which requires the least time coincides with the graph of an inverted cycloid. To cite another interesting property of this curve, suppose that A is the origin and B is the point with abscissa $\pi|a|$, that is, the lowest point on the cycloid occurring in the first arc to the right of A. It can be shown that if the bead is released at *any* point between A and B, the time required for it to reach B is always the same!

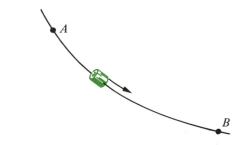

Figure 7.52

Variations of the cycloid occur in practical problems. For example, if a motorcycle wheel rolls along a straight road, then the curve traced by a fixed point on one of the spokes is a cycloid-like curve. In this case the curve does not have sharp corners, nor does it intersect the road (the x-axis) as does the cycloid. In like manner, if the wheel of a train rolls along a railroad track, then the curve traced by a fixed point on the circumference of the wheel (which extends below the track) contains loops at regular intervals. Observe in this event that as the train moves forward there are always points on the wheel that move backward! Several other cycloids are defined in Exercises 21 and 22.

EXERCISES 7.12

In each of Exercises 1–16, (a) sketch the graph of the curve C having the indicated parametric equations, and (b) find a rectangular equation of a graph that contains the points on C.

1   $x = t - 2,\ y = 2t + 3;\ 0 \le t \le 5$

2   $x = 1 - 2t,\ y = 1 + t;\ -1 \le t \le 4$

3   $x = t^2 + 1,\ y = t^2 - 1;\ -2 \le t \le 2$

4   $x = t^3 + 1,\ y = t^3 - 1;\ -2 \le t \le 2$

5   $x = 4t^2 - 5,\ y = 2t + 3;\ t$ in $\mathbb{R}$

6   $x = t^3,\ y = t^2;\ t$ in $\mathbb{R}$

7   $x = 2^t,\ y = 2^{-2t};\ t$ in $\mathbb{R}$

8   $x = \sqrt{t},\ y = 3t + 4;\ t \ge 0$

9   $x = 2 \sin t,\ y = 3 \cos t;\ 0 \le t \le 2\pi$

10   $x = \cos t - 2,\ y = \sin t + 3;\ 0 \le t \le 2\pi$

11   $x = \sec t,\ y = \tan t;\ -\pi/2 < t < \pi/2$

12   $x = \cos 2t,\ y = \sin t;\ -\pi \le t \le \pi$

13   $x = t^2,\ y = 2 \log t;\ t > 0$

14   $x = \cos^3 t,\ y = \sin^3 t;\ 0 \le t \le 2\pi$

15   $x = \sin t,\ y = \csc t;\ 0 < t \le \pi/2$

16   $x = 2^t,\ y = 2^{-t};\ t$ in $\mathbb{R}$

17   If $P_1(x_1, y_1)$ and $P_2(x_2, y_2)$ are distinct points, show that
$$x = (x_2 - x_1)t + x_1,\quad y = (y_2 - y_1)t + y_1$$
where t varies through $\mathbb{R}$, are parametric equations of the line l through P_1 and P_2. Find three other pairs of parametric equations for the line l. Show that there are an infinite number of different pairs of parametric equations for l.

18   What is the difference between the graph of the parabola $y = x^2$ and the graph of $x = t^2,\ y = t^4$, where t varies through $\mathbb{R}$?

19   Show that
$$x = a \cos t + h,\quad y = b \sin t + k$$
where t is in $\mathbb{R}$ are parametric equations of an ellipse with center at the point (h, k) and semi-axes of lengths a and b.

20   Find parametric equations for the parabola with

(a) vertex $V(0, 0)$ and focus $F(0, p)$.
(b) vertex $V(h, k)$ and focus $F(h, k + p)$.

21   A circle C of radius b rolls on the inside of a second circle having equation $x^2 + y^2 = a^2$, where $b < a$. Let P be a fixed point on C and let the initial position of P be $A(a, 0)$. If the parameter t is the angle from the positive x-axis to the line segment from O to the center of C, show that parametric equations for the curve traced by P (called a **hypocycloid**) are
$$x = (a - b) \cos t + b \cos \frac{a - b}{b} t$$
$$y = (a - b) \sin t - b \sin \frac{a - b}{b} t$$
where t is in $\mathbb{R}$. If $b = a/4$, show that
$$x = a \cos^3 t,\quad y = a \sin^3 t$$
and sketch the graph of the curve.

22   If the circle C of Exercise 21 rolls on the outside of the second circle, find parametric equations for the curve traced by P. (This curve is called an **epicycloid**).

7.13   REVIEW

Concepts

Define or discuss each of the following:

1   Equations of circles

2   Equations of lines

3   Inclination of a line

Exercises

1 (a) Find the center and radius of the circle that has equation $x^2 + y^2 - 18x + 10y + 6 = 0$.

(b) Find an equation for the circle concentric to the circle of part (a) and passing through the origin.

(c) Find an equation for the circle of radius 6 with center in the fourth quadrant and tangent to both axes.

2 Given the points $A(5, 2)$, $B(-1, 4)$, and $C(-2, -6)$, find each of the following.

(a) An equation for the line through B which is parallel to the line through A and C

(b) An equation for the line through B which is perpendicular to the line through A and C

(c) An equation for the line through C and the midpoint of the line segment AB

(d) An equation for the line through C which is parallel to the y-axis

(e) An equation for the line through B which is perpendicular to the line with equation $5x + 2y - 8 = 0$

In each of Exercises 3–8, find the foci and vertices, and sketch the graph of the conic that has the given equation.

3 $4y^2 = 9x$

4 $y - 5 = 6(x + 7)^2$

5 $y^2 = 144 - 9x^2$

6 $16y^2 = 144 + 9x^2$

7 $y^2 - x^2 - 8 = 0$

8 $x = 8y^2 - 3$

Find equations for the conics in Exercises 9–14.

9 The parabola with focus $(-8, 0)$ and directrix $x = 8$

10 The parabola with vertex at the origin, symmetric to the y-axis, and passing through the point $(3, -2)$

11 The ellipse with vertices $V(0, \pm 7)$ and foci $F(0, \pm 3)$

12 The hyperbola with foci $F(\pm 2, 0)$ and vertices $V(\pm 1, 0)$

13 The hyperbola with vertices $V(0, \pm 4)$ and asymptotes $y = \pm 5x$

14 The ellipse with foci $F(\pm 10, 0)$ and passing through the point $(2, \sqrt{2})$

Discuss and sketch the graph of each of the equations in Exercises 15–20, after making a suitable translation of axes.

15 $4x^2 + 9y^2 + 24x - 36y + 36 = 0$

16 $4x^2 - y^2 - 40x - 8y + 88 = 0$

17 $y^2 - 8x + 8y + 32 = 0$

18 $4x^2 + y^2 - 24x + 4y + 36 = 0$

19 $y^2 - 2x^2 + 6y + 8x - 3 = 0$

20 $x^2 - 9y^2 + 8x + 7 = 0$

Sketch the graphs of the equations in Exercises 21–28.

21 $r = -4\sin\theta$

22 $r = 3\cos 5\theta$

23 $r = 6 - 3\cos\theta$

24 $r^2 = 9\sin 2\theta$

25 $2r = \theta$

26 $r = \dfrac{8}{1 - 3\sin\theta}$

27 $r = 6 - r\cos\theta$

28 $r = 8\sec\theta$

Change the equations in Exercises 29–32 to polar equations.

29 $y^2 = 4x$

30 $x^2 + y^2 - 3x + 4y = 0$

31 $2x - 3y = 8$

32 $x^2 + y^2 = 2xy$

In each of Exercises 33–36, change the equation to an equation in x and y.

33 $r^2 = \tan\theta$

34 $r = 2\cos\theta + 3\sin\theta$

35 $r^2 = 4\sin 2\theta$

36 $\theta = \sqrt{3}$

In Exercises 37–39, sketch the graph of the curve and find a rectangular equation of a graph that contains the points on the curve.

37 $x = (1/t) + 1,\ y = (2/t) - t;\ 0 < t \le 4$

38 $x = \cos^2 t - 2,\ y = \sin t + 1;\ 0 \le t \le 2\pi$

39 $x = \sqrt{t},\ y = 2^{-t};\ t \ge 0$

40   Let the curves $C_1, C_2, C_3,$ and C_4 be given parametrically by

$$C_1 : x = t^2, y = t$$
$$C_2 : x = t^4, y = t^2$$
$$C_3 : x = \sin^2 t, y = \sin t$$
$$C_4 : x = 3^{2t}, y = -3^t$$

where t varies through $\mathbb{R}$. Sketch the graphs of $C_1, C_2, C_3,$ and C_4 and discuss their similarities and differences.

Table I. Common Logarithms

N	0	1	2	3	4	5	6	7	8	9
1.0	.0000	.0043	.0086	.0128	.0170	.0212	.0253	.0294	.0334	.0374
1.1	.0414	.0453	.0492	.0531	.0569	.0607	.0645	.0682	.0719	.0755
1.2	.0792	.0828	.0864	.0899	.0934	.0969	.1004	.1038	.1072	.1106
1.3	.1139	.1173	.1206	.1239	.1271	.1303	.1335	.1367	.1399	.1430
1.4	.1461	.1492	.1523	.1553	.1584	.1614	.1644	.1673	.1703	.1732
1.5	.1761	.1790	.1818	.1847	.1875	.1903	.1931	.1959	.1987	.2014
1.6	.2041	.2068	.2095	.2122	.2148	.2175	.2201	.2227	.2253	.2279
1.7	.2304	.2330	.2355	.2380	.2405	.2430	.2455	.2480	.2504	.2529
1.8	.2553	.2577	.2601	.2625	.2648	.2672	.2695	.2718	.2742	.2765
1.9	.2788	.2810	.2833	.2856	.2878	.2900	.2923	.2945	.2967	.2989
2.0	.3010	.3032	.3054	.3075	.3096	.3118	.3139	.3160	.3181	.3201
2.1	.3222	.3243	.3263	.3284	.3304	.3324	.3345	.3365	.3385	.3404
2.2	.3424	.3444	.3464	.3483	.3502	.3522	.3541	.3560	.3579	.3598
2.3	.3617	.3636	.3655	.3674	.3692	.3711	.3729	.3747	.3766	.3784
2.4	.3802	.3820	.3838	.3856	.3874	.3892	.3909	.3927	.3945	.3962
2.5	.3979	.3997	.4014	.4031	.4048	.4065	.4082	.4099	.4116	.4133
2.6	.4150	.4166	.4183	.4200	.4216	.4232	.4249	.4265	.4281	.4298
2.7	.4314	.4330	.4346	.4362	.4378	.4393	.4409	.4425	.4440	.4456
2.8	.4472	.4487	.4502	.4518	.4533	.4548	.4564	.4579	.4594	.4609
2.9	.4624	.4639	.4654	.4669	.4683	.4698	.4713	.4728	.4742	.4757
3.0	.4771	.4786	.4800	.4814	.4829	.4843	.4857	.4871	.4886	.4900
3.1	.4914	.4928	.4942	.4955	.4969	.4983	.4997	.5011	.5024	.5038
3.2	.5051	.5065	.5079	.5092	.5105	.5119	.5132	.5145	.5159	.5172
3.3	.5185	.5198	.5211	.5224	.5237	.5250	.5263	.5276	.5289	.5302
3.4	.5315	.5328	.5340	.5353	.5366	.5378	.5391	.5403	.5416	.5428
3.5	.5441	.5453	.5465	.5478	.5490	.5502	.5514	.5527	.5539	.5551
3.6	.5563	.5575	.5587	.5599	.5611	.5623	.5635	.5647	.5658	.5670
3.7	.5682	.5694	.5705	.5717	.5729	.5740	.5752	.5763	.5775	.5786
3.8	.5798	.5809	.5821	.5832	.5843	.5855	.5866	.5877	.5888	.5899
3.9	.5911	.5922	.5933	.5944	.5955	.5966	.5977	.5988	.5999	.6010
4.0	.6021	.6031	.6042	.6053	.6064	.6075	.6085	.6096	.6107	.6117
4.1	.6128	.6138	.6149	.6160	.6170	.6180	.6191	.6201	.6212	.6222
4.2	.6232	.6243	.6253	.6263	.6274	.6284	.6294	.6304	.6314	.6325
4.3	.6335	.6345	.6355	.6365	.6375	.6385	.6395	.6405	.6415	.6425
4.4	.6435	.6444	.6454	.6464	.6474	.6484	.6493	.6503	.6513	.6522
4.5	.6532	.6542	.6551	.6561	.6571	.6580	.6590	.6599	.6609	.6618
4.6	.6628	.6637	.6646	.6656	.6665	.6675	.6684	.6693	.6702	.6712
4.7	.6721	.6730	.6739	.6749	.6758	.6767	.6776	.6785	.6794	.6803
4.8	.6812	.6821	.6830	.6839	.6848	.6857	.6866	.6875	.6884	.6893
4.9	.6902	.6911	.6920	.6928	.6937	.6946	.6955	.6964	.6972	.6981
5.0	.6990	.6998	.7007	.7016	.7024	.7033	.7042	.7050	.7059	.7067
5.1	.7076	.7084	.7093	.7101	.7110	.7118	.7126	.7135	.7143	.7152
5.2	.7160	.7168	.7177	.7185	.7193	.7202	.7210	.7218	.7226	.7235
5.3	.7243	.7251	.7259	.7267	.7275	.7284	.7292	.7300	.7308	.7316
5.4	.7324	.7332	.7340	.7348	.7356	.7364	.7372	.7380	.7388	.7396
5.5	.7404	.7412	.7419	.7427	.7435	.7443	.7451	.7459	.7466	.7474
5.6	.7482	.7490	.7497	.7505	.7513	.7520	.7528	.7536	.7543	.7551
5.7	.7559	.7566	.7574	.7582	.7589	.7597	.7604	.7612	.7619	.7627
5.8	.7634	.7642	.7649	.7657	.7664	.7672	.7679	.7686	.7694	.7701
5.9	.7709	.7716	.7723	.7731	.7738	.7745	.7752	.7760	.7767	.7774
6.0	.7782	.7789	.7796	.7803	.7810	.7818	.7825	.7832	.7839	.7846
6.1	.7853	.7860	.7868	.7875	.7882	.7889	.7896	.7903	.7910	.7917
6.2	.7924	.7931	.7938	.7945	.7952	.7959	.7966	.7973	.7980	.7987
6.3	.7993	.8000	.8007	.8014	.8021	.8028	.8035	.8041	.8048	.8055
6.4	.8062	.8069	.8075	.8082	.8089	.8096	.8102	.8109	.8116	.8122
6.5	.8129	.8136	.8142	.8149	.8156	.8162	.8169	.8176	.8182	.8189
6.6	.8195	.8202	.8209	.8215	.8222	.8228	.8235	.8241	.8248	.8254
6.7	.8261	.8267	.8274	.8280	.8287	.8293	.8299	.8306	.8312	.8319
6.8	.8325	.8331	.8338	.8344	.8351	.8357	.8363	.8370	.8376	.8382
6.9	.8388	.8395	.8401	.8407	.8414	.8420	.8426	.8432	.8439	.8445
7.0	.8451	.8457	.8463	.8470	.8476	.8482	.8488	.8494	.8500	.8506
7.1	.8513	.8519	.8525	.8531	.8537	.8543	.8549	.8555	.8561	.8567
7.2	.8573	.8579	.8585	.8591	.8597	.8603	.8609	.8615	.8621	.8627
7.3	.8633	.8639	.8645	.8651	.8657	.8663	.8669	.8675	.8681	.8686
7.4	.8692	.8698	.8704	.8710	.8716	.8722	.8727	.8733	.8739	.8745
7.5	.8751	.8756	.8762	.8768	.8774	.8779	.8785	.8791	.8797	.8802
7.6	.8808	.8814	.8820	.8825	.8831	.8837	.8842	.8848	.8854	.8859
7.7	.8865	.8871	.8876	.8882	.8887	.8893	.8899	.8904	.8910	.8915
7.8	.8921	.8927	.8932	.8938	.8943	.8949	.8954	.8960	.8965	.8971
7.9	.8976	.8982	.8987	.8993	.8998	.9004	.9009	.9015	.9020	.9025
8.0	.9031	.9036	.9042	.9047	.9053	.9058	.9063	.9069	.9074	.9079
8.1	.9085	.9090	.9096	.9101	.9106	.9112	.9117	.9122	.9128	.9133
8.2	.9138	.9143	.9149	.9154	.9159	.9165	.9170	.9175	.9180	.9186
8.3	.9191	.9196	.9201	.9206	.9212	.9217	.9222	.9227	.9232	.9238
8.4	.9243	.9248	.9253	.9258	.9263	.9269	.9274	.9279	.9284	.9289
8.5	.9294	.9299	.9304	.9309	.9315	.9320	.9325	.9330	.9335	.9340
8.6	.9345	.9350	.9355	.9360	.9365	.9370	.9375	.9380	.9385	.9390
8.7	.9395	.9400	.9405	.9410	.9415	.9420	.9425	.9430	.9435	.9440
8.8	.9445	.9450	.9455	.9460	.9465	.9469	.9474	.9479	.9484	.9489
8.9	.9494	.9499	.9504	.9509	.9513	.9518	.9523	.9528	.9533	.9538
9.0	.9542	.9547	.9552	.9557	.9562	.9566	.9571	.9576	.9581	.9586
9.1	.9590	.9595	.9600	.9605	.9609	.9614	.9619	.9624	.9628	.9633
9.2	.9638	.9643	.9647	.9652	.9657	.9661	.9666	.9671	.9675	.9680
9.3	.9685	.9689	.9694	.9699	.9703	.9708	.9713	.9717	.9722	.9727
9.4	.9731	.9736	.9741	.9745	.9750	.9754	.9759	.9763	.9768	.9773
9.5	.9777	.9782	.9786	.9791	.9795	.9800	.9805	.9809	.9814	.9818
9.6	.9823	.9827	.9832	.9836	.9841	.9845	.9850	.9854	.9859	.9863
9.7	.9868	.9872	.9877	.9881	.9886	.9890	.9894	.9899	.9903	.9908
9.8	.9912	.9917	.9921	.9926	.9930	.9934	.9939	.9943	.9948	.9952
9.9	.9956	.9961	.9965	.9969	.9974	.9978	.9983	.9987	.9991	.9996

Table 2. Values of the Trigonometric Functions

t	t degrees	sin t	cos t	tan t	cot t	sec t	csc t	t degrees	t
.1222	7°00'	.1219	.9925	.1228	8.144	1.008	8.206	83°00'	1.4486
.1251	10	.1248	.9922	.1257	7.953	1.008	8.016	50	1.4457
.1280	20	.1276	.9918	.1287	7.770	1.008	7.834	40	1.4428
.1309	30	.1305	.9914	.1317	7.596	1.009	7.661	30	1.4399
.1338	40	.1334	.9911	.1346	7.429	1.009	7.496	20	1.4370
.1367	50	.1363	.9907	.1376	7.269	1.009	7.337	10	1.4341
.1396	8°00'	.1392	.9903	.1405	7.115	1.010	7.185	82°00'	1.4312
.1425	10	.1421	.9899	.1435	6.968	1.010	7.040	50	1.4283
.1454	20	.1449	.9894	.1465	6.827	1.011	6.900	40	1.4254
.1484	30	.1478	.9890	.1495	6.691	1.011	6.765	30	1.4224
.1513	40	.1507	.9886	.1524	6.561	1.012	6.636	20	1.4195
.1542	50	.1536	.9881	.1554	6.435	1.012	6.512	10	1.4166
.1571	9°00'	.1564	.9877	.1584	6.314	1.012	6.392	81°00'	1.4137
.1600	10	.1593	.9872	.1614	6.197	1.013	6.277	50	1.4108
.1629	20	.1622	.9868	.1644	6.084	1.013	6.166	40	1.4079
.1658	30	.1650	.9863	.1673	5.976	1.014	6.059	30	1.4050
.1687	40	.1679	.9858	.1703	5.871	1.014	5.955	20	1.4021
.1716	50	.1708	.9853	.1733	5.769	1.015	5.855	10	1.3992
.1745	10°00'	.1736	.9848	.1763	5.671	1.015	5.759	80°00'	1.3963
.1774	10	.1765	.9843	.1793	5.576	1.016	5.665	50	1.3934
.1804	20	.1794	.9838	.1823	5.485	1.016	5.575	40	1.3904
.1833	30	.1822	.9833	.1853	5.396	1.017	5.487	30	1.3875
.1862	40	.1851	.9827	.1883	5.309	1.018	5.403	20	1.3846
.1891	50	.1880	.9822	.1914	5.226	1.018	5.320	10	1.3817
.1920	11°00'	.1908	.9816	.1944	5.145	1.019	5.241	79°00'	1.3788
.1949	10	.1937	.9811	.1974	5.066	1.019	5.164	50	1.3759
.1978	20	.1965	.9805	.2004	4.989	1.020	5.089	40	1.3730
.2007	30	.1994	.9799	.2035	4.915	1.020	5.016	30	1.3701
.2036	40	.2022	.9793	.2065	4.843	1.021	4.945	20	1.3672
.2065	50	.2051	.9787	.2095	4.773	1.022	4.876	10	1.3643
.2094	12°00'	.2079	.9781	.2126	4.705	1.022	4.810	78°00'	1.3614
.2123	10	.2108	.9775	.2156	4.638	1.023	4.745	50	1.3584
.2153	20	.2136	.9769	.2186	4.574	1.024	4.682	40	1.3555
.2182	30	.2164	.9763	.2217	4.511	1.024	4.620	30	1.3526
.2211	40	.2193	.9757	.2247	4.449	1.025	4.560	20	1.3497
.2240	50	.2221	.9750	.2278	4.390	1.026	4.502	10	1.3468
.2269	13°00'	.2250	.9744	.2309	4.331	1.026	4.445	77°00'	1.3439
.2298	10	.2278	.9737	.2339	4.275	1.027	4.390	50	1.3410
.2327	20	.2306	.9730	.2370	4.219	1.028	4.336	40	1.3381
.2356	30	.2334	.9724	.2401	4.165	1.028	4.284	30	1.3352
.2385	40	.2363	.9717	.2432	4.113	1.029	4.232	20	1.3323
.2414	50	.2391	.9710	.2462	4.061	1.030	4.182	10	1.3294
.2443	14°00'	.2419	.9703	.2493	4.011	1.031	4.134	76°00'	1.3265
t		cos t	sin t	cot t	tan t	csc t	sec t	degrees	t

t	t degrees	sin t	cos t	tan t	cot t	sec t	csc t	t degrees	t
.0000	0°00'	.0000	1.0000	.0000	—	1.000	—	90°00'	1.5708
.0029	10	.0029	1.0000	.0029	343.8	1.000	343.8	50	1.5679
.0058	20	.0058	1.0000	.0058	171.9	1.000	171.9	40	1.5650
.0087	30	.0087	1.0000	.0087	114.6	1.000	114.6	30	1.5621
.0116	40	.0116	.9999	.0116	85.94	1.000	85.95	20	1.5592
.0145	50	.0145	.9999	.0145	68.75	1.000	68.76	10	1.5563
.0175	1°00'	.0175	.9998	.0175	57.29	1.000	57.30	89°00'	1.5533
.0204	10	.0204	.9998	.0204	49.10	1.000	49.11	50	1.5504
.0233	20	.0233	.9997	.0233	42.96	1.000	42.98	40	1.5475
.0262	30	.0262	.9997	.0262	38.19	1.000	38.20	30	1.5446
.0291	40	.0291	.9996	.0291	34.37	1.000	34.38	20	1.5417
.0320	50	.0320	.9995	.0320	31.24	1.001	31.26	10	1.5388
.0349	2°00'	.0349	.9994	.0349	28.64	1.001	28.65	88°00'	1.5359
.0378	10	.0378	.9993	.0378	26.43	1.001	26.45	50	1.5330
.0407	20	.0407	.9992	.0407	24.54	1.001	24.56	40	1.5301
.0436	30	.0436	.9990	.0437	22.90	1.001	22.93	30	1.5272
.0465	40	.0465	.9989	.0466	21.47	1.001	21.49	20	1.5243
.0495	50	.0494	.9988	.0495	20.21	1.001	20.23	10	1.5213
.0524	3°00'	.0523	.9986	.0524	19.08	1.001	19.11	87°00'	1.5184
.0553	10	.0552	.9985	.0553	18.07	1.002	18.10	50	1.5155
.0582	20	.0581	.9983	.0582	17.17	1.002	17.20	40	1.5126
.0611	30	.0610	.9981	.0612	16.35	1.002	16.38	30	1.5097
.0640	40	.0640	.9980	.0641	15.60	1.002	15.64	20	1.5068
.0669	50	.0669	.9978	.0670	14.92	1.002	14.96	10	1.5039
.0698	4°00'	.0698	.9976	.0699	14.30	1.002	14.34	86°00'	1.5010
.0727	10	.0727	.9974	.0729	13.73	1.003	13.76	50	1.4981
.0756	20	.0756	.9971	.0758	13.20	1.003	13.23	40	1.4952
.0785	30	.0785	.9969	.0787	12.71	1.003	12.75	30	1.4923
.0814	40	.0814	.9967	.0816	12.25	1.003	12.29	20	1.4893
.0844	50	.0843	.9964	.0846	11.83	1.004	11.87	10	1.4864
.0873	5°00'	.0872	.9962	.0875	11.43	1.004	11.47	85°00'	1.4835
.0902	10	.0901	.9959	.0904	11.06	1.004	11.10	50	1.4806
.0931	20	.0929	.9957	.0934	10.71	1.004	10.76	40	1.4777
.0960	30	.0958	.9954	.0963	10.39	1.005	10.43	30	1.4748
.0989	40	.0987	.9951	.0992	10.08	1.005	10.13	20	1.4719
.1018	50	.1016	.9948	.1022	9.788	1.005	9.839	10	1.4690
.1047	6°00'	.1045	.9945	.1051	9.514	1.006	9.567	84°00'	1.4661
.1076	10	.1074	.9942	.1080	9.255	1.006	9.309	50	1.4632
.1105	20	.1103	.9939	.1110	9.010	1.006	9.065	40	1.4603
.1134	30	.1132	.9936	.1139	8.777	1.006	8.834	30	1.4573
.1164	40	.1161	.9932	.1169	8.556	1.007	8.614	20	1.4544
.1193	50	.1190	.9929	.1198	8.345	1.007	8.405	10	1.4515
.1222	7°00'	.1219	.9925	.1228	8.144	1.008	8.206	83°00'	1.4486
		cos t	sin t	cot t	tan t	csc t	sec t	degrees	t

TABLE 2. VALUES OF THE TRIGONOMETRIC FUNCTIONS · A3

Table 2. Values of the Trigonometric Functions (cont'd.)

Upper table

t	degrees	csc t	sec t	cot t	tan t	cos t	sin t	degrees	t
1.2043	69°00'	2.790	1.071	2.605	.3839	.9336	.3584	21°00'	.3665
1.2014	50	2.769	1.072	2.583	.3872	.9325	.3611	10	.3694
1.1985	40	2.749	1.074	2.560	.3906	.9315	.3638	20	.3723
1.1956	30	2.729	1.075	2.539	.3939	.9304	.3665	30	.3752
1.1926	20	2.709	1.076	2.517	.3973	.9293	.3692	40	.3782
1.1897	10	2.689	1.077	2.496	.4006	.9283	.3719	50	.3811
1.1868	68°00'	2.669	1.079	2.475	.4040	.9272	.3746	22°00'	.3840
1.1839	50	2.650	1.080	2.455	.4074	.9261	.3773	10	.3869
1.1810	40	2.632	1.081	2.434	.4108	.9250	.3800	20	.3898
1.1781	30	2.613	1.082	2.414	.4142	.9239	.3827	30	.3927
1.1752	20	2.595	1.084	2.394	.4176	.9228	.3854	40	.3956
1.1723	10	2.577	1.085	2.375	.4210	.9216	.3881	50	.3985
1.1694	67°00'	2.559	1.086	2.356	.4245	.9205	.3907	23°00'	.4014
1.1665	50	2.542	1.088	2.337	.4279	.9194	.3934	10	.4043
1.1636	40	2.525	1.089	2.318	.4314	.9182	.3961	20	.4072
1.1606	30	2.508	1.090	2.300	.4348	.9171	.3987	30	.4102
1.1577	20	2.491	1.092	2.282	.4383	.9159	.4014	40	.4131
1.1548	10	2.475	1.093	2.264	.4417	.9147	.4041	50	.4160
1.1519	66°00'	2.459	1.095	2.246	.4452	.9135	.4067	24°00'	.4189
1.1490	50	2.443	1.096	2.229	.4487	.9124	.4094	10	.4218
1.1461	40	2.427	1.097	2.211	.4522	.9112	.4120	20	.4247
1.1432	30	2.411	1.099	2.194	.4557	.9100	.4147	30	.4276
1.1403	20	2.396	1.100	2.177	.4592	.9088	.4173	40	.4305
1.1374	10	2.381	1.102	2.161	.4628	.9075	.4200	50	.4334
1.1345	65°00'	2.366	1.103	2.145	.4663	.9063	.4226	25°00'	.4363
1.1316	50	2.352	1.105	2.128	.4699	.9051	.4253	10	.4392
1.1286	40	2.337	1.106	2.112	.4734	.9038	.4279	20	.4422
1.1257	30	2.323	1.108	2.097	.4770	.9026	.4305	30	.4451
1.1228	20	2.309	1.109	2.081	.4806	.9013	.4331	40	.4480
1.1199	10	2.295	1.111	2.066	.4841	.9001	.4358	50	.4509
1.1170	64°00'	2.281	1.113	2.050	.4877	.8988	.4384	26°00'	.4538
1.1141	50	2.268	1.114	2.035	.4913	.8975	.4410	10	.4567
1.1112	40	2.254	1.116	2.020	.4950	.8962	.4436	20	.4596
1.1083	30	2.241	1.117	2.006	.4986	.8949	.4462	30	.4625
1.1054	20	2.228	1.119	1.991	.5022	.8936	.4488	40	.4654
1.1025	10	2.215	1.121	1.977	.5059	.8923	.4514	50	.4683
1.0996	63°00'	2.203	1.122	1.963	.5095	.8910	.4540	27°00'	.4712
1.0966	50	2.190	1.124	1.949	.5132	.8897	.4566	10	.4741
1.0937	40	2.178	1.126	1.935	.5169	.8884	.4592	20	.4771
1.0908	30	2.166	1.127	1.921	.5206	.8870	.4617	30	.4800
1.0879	20	2.154	1.129	1.907	.5243	.8857	.4643	40	.4829
1.0850	10	2.142	1.131	1.894	.5280	.8843	.4669	50	.4858
1.0821	62°00'	2.130	1.133	1.881	.5317	.8829	.4695	28°00'	.4887

Bottom column labels (complementary reading): t · degrees · sec t · csc t · tan t · cot t · sin t · cos t · degrees

Lower table

t	degrees	csc t	sec t	cot t	tan t	cos t	sin t	degrees	t
1.3265	76°00'	4.134	1.031	4.011	.2493	.9703	.2419	14°00'	.2443
1.3235	50	4.086	1.031	3.962	.2524	.9696	.2447	10	.2473
1.3206	40	4.039	1.032	3.914	.2555	.9689	.2476	20	.2502
1.3177	30	3.994	1.033	3.867	.2586	.9681	.2504	30	.2531
1.3148	20	3.950	1.034	3.821	.2617	.9674	.2532	40	.2560
1.3119	10	3.906	1.034	3.776	.2648	.9667	.2560	50	.2589
1.3090	75°00'	3.864	1.035	3.732	.2679	.9659	.2588	15°00'	.2618
1.3061	50	3.822	1.036	3.689	.2711	.9652	.2616	10	.2647
1.3032	40	3.782	1.037	3.647	.2742	.9644	.2644	20	.2676
1.3003	30	3.742	1.038	3.606	.2773	.9636	.2672	30	.2705
1.2974	20	3.703	1.039	3.566	.2805	.9628	.2700	40	.2734
1.2945	10	3.665	1.039	3.526	.2836	.9621	.2728	50	.2763
1.2915	74°00'	3.628	1.040	3.487	.2867	.9613	.2756	16°00'	.2793
1.2886	50	3.592	1.041	3.450	.2899	.9605	.2784	10	.2822
1.2857	40	3.556	1.042	3.412	.2931	.9596	.2812	20	.2851
1.2828	30	3.521	1.043	3.376	.2962	.9588	.2840	30	.2880
1.2799	20	3.487	1.044	3.340	.2994	.9580	.2868	40	.2909
1.2770	10	3.453	1.045	3.305	.3026	.9572	.2896	50	.2938
1.2741	73°00'	3.420	1.046	3.271	.3057	.9563	.2924	17°00'	.2967
1.2712	50	3.388	1.047	3.237	.3089	.9555	.2952	10	.2996
1.2683	40	3.356	1.048	3.204	.3121	.9546	.2979	20	.3025
1.2654	30	3.326	1.049	3.172	.3153	.9537	.3007	30	.3054
1.2625	20	3.295	1.049	3.140	.3185	.9528	.3035	40	.3083
1.2595	10	3.265	1.050	3.108	.3217	.9520	.3062	50	.3113
1.2566	72°00'	3.236	1.051	3.078	.3249	.9511	.3090	18°00'	.3142
1.2537	50	3.207	1.052	3.047	.3281	.9502	.3118	10	.3171
1.2508	40	3.179	1.053	3.018	.3314	.9492	.3145	20	.3200
1.2479	30	3.152	1.054	2.989	.3346	.9483	.3173	30	.3229
1.2450	20	3.124	1.056	2.960	.3378	.9474	.3201	40	.3258
1.2421	10	3.098	1.057	2.932	.3411	.9465	.3228	50	.3287
1.2392	71°00'	3.072	1.058	2.904	.3443	.9455	.3256	19°00'	.3316
1.2363	50	3.046	1.059	2.877	.3476	.9446	.3283	10	.3345
1.2334	40	3.021	1.060	2.850	.3508	.9436	.3311	20	.3374
1.2305	30	2.996	1.061	2.824	.3541	.9426	.3338	30	.3403
1.2275	20	2.971	1.062	2.798	.3574	.9417	.3365	40	.3432
1.2246	10	2.947	1.063	2.773	.3607	.9407	.3393	50	.3462
1.2217	70°00'	2.924	1.064	2.747	.3640	.9397	.3420	20°00'	.3491
1.2188	50	2.901	1.065	2.723	.3673	.9387	.3448	10	.3520
1.2159	40	2.878	1.066	2.699	.3706	.9377	.3475	20	.3549
1.2130	30	2.855	1.068	2.675	.3739	.9367	.3502	30	.3578
1.2101	20	2.833	1.069	2.651	.3772	.9356	.3529	40	.3607
1.2072	10	2.812	1.070	2.628	.3805	.9346	.3557	50	.3636
1.2043	69°00'	2.790	1.071	2.605	.3839	.9336	.3584	21°00'	.3665

Bottom column labels (complementary reading): t · degrees · sec t · csc t · tan t · cot t · sin t · cos t · degrees

t	degrees	csc t	sec t	cot t	tan t	cos t	sin t	degrees	t
.9599	55°00'	1.743	1.221	1.428	.7002	.8192	.5736	35°00'	.6109
.9570	50	1.736	1.223	1.419	.7046	.8175	.5760	10	.6138
.9541	40	1.729	1.226	1.411	.7089	.8158	.5783	20	.6167
.9512	30	1.722	1.228	1.402	.7133	.8141	.5807	30	.6196
.9483	20	1.715	1.231	1.393	.7177	.8124	.5831	40	.6225
.9454	10	1.708	1.233	1.385	.7221	.8107	.5854	50	.6254
.9425	54°00'	1.701	1.236	1.376	.7265	.8090	.5878	36°00'	.6283
.9396	50	1.695	1.239	1.368	.7310	.8073	.5901	10	.6312
.9367	40	1.688	1.241	1.360	.7355	.8056	.5925	20	.6341
.9338	30	1.681	1.244	1.351	.7400	.8039	.5948	30	.6370
.9308	20	1.675	1.247	1.343	.7445	.8021	.5972	40	.6400
.9279	10	1.668	1.249	1.335	.7490	.8004	.5995	50	.6429
.9250	53°00'	1.662	1.252	1.327	.7536	.7986	.6018	37°00'	.6458
.9221	50	1.655	1.255	1.319	.7581	.7969	.6041	10	.6487
.9192	40	1.649	1.258	1.311	.7627	.7951	.6065	20	.6516
.9163	30	1.643	1.260	1.303	.7673	.7934	.6088	30	.6545
.9134	20	1.636	1.263	1.295	.7720	.7916	.6111	40	.6574
.9105	10	1.630	1.266	1.288	.7766	.7898	.6134	50	.6603
.9076	52°00'	1.624	1.269	1.280	.7813	.7880	.6157	38°00'	.6632
.9047	50	1.618	1.272	1.272	.7860	.7862	.6180	10	.6661
.9018	40	1.612	1.275	1.265	.7907	.7844	.6202	20	.6690
.8988	30	1.606	1.278	1.257	.7954	.7826	.6225	30	.6720
.8959	20	1.601	1.281	1.250	.8002	.7808	.6248	40	.6749
.8930	10	1.595	1.284	1.242	.8050	.7790	.6271	50	.6778
.8901	51°00'	1.589	1.287	1.235	.8098	.7771	.6293	39°00'	.6807
.8872	50	1.583	1.290	1.228	.8146	.7753	.6316	10	.6836
.8843	40	1.578	1.293	1.220	.8195	.7735	.6338	20	.6865
.8814	30	1.572	1.296	1.213	.8243	.7716	.6361	30	.6894
.8785	20	1.567	1.299	1.206	.8292	.7698	.6383	40	.6923
.8756	10	1.561	1.302	1.199	.8342	.7679	.6406	50	.6952
.8727	50°00'	1.556	1.305	1.192	.8391	.7660	.6428	40°00'	.6981
.8698	50	1.550	1.309	1.185	.8441	.7642	.6450	10	.7010
.8668	40	1.545	1.312	1.178	.8491	.7623	.6472	20	.7039
.8639	30	1.540	1.315	1.171	.8541	.7604	.6494	30	.7069
.8610	20	1.535	1.318	1.164	.8591	.7585	.6517	40	.7098
.8581	10	1.529	1.322	1.157	.8642	.7566	.6539	50	.7127
8.552	49°00'	1.524	1.325	1.150	.8693	.7547	.6561	41°00'	.7156
8.523	50	1.519	1.328	1.144	.8744	.7528	.6583	10	.7185
8.494	40	1.514	1.332	1.137	.8796	.7509	.6604	20	.7214
8.465	30	1.509	1.335	1.130	.8847	.7490	.6626	30	.7243
8.436	20	1.504	1.339	1.124	.8899	.7470	.6648	40	.7272
8.407	10	1.499	1.342	1.117	.8952	.7451	.6670	50	.7301
.8378	48°00'	1.494	1.346	1.111	.9004	.7431	.6691	42°00'	.7330
t		sec t	csc t	tan t	cot t	sin t	cos t	degrees	

Table 2. Values of the Trigonometric Functions (cont'd.)

t	degrees	csc t	sec t	cot t	tan t	cos t	sin t	degrees	t
.4887	28°00'	2.130	1.133	1.881	.5317	.8829	.4695	62°00'	1.0821
.4916	10	2.118	1.134	1.868	.5354	.8816	.4720	50	1.0792
.4945	20	2.107	1.136	1.855	.5392	.8802	.4746	40	1.0763
.4974	30	2.096	1.138	1.842	.5430	.8788	.4772	30	1.0734
.5003	40	2.085	1.140	1.829	.5467	.8774	.4797	20	1.0705
.5032	50	2.074	1.142	1.816	.5505	.8760	.4823	10	1.0676
.5061	29°00'	2.063	1.143	1.804	.5543	.8746	.4848	61°00'	1.0647
.5091	10	2.052	1.145	1.792	.5581	.8732	.4874	50	1.0617
.5120	20	2.041	1.147	1.780	.5619	.8718	.4899	40	1.0588
.5149	30	2.031	1.149	1.767	.5658	.8704	.4924	30	1.0559
.5178	40	2.020	1.151	1.756	.5696	.8689	.4950	20	1.0530
.5207	50	2.010	1.153	1.744	.5735	.8675	.4975	10	1.0501
.5236	30°00'	2.000	1.155	1.732	.5774	.8660	.5000	60°00'	1.0472
.5265	10	1.990	1.157	1.720	.5812	.8646	.5025	50	1.0443
.5294	20	1.980	1.159	1.709	.5851	.8631	.5050	40	1.0414
.5323	30	1.970	1.161	1.698	.5890	.8616	.5075	30	1.0385
.5352	40	1.961	1.163	1.686	.5930	.8601	.5100	20	1.0356
.5381	50	1.951	1.165	1.675	.5969	.8587	.5125	10	1.0327
.5411	31°00'	1.942	1.167	1.664	.6009	.8572	.5150	59°00'	1.0297
.5440	10	1.932	1.169	1.653	.6048	.8557	.5175	50	1.0268
.5469	20	1.923	1.171	1.643	.6088	.8542	.5200	40	1.0239
.5498	30	1.914	1.173	1.632	.6128	.8526	.5225	30	1.0210
.5527	40	1.905	1.175	1.621	.6168	.8511	.5250	20	1.0181
.5556	50	1.896	1.177	1.611	.6208	.8496	.5275	10	1.0152
.5585	32°00'	1.887	1.179	1.600	.6249	.8480	.5299	58°00'	1.0123
.5614	10	1.878	1.181	1.590	.6289	.8465	.5324	50	1.0094
.5643	20	1.870	1.184	1.580	.6330	.8450	.5348	40	1.0065
.5672	30	1.861	1.186	1.570	.6371	.8434	.5373	30	1.0036
.5701	40	1.853	1.188	1.560	.6412	.8418	.5398	20	1.0007
.5730	50	1.844	1.190	1.550	.6453	.8403	.5422	10	.9977
.5760	33°00'	1.836	1.192	1.540	.6494	.8387	.5446	57°00'	.9948
.5789	10	1.828	1.195	1.530	.6536	.8371	.5471	50	.9919
.5818	20	1.820	1.197	1.520	.6577	.8355	.5495	40	.9890
.5847	30	1.812	1.199	1.511	.6619	.8339	.5519	30	.9861
.5876	40	1.804	1.202	1.501	.6661	.8323	.5544	20	.9832
.5905	50	1.796	1.204	1.492	.6703	.8307	.5568	10	.9803
.5934	34°00'	1.788	1.206	1.483	.6745	.8290	.5592	56°00'	.9774
.5963	10	1.781	1.209	1.473	.6787	.8274	.5616	50	.9745
.5992	20	1.773	1.211	1.464	.6830	.8258	.5640	40	.9716
.6021	30	1.766	1.213	1.455	.6873	.8241	.5664	30	.9687
.6050	40	1.758	1.216	1.446	.6916	.8225	.5688	20	.9657
.6080	50	1.751	1.218	1.437	.6959	.8208	.5712	10	.9628
.6109	35°00'	1.743	1.221	1.428	.7002	.8192	.5736	55°00'	.9599
t		sec t	csc t	tan t	cot t	sin t	cos t	degrees	

TABLE 3. TRIGONOMETRIC FUNCTIONS OF RADIANS AND REAL NUMBERS   A5

Table 3. Trigonometric Functions of Radians and Real Numbers

t	sin t	cos t	tan t	cot t	sec t	csc t
.00	.0000	1.0000	.0000	—	1.0000	—
.01	.0100	1.0000	.0100	99.997	1.000	100.00
.02	.0200	.9998	.0200	49.993	1.000	50.00
.03	.0300	.9996	.0300	33.323	1.000	33.34
.04	.0400	.9992	.0400	24.987	1.001	25.01
.05	.0500	.9988	.0500	19.983	1.001	20.01
.06	.0600	.9982	.0601	16.647	1.002	16.68
.07	.0699	.9976	.0701	14.262	1.002	14.30
.08	.0799	.9968	.0802	12.473	1.003	12.51
.09	.0899	.9960	.0902	11.081	1.004	11.13
.10	.0998	.9950	.1003	9.967	1.005	10.02
.11	.1098	.9940	.1104	9.054	1.006	9.109
.12	.1197	.9928	.1206	8.293	1.007	8.353
.13	.1296	.9916	.1307	7.649	1.009	7.714
.14	.1395	.9902	.1409	7.096	1.010	7.166
.15	.1494	.9888	.1511	6.617	1.011	6.692
.16	.1593	.9872	.1614	6.197	1.013	6.277
.17	.1692	.9856	.1717	5.826	1.015	5.911
.18	.1790	.9838	.1820	5.495	1.016	5.586
.19	.1889	.9820	.1923	5.200	1.018	5.295
.20	.1987	.9801	.2027	4.933	1.020	5.033
.21	.2085	.9780	.2131	4.692	1.022	4.797
.22	.2182	.9759	.2236	4.472	1.025	4.582
.23	.2280	.9737	.2341	4.271	1.027	4.386
.24	.2377	.9713	.2447	4.086	1.030	4.207
.25	.2474	.9689	.2553	3.916	1.032	4.042
.26	.2571	.9664	.2660	3.759	1.035	3.890
.27	.2667	.9638	.2768	3.613	1.038	3.749
.28	.2764	.9611	.2876	3.478	1.041	3.619
.29	.2860	.9582	.2984	3.351	1.044	3.497
.30	.2955	.9553	.3093	3.233	1.047	3.384
.31	.3051	.9523	.3203	3.122	1.050	3.278
.32	.3146	.9492	.3314	3.018	1.053	3.179
.33	.3240	.9460	.3425	2.920	1.057	3.086
.34	.3335	.9428	.3537	2.827	1.061	2.999
.35	.3429	.9394	.3650	2.740	1.065	2.916
.36	.3523	.9359	.3764	2.657	1.068	2.839
.37	.3616	.9323	.3879	2.578	1.073	2.765
.38	.3709	.9287	.3994	2.504	1.077	2.696
.39	.3802	.9249	.4111	2.433	1.081	2.630

Table 2. Values of the Trigonometric Functions (cont'd.)

t	degrees	sin t	cos t	tan t	cot t	sec t	csc t	degrees	t
.7330	42°00'	.6691	.7431	.9004	1.111	1.346	1.494	48°00'	.8378
.7359	10	.6713	.7412	.9057	1.104	1.349	1.490	50	.8348
.7389	20	.6734	.7392	.9110	1.098	1.353	1.485	40	.8319
.7418	30	.6756	.7373	.9163	1.091	1.356	1.480	30	.8290
.7447	40	.6777	.7353	.9217	1.085	1.360	1.476	20	.8261
.7476	50	.6799	.7333	.9271	1.079	1.364	1.471	10	.8232
.7505	43°00'	.6820	.7314	.9325	1.072	1.367	1.466	47°00'	.8203
.7534	10	.6841	.7294	.9380	1.066	1.371	1.462	50	.8174
.7563	20	.6862	.7274	.9435	1.060	1.375	1.457	40	.8145
.7592	30	.6884	.7254	.9490	1.054	1.379	1.453	30	.8116
.7621	40	.6905	.7234	.9545	1.048	1.382	1.448	20	.8087
.7650	50	.6926	.7214	.9601	1.042	1.386	1.444	10	.8058
.7679	44°00'	.6947	.7193	.9657	1.036	1.390	1.440	46°00'	.8029
.7709	10	.6967	.7173	.9713	1.030	1.394	1.435	50	.7999
.7738	20	.6988	.7153	.9770	1.024	1.398	1.431	40	.7970
.7767	30	.7009	.7133	.9827	1.018	1.402	1.427	30	.7941
.7796	40	.7030	.7112	.9884	1.012	1.406	1.423	20	.7912
.7825	50	.7050	.7092	.9942	1.006	1.410	1.418	10	.7883
.7854	45°00'	.7071	.7071	1.0000	1.0000	1.414	1.414	45°00'	.7854
		cos t	sin t	cot t	tan t	csc t	sec t	t degrees	t

Table 3. *Trigonometric Functions of Radians and Real Numbers (cont'd.)*

t	sin t	cos t	tan t	cot t	sec t	csc t
1.20	.9320	.3624	2.572	.3888	2.760	1.073
1.21	.9356	.3530	2.650	.3773	2.833	1.069
1.22	.9391	.3436	2.733	.3659	2.910	1.065
1.23	.9425	.3342	2.820	.3546	2.992	1.061
1.24	.9458	.3248	2.912	.3434	3.079	1.057
1.25	.9490	.3153	3.010	.3323	3.171	1.054
1.26	.9521	.3058	3.113	.3212	3.270	1.050
1.27	.9551	.2963	3.224	.3102	3.375	1.047
1.28	.9580	.2867	3.341	.2993	3.488	1.044
1.29	.9608	.2771	3.467	.2884	3.609	1.041
1.30	.9636	.2675	3.602	.2776	3.738	1.038
1.31	.9662	.2579	3.747	.2669	3.878	1.035
1.32	.9687	.2482	3.903	.2562	4.029	1.032
1.33	.9711	.2385	4.072	.2456	4.193	1.030
1.34	.9735	.2288	4.256	.2350	4.372	1.027
1.35	.9757	.2190	4.455	.2245	4.566	1.025
1.36	.9779	.2092	4.673	.2140	4.779	1.023
1.37	.9799	.1994	4.913	.2035	5.014	1.021
1.38	.9819	.1896	5.177	.1931	5.273	1.018
1.39	.9837	.1798	5.471	.1828	5.561	1.017
1.40	.9854	.1700	5.798	.1725	5.883	1.015
1.41	.9871	.1601	6.165	.1622	6.246	1.013
1.42	.9887	.1502	6.581	.1519	6.657	1.011
1.43	.9901	.1403	7.055	.1417	7.126	1.010
1.44	.9915	.1304	7.602	.1315	7.667	1.009
1.45	.9927	.1205	8.238	.1214	8.299	1.007
1.46	.9939	.1106	8.989	.1113	9.044	1.006
1.47	.9949	.1006	9.887	.1011	9.938	1.005
1.48	.9959	.0907	10.983	.0910	11.029	1.004
1.49	.9967	.0807	12.350	.0810	12.390	1.003
1.50	.9975	.0707	14.101	.0709	14.137	1.003
1.51	.9982	.0608	16.428	.0609	16.458	1.002
1.52	.9987	.0508	19.670	.0508	19.695	1.001
1.53	.9992	.0408	24.498	.0408	24.519	1.001
1.54	.9995	.0308	32.461	.0308	32.476	1.000
1.55	.9998	.0208	48.078	.0208	48.089	1.000
1.56	.9999	.0108	92.620	.0108	92.626	1.000
1.57	1.0000	.0008	1255.8	.0008	1255.8	1.000

t	sin t	cos t	tan t	cot t	sec t	csc t
.40	.3894	.9211	.4228	2.365	1.086	2.568
.41	.3986	.9171	.4346	2.301	1.090	2.509
.42	.4078	.9131	.4466	2.239	1.095	2.452
.43	.4169	.9090	.4586	2.180	1.100	2.399
.44	.4259	.9048	.4708	2.124	1.105	2.348
.45	.4350	.9004	.4831	2.070	1.111	2.299
.46	.4439	.8961	.4954	2.018	1.116	2.253
.47	.4529	.8916	.5080	1.969	1.122	2.208
.48	.4618	.8870	.5206	1.921	1.127	2.166
.49	.4706	.8823	.5334	1.875	1.133	2.125
.50	.4794	.8776	.5463	1.830	1.139	2.086
.51	.4882	.8727	.5594	1.788	1.146	2.048
.52	.4969	.8678	.5726	1.747	1.152	2.013
.53	.5055	.8628	.5859	1.707	1.159	1.978
.54	.5141	.8577	.5994	1.668	1.166	1.945
.55	.5227	.8525	.6131	1.631	1.173	1.913
.56	.5312	.8473	.6269	1.595	1.180	1.883
.57	.5396	.8419	.6410	1.560	1.188	1.853
.58	.5480	.8365	.6552	1.526	1.196	1.825
.59	.5564	.8309	.6696	1.494	1.203	1.797
.60	.5646	.8253	.6841	1.462	1.212	1.771
.61	.5729	.8196	.6989	1.431	1.220	1.746
.62	.5810	.8139	.7139	1.401	1.229	1.721
.63	.5891	.8080	.7291	1.372	1.238	1.697
.64	.5972	.8021	.7445	1.343	1.247	1.674
.65	.6052	.7961	.7602	1.315	1.256	1.652
.66	.6131	.7900	.7761	1.288	1.266	1.631
.67	.6210	.7838	.7923	1.262	1.276	1.610
.68	.6288	.7776	.8087	1.237	1.286	1.590
.69	.6365	.7712	.8253	1.212	1.297	1.571
.70	.6442	.7648	.8423	1.187	1.307	1.552
.71	.6518	.7584	.8595	1.163	1.319	1.534
.72	.6594	.7518	.8771	1.140	1.330	1.517
.73	.6669	.7452	.8949	1.117	1.342	1.500
.74	.6743	.7385	.9131	1.095	1.354	1.483
.75	.6816	.7317	.9316	1.073	1.367	1.467
.76	.6889	.7248	.9505	1.052	1.380	1.452
.77	.6961	.7179	.9697	1.031	1.393	1.437
.78	.7033	.7109	.9893	1.011	1.407	1.422
.79	.7104	.7038	1.0009	.9908	1.421	1.408

TABLE 4. POWERS AND ROOTS   A7

Table 4. Powers and Roots

n	n^2	$\sqrt{n}$	n^3	$\sqrt[3]{n}$
51	2,601	7.141	132,651	3.708
52	2,704	7.211	140,608	3.733
53	2,809	7.280	148,877	3.756
54	2,916	7.348	157,464	3.780
55	3,025	7.416	166,375	3.803
56	3,136	7.483	175,616	3.826
57	3,249	7.550	185,193	3.849
58	3,364	7.616	195,112	3.871
59	3,481	7.681	205,379	3.893
60	3,600	7.746	216,000	3.915
61	3,721	7.810	226,981	3.936
62	3,844	7.874	238,328	3.958
63	3,969	7.937	250,047	3.979
64	4,096	8.000	262,144	4.000
65	4,225	8.062	274,625	4.021
66	4,356	8.124	287,496	4.041
67	4,489	8.185	300,763	4.062
68	4,624	8.246	314,432	4.082
69	4,761	8.307	328,509	4.102
70	4,900	8.367	343,000	4.121
71	5,041	8.426	357,911	4.141
72	5,184	8.485	373,248	4.160
73	5,329	8.544	389,017	4.179
74	5,476	8.602	405,224	4.198
75	5,625	8.660	421,875	4.217
76	5,776	8.718	438,976	4.236
77	5,929	8.775	456,533	4.254
78	6,084	8.832	474,552	4.273
79	6,241	8.888	493,039	4.291
80	6,400	8.944	512,000	4.309
81	6,561	9.000	531,441	4.327
82	6,724	9.055	551,368	4.344
83	6,889	9.110	571,787	4.362
84	7,056	9.165	592,704	4.380
85	7,225	9.220	614,125	4.397
86	7,396	9.274	636,056	4.414
87	7,569	9.327	658,503	4.431
88	7,744	9.381	681,472	4.448
89	7,921	9.434	704,969	4.465
90	8,100	9.487	729,000	4.481
91	8,281	9.539	753,571	4.498
92	8,464	9.592	778,688	4.514
93	8,649	9.644	804,357	4.531
94	8,836	9.695	830,584	4.547
95	9,025	9.747	857,375	4.563
96	9,216	9.798	884,736	4.579
97	9,409	9.849	912,673	4.595
98	9,604	9.899	941,192	4.610
99	9,801	9.950	970,299	4.626
100	10,000	10.000	1,000,000	4.642

Table 4. Powers and Roots

n	n^2	$\sqrt{n}$	n^3	$\sqrt[3]{n}$
1	1	1.000	1	1.000
2	4	1.414	8	1.260
3	9	1.732	27	1.442
4	16	2.000	64	1.587
5	25	2.236	125	1.710
6	36	2.449	216	1.817
7	49	2.646	343	1.913
8	64	2.828	512	2.000
9	81	3.000	729	2.080
10	100	3.162	1,000	2.154
11	121	3.317	1,331	2.224
12	144	3.464	1,728	2.289
13	169	3.606	2,197	2.351
14	196	3.742	2,744	2.410
15	225	3.873	3,375	2.466
16	256	4.000	4,096	2.520
17	289	4.123	4,913	2.571
18	324	4.243	5,832	2.621
19	361	4.359	6,859	2.668
20	400	4.472	8,000	2.714
21	441	4.583	9,261	2.759
22	484	4.690	10,648	2.802
23	529	4.796	12,167	2.844
24	576	4.899	13,824	2.884
25	625	5.000	15,625	2.924
26	676	5.099	17,576	2.962
27	729	5.196	19,683	3.000
28	784	5.292	21,952	3.037
29	841	5.385	24,389	3.072
30	900	5.477	27,000	3.107
31	961	5.568	29,791	3.141
32	1,024	5.657	32,768	3.175
33	1,089	5.745	35,937	3.208
34	1,156	5.831	39,304	3.240
35	1,225	5.916	42,875	3.271
36	1,296	6.000	46,656	3.302
37	1,369	6.083	50,653	3.332
38	1,444	6.164	54,872	3.362
39	1,521	6.245	59,319	3.391
40	1,600	6.325	64,000	3.420
41	1,681	6.403	68,921	3.448
42	1,764	6.481	74,088	3.476
43	1,849	6.557	79,507	3.503
44	1,936	6.633	85,184	3.530
45	2,025	6.708	91,125	3.557
46	2,116	6.782	97,336	3.583
47	2,209	6.856	103,823	3.609
48	2,304	6.928	110,592	3.634
49	2,401	7.000	117,649	3.659
50	2,500	7.071	125,000	3.684

Table 3. Trigonometric Functions of Radians and Real Numbers (cont'd.)

t	$\sin t$	$\cos t$	$\tan t$	$\cot t$	$\sec t$	$\csc t$
.80	.7174	.6967	1.030	.9712	1.435	1.394
.81	.7243	.6895	1.050	.9520	1.450	1.381
.82	.7311	.6822	1.072	.9331	1.466	1.368
.83	.7379	.6749	1.093	.9146	1.482	1.355
.84	.7446	.6675	1.116	.8964	1.498	1.343
.85	.7513	.6600	1.138	.8785	1.515	1.331
.86	.7578	.6524	1.162	.8609	1.533	1.320
.87	.7643	.6448	1.185	.8437	1.551	1.308
.88	.7707	.6372	1.210	.8267	1.569	1.297
.89	.7771	.6294	1.235	.8100	1.589	1.287
.90	.7833	.6216	1.260	.7936	1.609	1.277
.91	.7895	.6137	1.286	.7774	1.629	1.267
.92	.7956	.6058	1.313	.7615	1.651	1.257
.93	.8016	.5978	1.341	.7458	1.673	1.247
.94	.8076	.5898	1.369	.7303	1.696	1.238
.95	.8134	.5817	1.398	.7151	1.719	1.229
.96	.8192	.5735	1.428	.7001	1.744	1.221
.97	.8249	.5653	1.459	.6853	1.769	1.212
.98	.8305	.5570	1.491	.6707	1.795	1.204
.99	.8360	.5487	1.524	.6563	1.823	1.196
1.00	.8415	.5403	1.557	.6421	1.851	1.188
1.01	.8468	.5319	1.592	.6281	1.880	1.181
1.02	.8521	.5234	1.628	.6142	1.911	1.174
1.03	.8573	.5148	1.665	.6005	1.942	1.166
1.04	.8624	.5062	1.704	.5870	1.975	1.160
1.05	.8674	.4976	1.743	.5736	2.010	1.153
1.06	.8724	.4889	1.784	.5604	2.046	1.146
1.07	.8772	.4801	1.827	.5473	2.083	1.140
1.08	.8820	.4713	1.871	.5344	2.122	1.134
1.09	.8866	.4625	1.917	.5216	2.162	1.128
1.10	.8912	.4536	1.965	.5090	2.205	1.122
1.11	.8957	.4447	2.014	.4964	2.249	1.116
1.12	.9001	.4357	2.066	.4840	2.295	1.111
1.13	.9044	.4267	2.120	.4718	2.344	1.106
1.14	.9086	.4176	2.176	.4596	2.395	1.101
1.15	.9128	.4085	2.234	.4475	2.448	1.096
1.16	.9168	.3993	2.296	.4356	2.504	1.091
1.17	.9208	.3902	2.360	.4237	2.563	1.086
1.18	.9246	.3809	2.427	.4120	2.625	1.082
1.19	.9284	.3717	2.498	.4003	2.691	1.077

ANSWERS TO ODD-NUMBERED EXERCISES

Section 1.1, page 7

1 (a) $<$ (b) $>$ (c) $=$ **3** (a) $>$ (b) $<$ (c) $>$ **5** $-8 < -5$ **7** $0 > -1$ **9** $x < 0$
11 $3 < a < 5$ **13** $b \geq 2$ **15** $c \leq 1$ **17** (a) 5 (b) -5 (c) 13   **19** (a) 0 (b) $4 - \pi$ (c) -1
21 (a) 4 (b) 6 (c) 6 (d) 10   **23** (a) 12 (b) 3 (c) 3 (d) 9   **25** $3/2, -1$ **27** $2, -4/3$
29 $(2 \pm \sqrt{14})/2$ **31** $5/2$ **33** $1/2, -1/2, 3, -3$ **35** $\pm(1/6)\sqrt{30 + 6\sqrt{13}}, \pm(1/6)\sqrt{30 - 6\sqrt{13}}$

Section 1.2, page 14

1

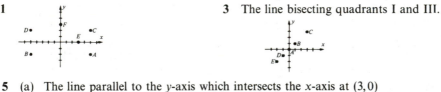

3 The line bisecting quadrants I and III.

5 (a) The line parallel to the y-axis which intersects the x-axis at $(3, 0)$
   (b) The line parallel to the x-axis which intersects the y-axis at $(0, -1)$
   (c) All points to the right of, and on, the y-axis
   (d) All points in quadrants I and III
   (e) All points under the x-axis
7 (a) $\sqrt{29}$ (b) $(5, -1/2)$ **9** (a) $\sqrt{13}$ (b) $(-7/2, -1)$ **11** (a) 4 (b) $(5, -3)$
13 Area $= 28$ **17** $(13, -28)$ **19** $d(A, P) = d(B, P)$
21 $\sqrt{x^2 + y^2} = 5$. A circle of radius 5 with center at the origin

Section 1.3, page 21

1   **3**   **5**   **7**   **9**   **11**

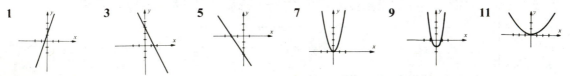

13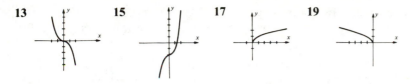

15

17

19

21 Circle of radius 4, center at the origin   **23** Circle of radius 1/3, center at the origin
25 Circle of radius 2, center at $(2, -1)$ **27** Circle of radius 3, center at $(0, 3)$
29 $(x - 3)^2 + (y + 2)^2 = 16$ **31** $(x - 1/2)^2 + (y + 3/2)^2 = 4$ **33** $x^2 + y^2 = 34$
35 $(x + 4)^2 + (y - 2)^2 = 4$ **37** $(x - 1)^2 + (y - 2)^2 = 34$

Section 1.4, page 26

1 3, 9, 4, 6   **3** $2, \sqrt{2} + 6, 12, 23$
5 (a) $5a - 2$ (b) $-5a - 2$ (c) $-5a + 2$ (d) $5a + 5h - 2$ (e) $5a + 5h - 4$ (f) 5
7 (a) $2a^2 - a + 3$ (b) $2a^2 + a + 3$ (c) $-2a^2 + a - 3$
   (d) $2a^2 + 4ah + 2h^2 - a - h + 3$ (e) $2a^2 - a + 2h^2 - h + 6$
   (f) $4a + 2h - 1$
9 (a) $3/a^2$ (b) $1/3a^2$ (c) $3a^4$ (d) $9a^4$ (e) $3a$ (f) $\sqrt{3a^2}$
11 (a) $2a/(a^2 + 1)$ (b) $(a^2 + 1)/2a$ (c) $2a^2/(a^4 + 1)$
   (d) $4a^2/(a^4 + 2a^2 + 1)$ (e) $2\sqrt{a}/(a + 1)$ (f) $\sqrt{2a^3 + 2a}/(a^2 + 1)$
13 $\{x : x \geq 5/3\}$ **15** $\{x : -2 \leq x \leq 2\}$
17 All real numbers except 0, 3, and -3 **19** All nonnegative real numbers except 4 and 3/2
21 $9/7$, $(a + 5)/7$, $\mathbb{R}$ **23** 19, $a^2 + 3$, all nonnegative real numbers   **25** $\sqrt[3]{4}, \sqrt[3]{a}, \mathbb{R}$ **27** Yes
29 No   **31** Yes   **33** No   **35** Odd   **37** Even   **39** Even   **41** Neither   **43** Neither
45 $r = C/2\pi$; $6/\pi \approx 1.9$ inches   **47** $V = 4x^3 - 100x^2 + 600x$
49 $P = 4\sqrt{A}$ **51** $d = 2\sqrt{t^2 + 2500}$ **53** Yes   **55** No   **57** Yes   **59** No

Section 1.5, page 35

1 Increasing on $\mathbb{R}$

3 Decreasing on $\mathbb{R}$

5 Increasing on $\{x : x \leq 0\}$
Decreasing on $\{x : x \geq 0\}$

7 Decreasing on $\{x : x \leq 0\}$
Increasing on $\{x : x \geq 0\}$

9 Increasing on $\{x : x \geq -4\}$

11 Increasing on $\{x : x \geq 0\}$

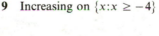

13 Decreasing on $\{x:x < 0\}$ and $\{x:x > 0\}$ **15** Decreasing on $\{x:x \le 2\}$ **17** Decreasing on $\{x:x \le 0\}$
Increasing on $\{x:x \ge 2\}$ Increasing on $\{x:x \ge 0\}$

   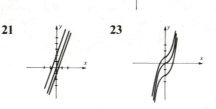

19 Neither increasing   **21**   **23**   **25**
nor decreasing

27   **29**

Section 1.6, Review Exercises, page 36

1 (a) $<$ (b) $>$ (c) $>$ **3** (a) 7 (b) -1 (c) 1/3   **5** 3/2, -4 **7** $\pm 5/2, \pm\sqrt{2}$
9 The points in quadrants II and IV

11   **13**   **15** Increasing on $\{x:x \le 0\}$
Decreasing on $\{x:x \ge 0\}$

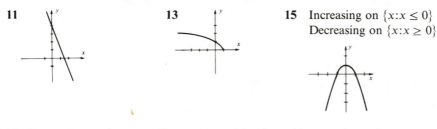

17 Decreasing on $\{x:x \le -5\}$ **19** Neither increasing nor decreasing   **21** Not one-to-one
Increasing on $\{x:x \ge -5\}$

23
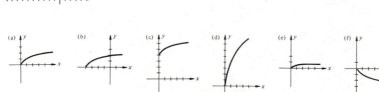
(a) (b) (c) (d) (e) (f)

CHAPTER 2

Section 2.1, page 44

1 $(-1, 0)$ **3** $(0, -1)$ **5** $(1, 0)$ **7** $(-1, 0)$ **9** $(0, -1)$ **11** $(-\sqrt{2}/2, -\sqrt{2}/2)$
13 $(\sqrt{2}/2, -\sqrt{2}/2)$ **15** $(-\sqrt{2}/2, \sqrt{2}/2)$ **17** $(1/2, -\sqrt{3}/2)$ **19** $(-\sqrt{3}/2, -1/2)$
21 $(-1/2, \sqrt{3}/2)$
23 (a) $(-3/5, -4/5)$ (b) $(-3/5, -4/5)$ (c) $(3/5, -4/5)$ (d) $(-3/5, 4/5)$
25 (a) $(8/17, -15/17)$ (b) $(8/17, -15/17)$ (c) $(-8/17, -15/17)$ (d) $(8/17, 15/17)$
27 (a) $(1, 0)$ (b) $(1, 0)$ (c) $(-1, 0)$ (d) $(1, 0)$
29 (a) $(-a/\sqrt{a^2 + b^2}, -b/\sqrt{a^2 + b^2})$ (b) $(-a/\sqrt{a^2 + b^2}, -b/\sqrt{a^2 + b^2})$
(c) $(a/\sqrt{a^2 + b^2}, -b/\sqrt{a^2 + b^2})$ (d) $(-a/\sqrt{a^2 + b^2}, b/\sqrt{a^2 + b^2})$
31 $\sqrt{3}/2$ **33** $-\sqrt{5}/3$ **35** $-1/2$ **37** $\sqrt{0.9999}$

Calculator Exercises

1 IV **3** III **5** III **7** III **9** -0.2419

Section 2.2, page 50

1 Divide both sides of $\sin^2 t + \cos^2 t = 1$ by $\sin^2 t$.
3 $\csc t = -5/3$, $\sec t = 5/4$, $\tan t = -3/4$, $\cot t = -4/3$
5 $\csc t = \sqrt{a^2 + b^2}/a$, $\sec t = \sqrt{a^2 + b^2}/b$, $\tan t = a/b$, $\cot t = b/a$
Values in Exercises 7–23 are given in the order $\sin t$, $\cos t$, $\tan t$, $\csc t$, $\sec t$, $\cot t$; a dash means the value is undefined.
7 $1, 0, —, 1, —, 0$ **9** $\sqrt{2}/2, -\sqrt{2}/2, -1, \sqrt{2}, -\sqrt{2}, -1$ **11** $0, -1, 0, —, -1, —$
13 $-1, 0, —, -1, —, 0$
15 $0, 1, 0, —, 1, —$ **17** $\sqrt{2}/2, -\sqrt{2}/2, -1, \sqrt{2}, -\sqrt{2}, -1$
19 $\sqrt{3}/2, 1/2, \sqrt{3}, 2\sqrt{3}/3, 2, \sqrt{3}/3$ **21** $1/2, -\sqrt{3}/2, -\sqrt{3}/3, 2, -2\sqrt{3}/3, -\sqrt{3}$
23 $-\sqrt{3}/2, -1/2, \sqrt{3}, -2\sqrt{3}/3, -2, \sqrt{3}/3$ **25** IV **27** III **29** II
31 III **33** I

Values in Exercises 35–41 are given in the order $\sin t$, $\cos t$, $\tan t$, $\csc t$, $\sec t$, $\cot t$.
35 $3/5, -4/5, -3/4, 5/3, -5/4, -4/3$ **37** $-5/13, 12/13, -5/12, -13/5, 13/12, -12/5$
39 $-2\sqrt{2}/3, -1/3, 2\sqrt{2}, -3\sqrt{2}/4, -3, \sqrt{2}/4$ **41** $\sqrt{15}/4, -1/4, -\sqrt{15}, 4\sqrt{15}/15, -4, -\sqrt{15}/15$
43 No; $|\sin t| \leq 1$ **45** (a) $\sqrt{2}/2$ (b) $-1/4$ **47** $(\cos t)(\sec t) = (\cos t)(1/\cos t) = 1$

Calculator Exercises

1 $\tan t = -0.3313$, $\cot t = -3.018$, $\sec t = -1.054$, $\csc t = 3.180$
3 $\sec t = 1.122$, $\csc t = 2.203$, $\cot t = 1.963$, $\sin t = 0.4540$
5 $\sin t = 0.9925$, $\tan t = -8.142$, $\sec t = -8.203$, $\csc t = 1.008$, $\cot t = -0.1228$

Section 2.3, page 54

1

-4π -3π -2π -π   0   π   2π 3π 4π

3 We shall give an indirect proof. Suppose there is a positive number k less than 2π such that $\sin(t + k) = \sin t$ for all t. Letting $t = 0$, we obtain $\sin k = \sin 0 = 0$. Since $0 < k < 2\pi$, it follows that $P(k)$ has coordinates

$(-1, 0)$. Consequently, $k = \pi$, and we may write $\sin(t + \pi) = \sin t$ for all t. In particular, if $t = \pi/2$, then $\sin(3\pi/2) = \sin \pi/2$, or $-1 = 1$, an absurdity. This completes the proof.

5 If $y/x = a$, where $x^2 + y^2 = 1$, then $\pm\sqrt{1 - x^2}/x = a$. Hence, $(1 - x^2)/x^2 = a^2$, and $1 - x^2 = a^2x^2$ or $1 = a^2x^2 + x^2 = (a^2 + 1)x^2$. Consequently, $x^2 = 1/(a^2 + 1)$ or $x = \pm 1/\sqrt{a^2 + 1}$. If $a > 0$, choose the point $P(x, y)$ on U where $x = 1/\sqrt{a^2 + 1}$. If $a < 0$, choose $P(x, y)$ such that $x = -1/\sqrt{a^2 + 1}$. Thus, there is always a point $P(x, y)$ on U such that $y/x = a$.

Section 2.4, page 60

1 $480°, 840°, -240°, -600°$ **3** $495°, 855°, -225°, -585°$ **5** $330°, 690°, -390°, -750°$
7 $260°, 980°, -100°, -460°$ **9** $17\pi/6, 29\pi/6, -7\pi/6, -19\pi/6$ **11** $7\pi/4, 15\pi/4, -9\pi/4, -17\pi/4$
13 $5\pi/6$ **15** $-\pi/3$ **17** $5\pi/4$ **19** $5\pi/2$ **21** $2\pi/5$ **23** $5\pi/9$ **25** $120°$ **27** $330°$
29 $135°$ **31** $-630°$ **33** $1260°$ **35** $20°$ **37** $114°\,35'\,30''$ **39** $286°\,28'\,44''$
41 (a) 1.75 (b) $100.27°$ **43** 6.98 meters   **45** $8.59\,\text{km}$
47 Approximations (in miles): (a) 4189 (b) 3142 (c) 2094 (d) 698 (e) 70
49 $1/8$ radian $= (45/2\pi)° \approx 7°\,10'$

Calculator Exercises

1 1.2811 **3** 8.4173 **5** $149.7651°$
7 Approximations (in miles): (a) 4150.26 (b) 3112.69 (c) 2075.13 (d) 691.71 (e) 69.17
9 Approximately 0.126 radians, or $7.219°$

Section 2.5, page 68

Answers to Exercises 1–29 are in the order sin, cos, tan, csc, sec, cot.

1 $-3/5, 4/5, -3/4, -5/3, 5/4, -4/3$ **3** $-5\sqrt{29}/29, -2\sqrt{29}/29, 5/2, -\sqrt{29}/5, -\sqrt{29}/2, 2/5$
5 $4\sqrt{17}/17, -\sqrt{17}/17, -4, \sqrt{17}/4, -\sqrt{17}, -1/4$ **7** $-7\sqrt{53}/53, -2\sqrt{53}/53, 7/2, -\sqrt{53}/7, -\sqrt{53}/2, 2/7$
9 $4/5, 3/5, 4/3, 5/4, 5/3, 3/4$ **11** $1, 0, -, 1, -, 0$ **13** $\sqrt{2}/2, -\sqrt{2}/2, -1, \sqrt{2}, -\sqrt{2}, -1$
15 $-\sqrt{2}/2, \sqrt{2}/2, -1, -\sqrt{2}, \sqrt{2}, -1$ **17** $0, 1, 0, -, 1, -$ **21** $4/5, 3/5, 4/3, 5/4, 5/3, 3/4$
23 $2\sqrt{13}/13, 3\sqrt{13}/13, 2/3, \sqrt{13}/2, \sqrt{13}/3, 3/2$ **25** $2/5, \sqrt{21}/5, \sqrt{21}/21, 5/2, 5\sqrt{21}/21, \sqrt{21}/2$
27 $a/\sqrt{a^2 + b^2}, b/\sqrt{a^2 + b^2}, a/b, \sqrt{a^2 + b^2}/a, \sqrt{a^2 + b^2}/b, b/a$
29 $b/c, \sqrt{c^2 - b^2}/c, b/\sqrt{c^2 - b^2}, c/b, c/\sqrt{c^2 - b^2}, \sqrt{c^2 - b^2}/b$

Calculator Exercises

1 Table A is exact. Calculator answers are approximations.
3 $0.743, 0.669, 1.110, 1.346, 1.494, 0.901$

Section 2.6, page 79

1 (a) $\pi/4$ (b) $\pi/3$ (c) $\pi/6$ **3** (a) $\pi/4$ (b) $\pi/6$ (c) $\pi/3$ **5** (a) 1.5 (b) $2\pi - 5$
7 (a) $60°$ (b) $20°$ (c) $70°$ **9** (a) $49°\,20'$ (b) $45°$ (c) $80°\,35'$ **11** (a) $\sqrt{3}/2$ (b) $-\sqrt{3}/2$
13 (a) -1 (b) -1 **15** (a) $-2\sqrt{3}/3$ (b) -2 **17** 0.2644 **19** 1.540 **21** 1.431
23 0.7826 **25** 6.197 **27** -1.019 **29** -0.3035 **31** 0.4440 **33** -0.1426 **35** 1.032
37 0.7911 **39** 0.5217 **41** 3.436 **43** 0.5315 **45** 1.3521 **47** 0.7703
49 $21°\,33', 158°\,27'$ **51** $26°\,45', 206°\,45'$ **53** $69°\,44', 290°\,16'$ **55** $43°\,48', 316°\,12'$

Section 2.7, page 86

1 (c) $[-2\pi, -3\pi/2), (-3\pi/2, -\pi], [0, \pi/2), (\pi/2, \pi]$ (d) $[-\pi, -\pi/2), (-\pi/2, 0], [\pi, 3\pi/2), (3\pi/2, 2\pi]$

3 (a) $\csc(-t) = 1/\sin(-t) = 1/(-\sin t) = -(1/\sin t) = -\csc t$

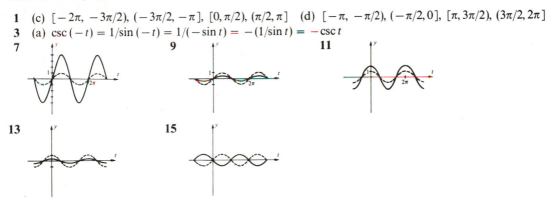

Section 2.8, page 93

1 The amplitudes and periods are (a) $4, 2\pi$ (b) $1, \pi/2$ (c) $1/4, 2\pi$ (d) $1, 8\pi$ (e) $2, 8\pi$ (f) $1/2, \pi/2$
(g) $4, 2\pi$ (h) $1, \pi/2$

3 The amplitudes and periods are (a) $3, 2\pi$ (b) $1, 2\pi/3$ (c) $1/3, 2\pi$ (d) $1, 6\pi$ (e) $2, 6\pi$ (f) $1/3, \pi$
(g) $3, 2\pi$ (h) $1, 2\pi/3$

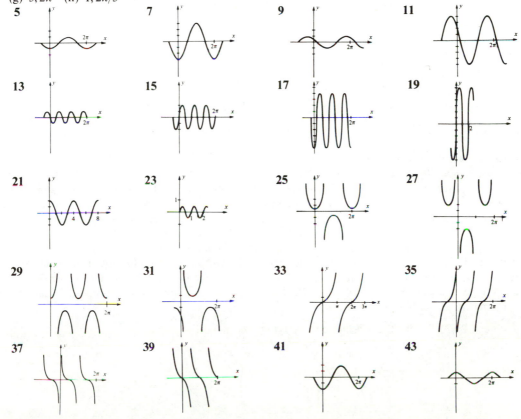

Section 2.9, page 96

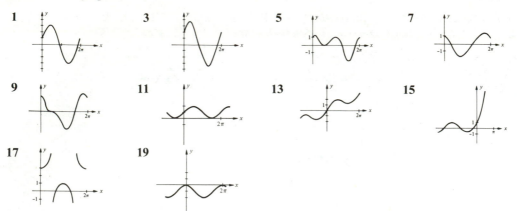

Section 2.10, page 101

1   $\beta = 60°$, $a = 20\sqrt{3}/3 \approx 12$, $c = 40\sqrt{3}/3 \approx 23$ 3 $\alpha = 38°$, $b \approx 19$, $c \approx 24$

5   $\beta = 72°20'$, $b \approx 14.1$, $c \approx 14.8$

7   $\alpha = 18°9'$, $a \approx 78.67$, $c \approx 252.6$ 9 $\alpha \approx 29°$, $\beta \approx 61°$, $c \approx 51$ 11 $\alpha \approx 69°$, $\beta \approx 21°$, $a \approx 5.4$

13   $\beta = 52°14'$, $a \approx 396.7$, $c \approx 647.7$ 15 $\alpha \approx 49°40'$, $\beta \approx 40°20'$, $b \approx 522$ 17 $51°$

19   70.6 meters   21   20.2 meters   23   29.7 km   25 $d \approx 160$ meters

27   $192\,(\sin 22°30') \approx 73.5$ cm   29   9,659 ft   31   126 mph   33   28,800 ft   35   55 miles

37   325 miles   39 $h = d(\tan \beta - \tan \alpha)$

Calculator Exercises

1   $\beta = 48.73°$, $b \approx 358.5$, $c \approx 476.9$ 3 $\alpha \approx 52.94°$, $b \approx 0.3484$, $c \approx 0.5781$ 5 $\alpha \approx 87.29°$,
$\alpha \approx 151,000$, $c \approx 151,200$

7   $c \approx 48.67$, $\alpha \approx 74.36°$, $\beta \approx 15.64°$ 9 $\alpha \approx 60.97°$, $\beta \approx 29.03°$, $a \approx 4437$

Section 2.11, page 107

1   (a) $\omega = 200\pi$ radians per minute
   (b) In cm: $x = 40\cos 200\pi t$, $y = 40\sin 200\pi t$

3   Amplitude 10 cm, period 1/3 second, frequency 3 oscillations per second. The point is at the origin at $t = 0$. It then moves upward with decreasing speed, reaching the point with coordinate 10 at $t = 1/12$. It then reverses direction and moves downward, gaining speed until it reaches the origin at $t = 1/6$. It continues downward, with decreasing speed, reaching the point with coordinate -10 at $t = 1/4$. It then reverses direction and moves upward with increasing speed, returning to the origin at $t = 1/3$.

5   Amplitude 4 cm, period 4/3 second, frequency 3/4 oscillations per second. The motion is similar to that in Exercise 3; however, the point starts 4 units above the origin and moves downward, reaching O at $t = 1/3$, and the point with coordinate -4 at $t = 2/3$. It then reverses direction and moves upward, reaching O at $t = 1$ and its initial point at $t = 4/3$.

7   $d = 5\cos (2\pi/3)t$ 9   Current lags emf by 1/1440 seconds.

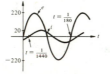

Section 2.12, Review Exercises, page 108

1 $(-1, 0)$, $(0, -1)$, $(0, 1)$, $(-\sqrt{2}/2, -\sqrt{2}/2)$, $(1, 0)$, $(\sqrt{3}/2, 1/2)$ **3** (a) II   (b) III   (c) IV

5 The order will be sin, cos, tan, csc, sec, cot:

  (a) 1, 0, —, 1, —, 0

  (b) $\sqrt{2}/2$, $-\sqrt{2}/2$, -1, $\sqrt{2}$, $-\sqrt{2}$, -1

  (c) 0, 1, 0, —, 1, —

  (d) $-1/2$, $\sqrt{3}/2$, $-\sqrt{3}/3$, -2, $2\sqrt{3}/3$, $-\sqrt{3}$

7 $810°$, $-120°$, $315°$, $900°$, $36°$ **9** $65°$, $42° 50'$, $8°$

11 The order will be sin, cos, tan, csc, sec, cot:

  (a) $-4/5$, $3/5$, $-4/3$, $-5/4$, $5/3$, $-3/4$

  (b) $2\sqrt{13}/13$, $-3\sqrt{13}/13$, $-2/3$, $\sqrt{13}/2$, $-\sqrt{13}/3$, $-3/2$

  (c) -1, 0, —, -1, —, 0

13 (a) 0.8500 (b) 2.972 (c) 1.112

15
17
19
21

23
25
27
29

CHAPTER 3

Section 3.1, page 113

The following are arranged in the order $\sin t$, $\cos t$, $\tan t$, $\csc t$, $\sec t$, $\cot t$:

1 $-\sqrt{3}/2$, $1/2$, $-\sqrt{3}$, $-2\sqrt{3}/3$, 2, $-\sqrt{3}/3$ **3** $\sqrt{2}/2$, $-\sqrt{2}/2$, -1, $\sqrt{2}$, $-\sqrt{2}$, -1

5 $-1/2$, $\sqrt{3}/2$, $-\sqrt{3}/3$, -2, $2\sqrt{3}/3$, $-\sqrt{3}$

7 0, -1, 0, —, -1, —   **9** $-3/5$, $-4/5$, $3/4$, $-5/3$, $-5/4$, $4/3$

11 $12/13$, $-5/13$, $-12/5$, $13/12$, $-13/5$, $-5/12$

13 $-2/3$, $\sqrt{5}/3$, $-2\sqrt{5}/5$, $-3/2$, $3\sqrt{5}/5$, $-\sqrt{5}/2$ **15** $1/8$, $-\sqrt{63}/8$, $-\sqrt{63}/63$, 8, $-8\sqrt{63}/63$, $-\sqrt{63}$

33 $\cos t = \pm\sqrt{1 - \sin^2 t}$, $\tan t = \pm\sin t/\sqrt{1 - \sin^2 t}$,

   $\csc t = 1/\sin t$, $\sec t = \pm 1/\sqrt{1 - \sin^2 t}$, $\cot t = \pm\sqrt{1 - \sin^2 t}/\sin t$

35 $\sin t = \pm\tan t/\sqrt{1 + \tan^2 t}$ **37** $\sec t = \pm\csc t/\sqrt{\csc^2 t - 1}$

Section 3.3, page 122

In the following, n denotes any integer.

1 $(2\pi/3) + 2\pi n$, $(4\pi/3) + 2\pi n$ **3** $(\pi/4) + (\pi/2)n$ **5** $2\pi n$, $(3\pi/2) + 2\pi n$

7 $(\pi/3) + \pi n$, $(2\pi/3) + \pi n$ **9** $(4\pi/3) + 2\pi n$, $(5\pi/3) + 2\pi n$ **11** $(\pi/6) + \pi n$, $(5\pi/6) + \pi n$

13 $(7\pi/6) + 2\pi n$, $(11\pi/6) + 2\pi n$ **15** $(\pi/12) + n\pi$, $(5\pi/12) + n\pi$

17 $\pi/3$, $2\pi/3$, $4\pi/3$, $5\pi/3$; $60°$, $120°$, $240°$, $300°$

19 $\pi/6$, $5\pi/6$, $3\pi/2$; $30°$, $150°$, $270°$ **21** 0, π, $\pi/4$, $3\pi/4$, $5\pi/4$, $7\pi/4$; $0°$, $180°$, $45°$, $135°$, $225°$, $315°$
23 $\pi/2$, $3\pi/2$, $2\pi/3$, $4\pi/3$; $90°$, $270°$, $120°$, $240°$ **25** No solutions   **27** $11\pi/6$, $\pi/2$; $330°$, $90°$
29 0, $\pi/2$; $0°$, $90°$ **31** 0; $0°$ **33** $7\pi/6$, $11\pi/6$, $\pi/2$, $3\pi/2$; $210°$, $330°$, $90°$, $270°$
35 $3\pi/4$, $7\pi/4$; $135°$, $315°$ **37** $15°\,30'$, $164°\,30'$ **39** $41°\,50'$, $138°\,10'$, $194°\,30'$, $345°\,30'$

Section 3.4, page 130

1 (a) $\cos 43°23'$ (b) $\sin 16°48'$ (c) $\cot \pi/3$ **3** (a) $\sin 3\pi/20$ (b) $\cos(2\pi-1)/4$ (c) $\cot(\pi-2)/2$
5 (a) $(\sqrt{2}+1)/2$ (b) $(\sqrt{2}-\sqrt{6})/4$ **7** (a) $\sqrt{3}+1$ (b) $-2-\sqrt{3}$
9 (a) $(\sqrt{2}-1)/2$ (b) $(\sqrt{6}+\sqrt{2})/4$
11 $\cos 25°$ **13** $\sin(-5°)$ **15** $-\sin 5°$ **17** $36/85$, $77/85$; I
19 $3/5$, $4/5$, $3/4$, $-117/125$, $44/125$, $-117/44$
41 $\sin u \cos v \cos w + \cos u \sin v \cos w + \cos u \cos v \sin w - \sin u \sin v \sin w$
49 0, $\pi/3$, $2\pi/3$, π, $4\pi/3$, $5\pi/3$; $0°$, $60°$, $120°$, $180°$, $240°$, $300°$ **51** $f(x) = 2\cos(2x-\pi/6)$; 2, π, $\pi/12$
53 $f(x) = 2\sqrt{2}\cos(3x+\pi/4)$; $2\sqrt{2}$, $2\pi/3$, $-\pi/12$

Section 3.5, page 137

1 $24/25$, $-7/25$, $-24/7$ **3** $-4\sqrt{2}/9$, $-7/9$, $4\sqrt{2}/7$ **5** $\sqrt{10}/10$, $3\sqrt{10}/10$, $1/3$
7 $-\sqrt{2+\sqrt{2}}/2$, $\sqrt{2-\sqrt{2}}/2$, $-\sqrt{2}-1$ **9** (a) $\sqrt{2-\sqrt{2}}/2$ (b) $\sqrt{2-\sqrt{3}}/2$ (c) $\sqrt{2}+1$
29 $\frac{3}{8} + \frac{1}{2}\cos\theta + \frac{1}{8}\cos 2\theta$ **31** 0, $2\pi/3$, π, $4\pi/3$; $0°$, $120°$, $180°$, $240°$ **33** $\pi/3$, π, $5\pi/3$; $60°$, $180°$, $300°$
35 0, π; $0°$, $180°$ **37** 0, $\pi/3$, $5\pi/3$; $0°$, $60°$, $300°$

Calculator Exercises

1 -0.8217

Section 3.6, page 141

1 $\sin 12\theta + \sin 6\theta$ **3** $(1/2)\cos 4t - (1/2)\cos 10t$ **5** $(1/2)\cos 10u + (1/2)\cos 2u$
7 $(3/2)\sin 3x + (3/2)\sin x$ **9** $2\cos 2\theta \sin 4\theta$ **11** $-2\sin 4x \sin x$ **13** $-2\cos 5t \sin 2t$
15 $2\cos(3x/2)\cos(x/2)$
25 $(1/2)\sin(a+b)x + (1/2)\sin(a-b)x$ **27** $n\pi/4$, where n is any integer
29 $n\pi/2$, where n is any integer.

Section 3.7, page 150

1 (a) $\pi/6$ (b) $\pi/3$ **3** (a) 0 (b) $\pi/2$ **5** (a) $\pi/2$ (b) 0 **7** (a) $\pi/3$ (b) $-\pi/3$
9 (a) $-\pi/4$ (b) $-\pi/6$ **11** -0.7069 **13** 1.1403 **15** $\sqrt{3}/2$ **17** $3/5$
19 $-\pi/4$ **21** 0 **23** $-77/36$ **25** $-24/25$ **27** $u\sqrt{1+u^2}/(1+u^2)$
29 $\sqrt{2+2u}/2$ **39** $\cot^{-1} u = v$ if and only if $\cot v = u$.

43   **45**   **47**   **49**   **51**

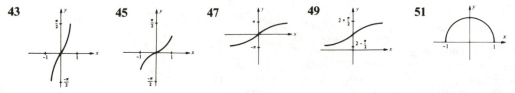

55 $\arctan(-9 \pm \sqrt{57})/4$ **57** $\arccos(\pm\sqrt{15}/5)$, $\arccos(\pm\sqrt{3}/3)$,   **59** $\arcsin(\pm\sqrt{30}/6)$

Calculator Exercises

1 $-0.3478, -1.3336$ **3** $0.6847, 2.4569, 0.9553, 2.1863$ **5** ± 1.1503

Section 3.8, Review Exercises, page 152

17 $\pi/2, 3\pi/2, \pi/4, 3\pi/4, 5\pi/4, 7\pi/4; 90°, 270°, 45°, 135°, 225°, 315°$ **19** $0, \pi; 0°, 180°$
21 $0, \pi; 0°, 180°$ **23** $\pi/2, 7\pi/6, 11\pi/6; 90°, 210°, 330°$
25 $\pi/6, 5\pi/6, \pi/3, 5\pi/3; 30°, 150°, 60°, 300°$ **27** $\pi/3, 5\pi/3; 60°, 300°$ **29** $\sqrt{2-\sqrt{3}}/2$ or $(\sqrt{2}-\sqrt{6})/4$
31 $\sqrt{2-\sqrt{3}}/2$ or $(\sqrt{2}-\sqrt{6})/4$ **33** $84/85$ **35** $-36/77$ **37** $240/289$ **39** $24/7$ **41** $1/3$
43 (a) $(1/2)\cos 3t - (1/2)\cos 11t$ (b) $(1/2)\cos(u/12) + (1/2)\cos(5u/12)$, (c) $3\sin 8x - 3\sin 2x$
45 $5\pi/6$ **47** π **49** $1/2$ **51** $-7/25$ **53** $\pi/2$
55

CHAPTER 4

Section 4.1, page 159

1 $\beta \approx 62°, b \approx 14.1, c \approx 15.6$ **3** $\gamma \approx 100°10', b \approx 55.1, c \approx 68.7$ **5** $\alpha \approx 58°40', a \approx 487, b \approx 442$
7 $\beta \approx 53°40', \gamma \approx 61°10', c \approx 20.6$ **9** $\alpha \approx 77°30', \beta \approx 49°10', b \approx 108; \alpha \approx 102°30', \beta \approx 24°10',$
$b \approx 58.7$ **11** $\alpha \approx 20°30', \gamma \approx 46°20', a \approx 94.5$ **13** 219 **15** 50 feet **17** 2.7 miles
19 3.7 miles from A and 5.4 miles from B **21** 627 meters

Calculator Exercises

1 $\alpha = 119.7°, a \approx 371.5, c \approx 243.5$ **3** $\beta = 49.36°, a \approx 49.78, c \approx 23.39$
5 $\alpha \approx 25.993°, \gamma \approx 32.383°, a \approx 0.146$

Section 4.2, page 163

1 $a \approx 26, \beta \approx 41°, \gamma \approx 79°$ **3** $b \approx 177, \alpha \approx 25°10', \gamma \approx 4°50'$ **5** $c \approx 2.75, \alpha \approx 21°10', \beta \approx 43°40'$
7 $\alpha \approx 29°, \beta \approx 47°, \gamma \approx 104°$ **9** $\alpha \approx 12°30', \beta \approx 136°30', \gamma \approx 31°$ **11** $63, 87$ inches
13 92 feet **15** 24 miles **17** 39 miles **19** Approximately 2.3 miles
21 Approximately N55 31'E

Calculator Exercises

1 $\alpha \approx 40.8, \beta \approx 26.9°, \gamma \approx 104.8°$ **3** $c \approx 0.487, \beta \approx 5.12°, \alpha \approx 168.03°$ **5** $\alpha \approx 157°16', \beta \approx 7°49',$
$\gamma \approx 14°55'$

Section 4.4, page 169

(Answers are in square units)
1 260 **3** $1,125$ **5** 72.3 **7** 879 **9** 2.9 **11** 517 **13** 1.6 acres

Calculator Exercises

1 19540 **3** 441.7 **5** 25820 **7** 14220

Section 4.5, page 178

1 $\langle 3,1 \rangle, \langle 1,-7 \rangle, \langle 13,8 \rangle, \langle 3,-32 \rangle$ **3** $\langle -15,6 \rangle, \langle 1,-2 \rangle, \langle -68,28 \rangle, \langle 12,-12 \rangle$
5 $4\mathbf{i} - 3\mathbf{j}, -2\mathbf{i} + 7\mathbf{j}, 19\mathbf{i} - 17\mathbf{j}, -11\mathbf{i} + 33\mathbf{j}$ **7** $-2\mathbf{i} - 5\mathbf{j}, -6\mathbf{i} + 7\mathbf{j}, -6\mathbf{i} - 26\mathbf{j}, -26\mathbf{i} + 34\mathbf{j}$
9 $-3\mathbf{i} + 2\mathbf{j}, 3\mathbf{i} + 2\mathbf{j}, -15\mathbf{i} + 8\mathbf{j}, 15\mathbf{i} + 8\mathbf{j}$

27 $3\sqrt{2}, 7\pi/4$ **29** $5, \pi$ **31** $\sqrt{41}, \arccos(-4\sqrt{41}/41)$ **33** $18, 3\pi/2$
35 89 kg, S66°W   **37** 5.8 lb, 129°   **39** 56°, 232 mph   **41** 420 mph, 244°
43 N20° 30′W

Section 4.6, page 187

1 (a) 24   (b) $\arccos(24/\sqrt{29}\sqrt{45}) \approx 48° 22'$ **3** (a) -14 (b) $\arccos(-14/\sqrt{17}\sqrt{13}) \approx 160° 21'$
5 (a) 45   (b) $\arccos(5/\sqrt{41}) \approx 38° 40'$ **7** $(4)(2) + (-1)(8) = 0$ **9** $(0)(-7) + (-4)(0) = 0$
11 6/5   **13** (a) -23 (b) -23 **15** -51 **17** $17\sqrt{26}/26 \approx 3.34$ **19** 11/5   **21** 7
23 28   **25** 12

Section 4.7, Review Exercises, page 188

1 $a = 50\sqrt{6}, c = 50(1 + \sqrt{3}), \gamma = 75°$ **3** $a = \sqrt{43}, \gamma = \cos^{-1}(5\sqrt{43}/86), \beta = \cos^{-1}(4\sqrt{43}/43)$
5 $c = 10, \alpha = 60°, \beta = 60°$ **7** $\gamma = 59° 50', b \approx 60.4, c \approx 71.0$ **9** $\alpha = 15°, \beta \approx 30°, \gamma \approx 135°$
11 $\beta \approx 61° 40', \gamma \approx 94° 10', c \approx 780$ or $\beta \approx 118° 20', \gamma \approx 37° 30', c \approx 476$ **13** 2137 square units
15 $\langle -2,-3 \rangle, \langle -6,13 \rangle, \langle -8,10 \rangle, \langle -1,4 \rangle$
17 (a) 80
    (b) $\arccos(2/\sqrt{5}) \approx 26° 34'$
    (c) $2\sqrt{10}$

CHAPTER 5

Section 5.1, page 194

1 $-2 + 6i$ **3** $-2 + 4i$ **5** $7 - 5i$ **7** $-4 - i$ **9** $4 + 7i$ **11** $-6 + 3i$
13 $-10 + 5i$ **15** $20 - 10i$ **17** 25   **19** $-72 - 36i$ **21** $32 - 44i$ **23** 15   **25** 10
27 $5 + 12i$ **29** $7 + 17i$ **31** 1   **33** -1 **35** i **37** $x = -8/5, y = 3$ **39** $x = -1/2,$
    $y = -1/7$

Section 5.2, page 197

1 $(3/13) - (2/13)i$ **3** $(35/61) + (42/61)i$ **5** $(-1/5) - (11/10)i$ **7** $(-7/13) + (17/13)i$
9 $-7 - 21i$ **11** $(12/17) - (54/17)i$ **13** $(42/5) - (9/5)i$ **15** $(-1/4) - (1/4)i$
17 $-2 - i$ **19** $(1/125)i$ **21** 5   **23** $\sqrt{85}$ **25** 8   **27** 1

The geometric representations in Exercises 29–37 are the following points:
29 $P(4,2)$ **31** $P(3,-5)$ **33** $P(-3,6)$ **35** $P(-6,4)$ **37** $P(0,2)$
39 $(26/29) - (7/29)i$ **41** $(-1/2)i$

Section 5.3, page 200

1 -5 **3** $-3 + 7i$ **5** 54 **7** $-2 + 2i$

9 $-10\sqrt{10}\,i$ **11** $(11/10) - (13/10)i$ **13** $(3 \pm \sqrt{31}\,i)/2$

15 $-1 \pm 2i$ **17** $(-1 \pm \sqrt{47}\,i)/8$ **19** $5, (-5 \pm 5\sqrt{3}\,i)/2$

21 $2, -2, -1 \pm \sqrt{3}\,i, 1 \pm \sqrt{3}\,i$ **23** $\pm 2i, \pm(3/2)i$

25 $0, (-3 \pm \sqrt{7}\,i)/2$ **27** $x^2 - 8x + 17 = 0$ **29** $x^2 + 6x + 13 = 0$ **31** $x^2 + 25 = 0$

33 $x^2 - (10 + i)x + 10i = 0$ **35** $x^2 + 1 = 0$ **37** $x^2 - 5ix - 6 = 0$

Section 5.4, page 204

1 $\sqrt{2}\,(\cos 7\pi/4 + i\sin 7\pi/4)$ **3** $8\,(\cos 5\pi/6 + i\sin 5\pi/6)$ **5** $20(\cos 3\pi/2 + i\sin 3\pi/2)$

7 $10(\cos 4\pi/3 + i\sin 4\pi/3)$ **9** $7(\cos \pi + i\sin \pi)$ **11** $\sqrt{5}\,(\cos \theta + i\sin \theta)$, where $\theta = \arctan(1/2)$

13 $4\sqrt{2}\,(\cos 5\pi/4 + i\sin 5\pi/4)$ **15** $6(\cos \pi/2 + i\sin \pi/2)$ **17** $8(\cos 5\pi/6 + i\sin 5\pi/6)$

19 $12(\cos 0 + i\sin 0)$ **21** $-2, i$ **23** $10\sqrt{3} - 10i, (-2\sqrt{3}/5) + (2/5)i$ **25** $40, 5/2$

27 $8 - 4i, (8/5) + (4/5)i$

29 $z_1 z_2 z_3 = r_2 r_2 r_3 [\cos(\theta_1 + \theta_2 + \theta_3) + i\sin(\theta_1 + \theta_2 + \theta_3)],$
$z_1 z_2 \cdots z_n = (r_1 r_2 \cdots r_n)[\cos(\theta_1 + \theta_2 + \cdots + \theta_n) + i\sin(\theta_1 + \theta_2 + \cdots + \theta_n)]$

Section 5.5, page 209

1 $-972 - 972i$ **3** $-32i$ **5** -8 **7** $-(\sqrt{2}/2) - (\sqrt{2}/2)i$ **9** $(-1/2) - (\sqrt{3}/2)i$

11 $-64\sqrt{3} - 64i$ **13** $(\sqrt{6}/2) + (\sqrt{2}/2)i, -(\sqrt{6}/2) - (\sqrt{2}/2)i$

15 $(\sqrt[4]{2}/2) + (\sqrt[4]{18}/2)i, -(\sqrt[4]{18}/2) + (\sqrt[4]{4}/2)i, (\sqrt[4]{18}/2) - (\sqrt[4]{2}/2)i, -(\sqrt[4]{2}/2) - (\sqrt[4]{18}/2)i$

17 $3i, -(3\sqrt{3}/2) - (3/2)i, (3\sqrt{3}/2) - (3/2)i$ **19** $\pm 1, (1/2) \pm (\sqrt{3}/2)i, (-1/2) \pm (\sqrt{3}/2)i$

21 $\sqrt[5]{2}\,[\cos \theta + i\sin \theta]$, where $\theta = 9°, 81°, 153°, 225°, 297°$ **23** $\pm 2, \pm 2i$

25 $\pm 2i, \pm\sqrt{3} + i, \pm\sqrt{3} - i$

27 $2i, -\sqrt{3} - i, \sqrt{3} - i$ **29** $3\cos \theta + 3\sin \theta i$, where $\theta = 0, 2\pi/5, 4\pi/5, 6\pi/5, 8\pi/5$

Section 5.6, Review Exercises, page 210

1 $-1 + 8i$ **3** $-28 + 6i$ **5** $40 + 56i$ **7** 97 **9** $16 + 15i$ **11** $(7/13) + (17/13)i$

13 $(5/82) + (2/41)i$ **15** $2\sqrt{34}$ **17** $-19 - 7i$ **19** $-i$ **21** $(1 \pm \sqrt{14}\,i)/5$

23 $\pm (\sqrt{14}/2)i, \pm (2\sqrt{3}/3)i$ **25** $x^2 - 14x + 50 = 0$ **27** $x^2 + 2x + 17 = 0$

29 $10\sqrt{2}\,[\cos 3\pi/4 + i\sin 3\pi/4]$ **31** $17[\cos \pi + i\sin \pi]$ **33** $10[\cos 7\pi/6 + i\sin 7\pi/6]$

35 $-512i$ **37** $-972 + 972i$ **39** $-3, (3/2) \pm (3\sqrt{3}/2)i$

CHAPTER 6

Section 6.1, page 217

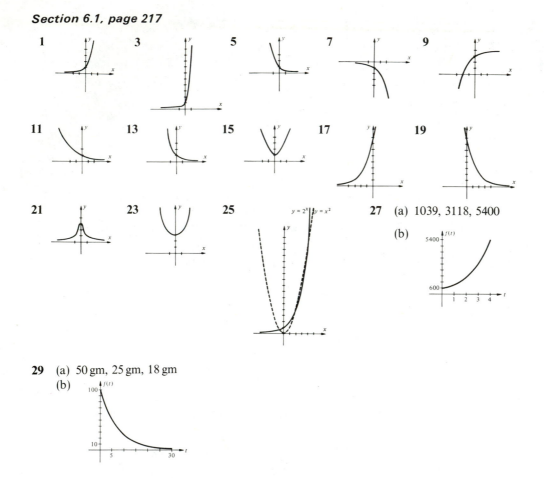

27 (a) 1039, 3118, 5400

(b)

29 (a) 50 gm, 25 gm, 18 gm

(b)

31 $-1/1600$ **33** $1,010.00, $1,020.10, $1,061.52, $1,126.83   **35** (a) $7800 (b) $4,790 (c) $2,942
37 a^x is not always real if $a < 0$.   **39** Reflection through the x-axis.

Calculator Exercises

1 4.7288, 4.6555, 4.7070, 4.7277, 4.7287   **3** $<$

7

9 (a) $1,061.36 (b) $1,126.49 (c) $1,346.86 (d) $1,814.01   **11** (a) 5 years (b) 8 years
(c) 12.5 years

13

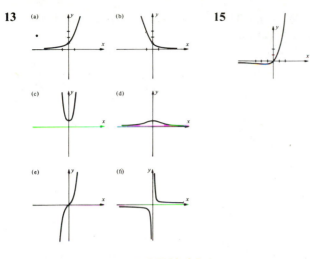

(a) (b) (c) (d) (e) (f)

15

17 2.7048, 2.7169, 2.7181, 2.7183, 2.7183; $f(x)$ gets closer to e as x gets closer to 0.   **19** 7.44

21

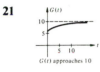

$G(t)$ approaches 10

Section 6.2, page 225

1 $\log_4 64 = 3$ **3** $\log_2 128 = 7$ **5** $\log_{10} (0.001) = -3$ **7** $\log_t s = r$ **9** $10^3 = 1000$
11 $3^{-5} = 1/243$ **13** $7^0 = 1$ **15** $t^p = r$ **17** -2 **19** 2   **21** 5   **23** 1/3   **25** -1
27 -3 **29** 16   **31** 0.3   **33** 2.4   **35** -0.25 **37** 1.8   **39** 1.25   **41** 13
43 27   **45** 1/5, $-1/5$ **47** 2, 3   **49** $\sqrt[3]{7}$ **51** 7/2   **53** No solution   **55** 1
57 $2 + \sqrt{8}$ **59** $2\log_a x + \log_a y - 3\log_a z$ **61** $(1/2)\log_a x + 2\log_a z - 4\log_a y$
63 $(2/3)\log_a x - (1/3)\log_a y - (5/3)\log_a z$ **65** $(1/2)\log_a x + (1/4)\log_a y + (3/4)\log_a z$
67 $\log_a (x^2 \sqrt[3]{x-2}/(2x+3)^5)$ **69** $\log_a x^4/y^{5/3}$

Calculator Exercises
7 1.8928   **9** 2.1252

Section 6.3, page 229

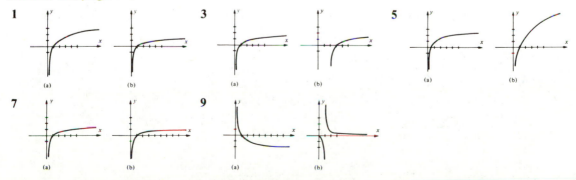

1 (a) (b)   **3** (a) (b)   **5** (a) (b)
7 (a) (b)   **9** (a) (b)

11   They are reflections of each other through the line $y = x$. They are inverse functions of each other.
13 $t = -1600 \log_2 (q/q_0)$ **15** $t = (1/k) (\ln Q - \ln Q_0)$
17   (a) 10   (b) 30   (c) 40   **19**   (a) 2   (b) 4   (c) 5

Calculator Exercises

1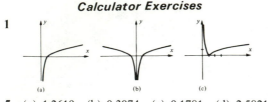
  (a)   (b)   (c)

5   (a) 1.2619   (b) 0.3074   (c) 0.1781   (d) 2.5821   (e) -0.1203

Section 6.4, page 237

1   2.5403; 7.5403 $-$ 10; 0.5403   **3**   9.7324 $-$ 10; 2.7324; 5.7324   **5**   1.7796; 5.7796 $-$ 10; 2.7796
7   3.3044; 0.8261; 6.6956 $-$ 10   **9**   9.9235 $-$ 10; 0.0765; 9.9915 $-$ 10   **11**   4.0428   **13**   2.0878
15   8.1462   **17**   4,240   **19**   8.85   **21**   162,000   **23**   0.543   **25**   0.0677   **27**   189
29   0.0237   **31**   (a) 2.2   (b) 5   (c) 8.3   **33**   Acidic if pH < 7, basic if pH > 7 **35** $\alpha \approx 54.5$
37   1.4062   **39**   3.7294   **41**   7.1000 $-$ 10   **43**   5.0913   **45**   9.8913 $-$ 10   **47**   2.5851
49   27.78   **51**   49,330   **53**   0.1467   **55**   0.006536   **57**   1.367   **59**   0.001345

Section 6.5, page 240

1 $\log 7/\log 10$ **3** $\log 3/\log 4$ **5** $4 - (\log 5/\log 3)$ **7** $(\log 2 - \log 81)/\log 24$ **9** $-\log 8/\log 2$
11   5   **13** $(2/3)\sqrt{1001/111}$ **15**   100, 1   **17** 10^{100} **19**   10,000   **21** $x = \log (y \pm \sqrt{y^2 - 1})$
23 $x = (1/2)\log (1 + y)/(1 - y)$ **25** $x = \ln (y + \sqrt{y^2 + 1})$ **27** $x = (1/2)\ln (1 + y)/(1 - y)$
29 $t = -(L/R)\ln (1 - Ri/E)$ **31**   (a) $I = I_0 10^{x/10}$

Calculator Exercises

1 $x \approx 1.2091$ **3** $x \approx \pm 1.347$ **5**   139 months   **7**   110 days   **9**   0.807

Section 6.6, page 244

1   36,500   **3**   4.26   **5**   1,750,000   **7**   0.876   **9**   6.20   **11**   22.0   **13**   22.1
15   0.000724   **17**   1.37
19   1.99   **21**   90.27   **23**   0.9356   **25**   3.068   **27**   88.6 square units   **29**   1.84 seconds

Section 6.7, Review Exercises, page 245

1 -4 **3**   4   **5**   6
7   **9**   **11**   **13**   **15**

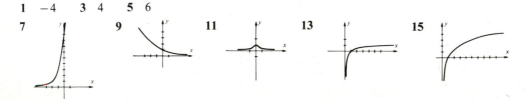

17 9   **19** 1   **21** $\log(16/3)/\log 2$ **23** $\log(3/8)/\log(32/9)$ **25** $4\log x + (2/3)\log y - (1/3)\log z$
27 $x = (1/2)\log(y+1)/(y-1)$ **29** 1.6796   **31** 5.4780   **33** 315.9   **35** 0.06266
37 25,800   **39** 31.4

CHAPTER 7

Section 7.1, page 249

1 $x^2 + y^2 - 6x + 8y + 21 = 0$ **3** $x^2 + y^2 - 12x + 4y + 31 = 0$ **5** $x^2 + y^2 - 6x - 2y - 7 = 0$
7 $(-1, 5); 4$ **9** $(0, 3); 2$ **11** $(5, -4); \sqrt{41}$ **13** $(-1, 1); 1/2$ **15** $(1/2, -1/3); 1/6$
17 $x^2 + y^2 - 3x + 9y - 20 = 0$

Section 7.2, page 257

1 $m = 8$ **3** $m = 1/11$ **5** $m = -1/4$ **9** $x - 3y - 11 = 0$ **11** $x + 5y + 23 = 0$
13 $4x + y - 7 = 0$
15 $7x - 3y + 21 = 0$ **17** (a) $y = -3$ (b) $x = 7$ **19** $y = -x$ **21** $13x - 8y + 132 = 0$
23 $8x - 15y - 13 = 0, x + 6y + 1 = 0, 10x - 3y - 11 = 0$ **25** $m = 2/5, b = 2$ **27** $m = -3/5, b = 0$
29 $m = 0, b = -2$ **31** $m = -5/6, b = 10/3$ **33** $m = 0, b = 0$ **35** $\dfrac{x}{(3/2)} + \dfrac{y}{(-3)} = 1$

Section 7.3, page 263

1 (a) $135°$ (b) $30°$ (c) $\tan^{-1}2$ (d) $20°$ **3** (a) 0 (b) $-\sqrt{3}$ (c) 1 (d) $4/3$
7 $5x + 2y - 29 = 0$ **9** $5x - 3y + 41 = 0$
11 $5x - 7y + 15 = 0$ **13** $x + 6y - 9 = 0; 4x + y - 4 = 0; 3x - 5y + 5 = 0; (15/23, 32/23)$
15 (a) $10/11$ (b) $1/8$ **17** $83°, 23°, 74°$ **19** $m = (6 \pm 5\sqrt{3})/3$

Section 7.5, page 269

1 $F(3, 0); x = -3$ **3** $F(0, -2); y = 2$ **5** $F(-5/16, 0); x = 5/16$

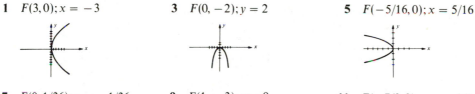

7 $F(0, 1/36); y = -1/36$,   **9** $F(1, -3); x = 0$ **11** $F(-7/2, 2); x = -9/2$

13 $F(-5, -97/16); y = -95/16$ **15** $F(-9/2, 0); x = 11/2$

17 $y^2 = -24x$ **19** $(x-2)^2 = 12(y-2)^2$ **21** $2x^2 = -9y$ **23** 9/16 feet from the vertex

Section 7.6, page 274

1 $V(\pm 7, 0); F(\pm \sqrt{24}, 0)$ **3** $V(0, \pm 6); F(0, \pm 4\sqrt{2})$ **5** $V(\pm 2, 0); F(\pm 1, 0)$

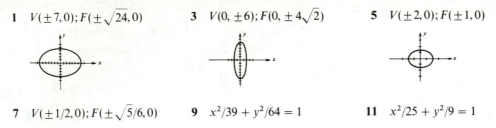

7 $V(\pm 1/2, 0); F(\pm \sqrt{5/6}, 0)$ **9** $x^2/39 + y^2/64 = 1$ **11** $x^2/25 + y^2/9 = 1$

13 $91x^2 + 16y^2 = 1600$ **15** $\{(2,2), (4,1)\}$ **17** $2\sqrt{21}$ feet
19 If the eccentricity is close to 1, the ellipse is very flat. If the eccentricity is close to zero, the ellipse is almost circular.

Section 7.7, page 281

1 $V(\pm 7, 0); F(\pm \sqrt{74}, 0); y = \pm 5x/7$ **3** $V(0, \pm 7); F(0, \pm \sqrt{74}); y = \pm 7x/5$

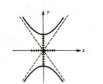

5 $V(0, \pm 6); F(0, \pm 2\sqrt{10}); y = \pm 3x$ **7** $V(\pm 1, 0); F(\pm \sqrt{2}, 0); y = \pm x$

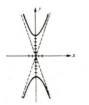

9 $V(\pm 1/4, 0); F(\pm \sqrt{13}/12, 0); y = \pm 2x/3$

11 $x^2/25 - y^2/39 = 1$ **13** $4y^2 - 5x^2 = 20$ **15** $x^2 - 4y^2 = 100$ **17** $\{(0,4), (8/3, 20/3)\}$
19 Conjugate hyperbolas have the same asymptotes.

Section 7.8, page 287

1 Parabola; $V(1, -3)$; $F(4, -3)$
3 Ellipse; center $(-5, 4)$; vertices $(-9, 4)$ and $(-1, 4)$; endpoints of minor axis $(-5, 7)$ and $(-5, 1)$
5 Hyperbola; center $(2, -7)$; vertices $(-4, -7)$ and $(8, -7)$; endpoints of conjugate axis $(2, 0)$ and $(2, -14)$
7 Ellipse; center $(-2, 2)$, vertices $(-2, 3)$ and $(-2, 1)$; endpoints of minor axis $(-5/2, 3)$ and $(-3/2, 3)$

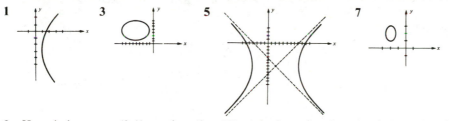

9 Hyperbola; center $(3, 0)$; vertices $(3, \pm 10)$; endpoints of conjugate axis $(-1, 0)$ and $(7, 0)$
11 Ellipse; center $(-3, 5)$; endpoints of major axis $(-3, 9)$ and $(-3, 1)$; end points of minor axis $(-5, 5)$ and $(-1, 5)$
13 Ellipse; center $(6, 2)$; vertices $(6, 5)$ and $(6, -1)$; endpoints of minor axis $(5, 2)$ and $(7, 2)$
15 Parabola; $V(-2, 10)$; $F(-2, 85/8)$

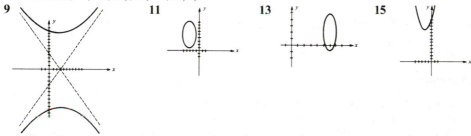

17 Hyperbola; center $(-5, -3)$; vertices $(-5, 1)$ and $(-5, -7)$; endpoints of conjugate axis $(-3, -3)$ and $(-7, -3)$
19 Hyperbola; center $(2, 6)$; vertices $(0, 6)$ and $(4, 6)$; endpoints of conjugate axis $(2, 0)$ and $(2, 12)$

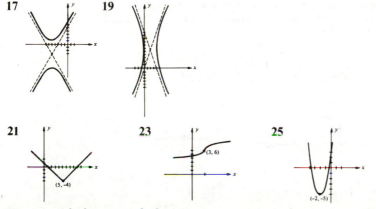

27 $(x - h)^2/a^2 - (y - k)^2/b^2 = 1$

Section 7.9, page 291

Answers 1–7 contain equations in x' and y' resulting from a rotation of axes.
1 Ellipse; $(x')^2 + 16(y')^2 = 16$ 3 Hyperbola; $4(x')^2 - (y')^2 = 1$ 5 Ellipse; $(x')^2 + 9(y')^2 = 9$

7 Parabola; $(y')^2 = 4(x' - 1)$

9 Sketch of proof: It can be shown that $B^2 - 4AC = B'^2 - 4A'C'$. For a suitable rotation of axes, we obtain $B' = 0$ and the general quadratic equation has the form $A'x'^2 + C'y'^2 + D'x' + E'y' + F' = 0$. Except for degenerate cases, the graph of the latter equation is an ellipse, hyperbola, or parabola if $A'C' > 0$, $A'C' < 0$, or $A'C' = 0$, respectively. However, if $B' = 0$, then $B^2 - 4AC = -4A'C'$, and hence, the graph is an ellipse, hyperbola, or parabola if $B^2 - 4AC < 0$, $B^2 - 4AC > 0$, or $B^2 - 4AC = 0$, respectively.

Section 7.10, page 297

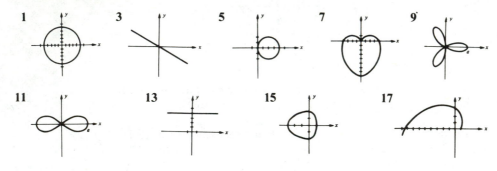

19 $r = -3\sec\theta$ **21** $r = 4$ **23** $r = 6\csc\theta$ **25** $r^2 = 6\sec 2\theta$ **27** $x = 5$

29 $x^2 + y^2 - 6y = 0$ **31** $x^2 + y^2 = a^2$ **33** $x^2(x^2 + y^2) = y^2$

Section 7.11, page 301

1 Ellipse; vertices $(3/2, \pi/2)$ and $(3, 3\pi/2)$; foci $(0,0)$ and $(3/2, 3\pi/2)$

3 Hyperbola; vertices $(-3, 0)$ and $(3/2, \pi)$; foci $(0,0)$ and $(-9/2, 0)$

5 Parabola; $V(3/4, 0)$, $F(0,0)$ **7** Ellipse; vertices $(-4, 0)$ and $(-4/3, \pi)$; foci $(0,0)$ and $(-8/3, 0)$

9 Hyperbola (except for the points $(\pm 3, 0)$); vertices $(6/5, \pi/2)$ and $(-6, 3\pi/2)$; foci $(0,0)$ and $(-36/5, 3\pi/2)$

11 $9x^2 + 8y^2 + 12y - 36 = 0$ **13** $y^2 - 8x^2 - 36x - 36 = 0$ **15** $4y^2 = 9 - 12x$

17 $3x^2 + 4y^2 + 8x - 16 = 0$ **19** $4x^2 - 5y^2 + 36y - 36 = 0$

21 $r = 2/(1 + \cos\theta)$; $e = 1$, $r = 2\sec\theta$ **23** $r = 4/(1 + 2\sin\theta)$, $e = 2$, $r = 2\csc\theta$

25 $r = 2/(3 + \cos\theta)$, $e = 1/3$, $r = 2\sec\theta$ **27** $r = 2/(3 + \cos\theta)$ **29** $r = 12/(1 - 4\sin\theta)$

31 $r = 5/(1 + \cos\theta)$ **33** $r = 8/(1 + \sin\theta)$

Section 7.12, page 307

1 $y = 2x + 7$ **3** $y = x - 2$ **5** $x = y^2 - 6y + 4$ **7** $y = 1/x^2$

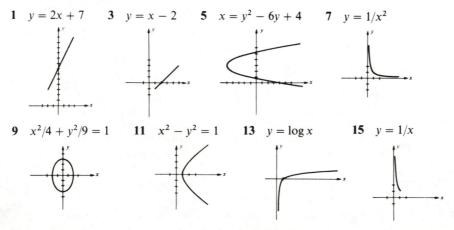

9 $x^2/4 + y^2/9 = 1$ **11** $x^2 - y^2 = 1$ **13** $y = \log x$ **15** $y = 1/x$

17 $x = (x_2 - x_1)t^n + x_1, y = (y_2 - y_1)t^n + y_1$, are parametric equations for l, if n is any odd positive integer.

Section 7.13, Review Exercises, page 308

1 (a) $(9, -5)$; 10 (b) $x^2 + y^2 - 18x + 10y = 0$ (c) $x^2 + y^2 - 12x + 12y = 0$

3 $V(0,0)$; $F(9/16, 0)$ **5** $V(0, \pm 12)$; $F(0, \pm 8\sqrt{2})$ **7** $V(0, \pm \sqrt{8})$; $F(0, \pm 4)$

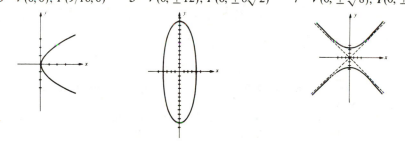

9 $y^2 = -32x$ **11** $y^2/49 + x^2/40 = 1$ **13** $y^2 - 25x^2 = 16$
15 Ellipse; center $(-3, 2)$; vertices $(-6, 2)$ and $(0, 2)$; endpoints of minor axis $(-3, 0)$ and $(-3, 4)$
17 Parabola; $V(2, -4)$; $F(4, -4)$
19 Hyperbola; center $(2, -3)$; vertices $(2, -1)$ and $(2, -5)$; endpoints of conjugate axis $(2 \pm \sqrt{2}, -3)$

15 **17** **19**

21 **23** **25** **27**

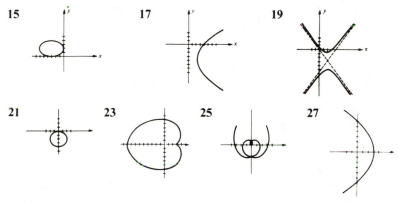

29 $r \sin^2 \theta = 4 \cos \theta$ **31** $r(2\cos \theta - 3 \sin \theta) = 8$ **33** $x^3 + xy^2 = y$ **35** $(x^2 + y^2)^2 = 8xy$
37 $y = 2(x - 1) - 1/(x - 1)$ **39** $y = 2^{-x^2}$

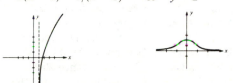

INDEX

ALGEBRAIC RELATIONSHIPS

Exponents and Radicals

If n is a positive integer, then

$$a^n = \underbrace{a \cdot a \cdot \cdots \cdot a}_{n \text{ factors}}; \; a^{-n} = \frac{1}{a^n}; \; a^0 = 1;$$

$$\sqrt[n]{b} = a \quad \text{if and only if} \quad a^n = b; \; b^{m/n} = (\sqrt[n]{b})^m = \sqrt[n]{b^m}$$

Laws of Exponents

$$a^m a^n = a^{m+n}$$

$$(a^m)^n = a^{mn}$$

$$(ab)^n = a^n b^n$$

$$\left(\frac{a}{b}\right)^n = \frac{a^n}{b^n}$$

$$\frac{a^m}{a^n} = a^{m-n}$$

Laws of Radicals

$$\sqrt[n]{ab} = \sqrt[n]{a}\sqrt[n]{b}$$

$$\sqrt[n]{\frac{a}{b}} = \frac{\sqrt[n]{a}}{\sqrt[n]{b}}$$

$$\sqrt[m]{\sqrt[n]{a}} = \sqrt[mn]{a}$$

Factoring Formulas

$$x^2 - y^2 = (x + y)(x - y)$$

$$x^2 + 2xy + y^2 = (x + y)^2$$

$$x^2 - 2xy + y^2 = (x - y)^2$$

$$x^3 - y^3 = (x - y)(x^2 + xy + y^2)$$

$$x^3 + y^3 = (x + y)(x^2 - xy + y^2)$$

Absolute Value

$$|a| = \begin{cases} a & \text{if } a \geq 0. \\ -a & \text{if } a < 0. \end{cases}$$

Quadratic Formula

The roots of $ax^2 + bx + c = 0$, where $a \neq 0$, are $\dfrac{-b \pm \sqrt{b^2 - 4ac}}{2a}$

Laws of Logarithms

$$\log_a xy = \log_a x + \log_a y$$

$$\log_a \frac{x}{y} = \log_a x - \log_a y$$

$$\log_a x^r = r \log_a x$$